MATHEMATICS FOR MANAGERIAL AND
SOCIAL SCIENCES

# WILLIAM L. HART
*UNIVERSITY OF MINNESOTA*

# MATHEMATICS
## *for managerial and social sciences*

PRINDLE, WEBER & SCHMIDT, INCORPORATED

*Boston*          *London*          *Sydney*

Library of Congress Catalog Card Number: 78–99938

Printed in the United States of America

SBN 87150 096 5

# Preface

In all of the social sciences, the study of quantitative aspects of the theory and its applications is increasingly dependent upon mathematical methods. Their bases range from mere arithmetic through advanced parts of various fields of mathematics. Hence, in the case of students planning advanced specialization in a social science, extensive mathematical programs of study at the college level have been recommended. However, such ambitious preparation cannot be expected with the students in a great many of the undergraduate courses in the social sciences and in business administration. Nevertheless, in these courses, use of certain mathematical methods of college level clarifies important parts of the content and simplifies their presentation. This text has the objective of giving a mathematical basis for the preceding method of instruction, with the extent of the book tailored to fit a three-hour course for one semester.

## PLAN OF THE TEXT

The student is assumed to have a reasonable foundation in algebra, perhaps somewhat forgotten, but subject to recall. Approximately the first fourth of the text is devoted to a brief review of fundamentals followed by content pointed at later use in this text. Thereafter, in five relatively independent parts, as follows, a mathematical basis is given which then is used* in corresponding applications.

---

* An exception to this statement occurs in Part IV, where the applications are purely mathematical. However, use of Part IV would be implied if Part V were employed extensively outside of this text. Also, Part IV supplies the basis for applications not considered in this book.

(I) *Linear equations and inequalities in two variables, and a chapter on linear programming with two independent variables*: applications involving linear demand and supply equations, and market equilibrium in Economics; linear programming in various settings.

(II) *Combinatorics, and probability for a finite sample space*: introduction of random variables; expected value of a random variable; Bernoulli spaces; the binomial distribution; conditional probability and Bayesian methods; applications throughout in diverse fields, including problems of types arising in quality control.

(III) *An introduction to differential and integral calculus on an intuitional basis*: restricted primarily to polynomial functions but with optional extension of the differential calculus to cover all algebraic functions; applications of derivatives, maxima, minima, differentials, and simple differential equations in Economics and other fields; fundamental theorem of integral calculus; linear distribution of mass, as an introduction to the concept of a probability density function for a continuous random variable in statistics.

(IV) *Matrices, determinants, and solution of systems of linear equations*: solution of such systems by triangulation of a matrix; elementary algebra of matrices; multiplication of matrices and the inverse of a square matrix; solution of linear systems by determinants and by multiplication with an inverse matrix.

(V) *Introduction to least square approximation*: the mean and the variance of a sample of values of a random variable; least square solution of linear systems; curve fitting in the sense of least squares, primarily for the linear case; trend lines for time series in Economics, business, and other fields; lines of regression for two variables as lines of best fit, with introduction of the coefficient of correlation.

## NATURE OF THE APPLIED PROBLEMS

The applications are presented in such a manner as to be plainly of a natural variety, under the assumption that the student is aware of the fields of application but has not necessarily studied them in other courses. The text makes no pretense of covering all possible types of applications of the mathematical content which is presented. Also, many of the examples necessarily are extremely simplified and artificial in data, due to the lack of a basis in the fields from which the data are selected. However, in all cases, it is endeavored to give the flavor of the real situation which is illustrated by the simplified setting in the text. The wide range of applications should cause the student to develop interest in the corresponding fields. Also, it is hoped that he will be impressed by the fact that, even with the moderate mathematical basis of this text, significant applications are possible.

## *THE PRELIMINARY CONTENT*

The first chapter presents briefly, with exercises for students, a review of the basic algebraic terminology and content which must be used in the course. The second chapter introduces sets and simple operations on them (not set algebra) which will be employed. This chapter also presents linear inequalities in one variable with emphasis on two objectives. First, such inequalities and their graphs on a number scale provide ideal experience illustrating unions and intersections of sets. Second, acquaintance with single inequalities in one variable, and systems of such inequalities, is an indispensable first stage leading to use, later, of single inequalities or systems of inequalities which are linear in two variables. In turn, this content is the basis for linear programming. An extensive third chapter gives the foundation for graphs of equations, and functions and their graphs, with the functions and equations restricted to simple types. The level of mathematical sophistication throughout the remainder of the text is consistent with the preparation in Chapters 1–3.

## *FLEXIBLE FEATURES*

The text provides sixty-six exercises for students. Beyond Chapter 1, with some exceptions, each exercise may be considered suitable for a single assignment. With a well-prepared class, the teacher may desire to cover early parts of the book with considerable speed. Then, various supplementary sections* could be included in order to use all available time in the course. If a class requires slow treatment of early chapters, then omission of supplementary sections would permit inclusion of the cores of all chapters in the course. If a particularly brief course is desired by the teacher, the relative independence of Parts (I)–(V), as described in this Preface, would permit omission of whole chapters without handicap in covering the rest of the book.

WILLIAM L. HART

* Marked with a black star, to indicate the possibility of omission without destroying continuity in the treatment.

# Contents

10 | MATRICES, DETERMINANTS, AND SYSTEMS OF
   LINEAR EQUATIONS

11 | INTRODUCTION TO LEAST SQUARE
   APPROXIMATION

MATHEMATICS FOR MANAGERIAL AND
SOCIAL SCIENCES

# 1 | BASIC CONTENT

## 1. The system of real numbers

In this text, unless otherwise specified, the number system involved will be the familiar system of real* numbers. They are classified, for one purpose, as positive, negative, or zero, which is not called either positive or negative. It is assumed that the student is familiar with the operations of addition, subtraction, multiplication, and division as applied to real numbers.

ILLUSTRATION 1. A sign, $+$ or $-$, preceding a symbol for a number is equivalent to multiplication of the number by $+1$ or by $-1$, respectively. The familiar laws of signs for multiplication or division of real numbers then become simple consequences of the following facts:

$$(+1)(+1) = +1; \qquad (-1)(-1) = +1; \qquad (+1)(-1) = -1.$$

Thus, $(-3)(-5) = 15$, understood as $+15$ with the plus sign omitted; and $(-3)(5) = (-3)(+5) = -15$. We refer to $-3$ and $5$ (or, $+5$) as having *opposite signs*.

We recall that the number 0 cannot be used as a divisor; or, in algebra, $\frac{N}{0}$ is *not defined* for any number $N$. However, we may *add* 0, *multiply* by 0, or *divide* 0 by any number not zero. Thus, for any number $N$, we have $0 \cdot N = 0$ and $0 + N = N$. Also,

$$\frac{0}{N} = 0 \qquad if \qquad N \neq 0.$$

---

* Imaginary numbers will be introduced briefly later.

*I*

The system of real numbers includes the integers, consisting of the endless set of positive integers, $1, 2, 3, \cdots$, the endless set of negative integers, $-1, -2, -3, \cdots$, and 0. A real number $N$ is called a **rational number** if it can be expressed as the quotient of two integers, or as a fraction $p/q$ where $p$ and $q$ are integers and $q \neq 0$. A real number which is not a rational number is called an **irrational number**.

ILLUSTRATION 2.   $\frac{2}{3}$, $\frac{5}{7}$, and .003 or 3/1000 are rational numbers. Any integer is a rational number. For instance, $6 = 6/1$ is a rational number. Examples of irrational numbers are the endless nonrepeating decimals $\sqrt{2}$ or $1.414\cdots$ and $\pi = 3.14159\cdots$. The decimal form for an irrational number is an endless nonrepeating decimal. The decimal forms for rational numbers are repeating decimals, including as special cases the terminating decimals (where the numeral 0 is in each decimal place from a certain place onward to the right). For instance,

$$\tfrac{3}{4} = .7500\cdots; \qquad \tfrac{1}{3} = .333\cdots.$$

The **negative** of a number $N$ is defined as $(-1)(N)$ or $-N$. Each negative number is the negative of a corresponding positive number, and *that* number is the negative of its corresponding negative number. Thus,

$$(-5) = (-1)(5); \qquad 5 = (-1)(-5) = (-1)(-1)5 = 5.$$

Suppose that $a$, $b$, $c$, and $d$ are any real numbers, with $b \neq 0$ and $d \neq 0$, then

$$\frac{a}{b} = \frac{c}{d} \qquad means\ that \qquad ad = bc; \tag{1}$$

$$\frac{a}{b} \cdot \frac{c}{d} = \frac{ac}{bd}; \tag{2}$$

$$\frac{a}{b} + \frac{c}{d} = \frac{ad + bc}{bd}. \tag{3}$$

If $b$, $c$, and $d$ are not zero,

$$\frac{\dfrac{a}{b}}{\dfrac{c}{d}} = \frac{a}{b} \cdot \frac{d}{c} = \frac{ad}{bc}. \tag{4}$$

The **reciprocal** of a real number $N \neq 0$ is defined as $1/N$.

ILLUSTRATION 3.   The reciprocal of 3 is $\frac{1}{3}$ and of $\frac{5}{7}$ is

$$\frac{1}{\frac{5}{7}} = \frac{1}{1} \cdot \frac{7}{5} = \frac{7}{5}.$$

The reciprocal of any fraction $a/b$, where $a \neq 0$ and $b \neq 0$, is *the fraction inverted*, or

$$\frac{1}{\dfrac{a}{b}} = \frac{1}{1} \cdot \frac{b}{a} = \frac{b}{a}.$$

ILLUSTRATION 4.    $(2\tfrac{3}{5})(4\tfrac{2}{3}) = \left(\dfrac{13}{5}\right)\left(\dfrac{14}{3}\right) = \dfrac{182}{15}.$

$$(2\tfrac{3}{4}) \div 6 = \frac{11}{4} \div \frac{6}{1} = \frac{11}{4} \cdot \frac{1}{6} = \frac{11}{24}.$$

$$\frac{a}{b} \div c = \frac{a}{b} \div \frac{c}{1} = \frac{a}{b} \cdot \frac{1}{c} = \frac{a}{bc}.$$

A fraction is not altered in value if both numerator and denominator are multiplied (or, divided) by the same number, not zero. A fraction is said to be in its **lowest terms** if both numerator and denominator have been divided by all common factors.

ILLUSTRATION 5.    To change 65/26 to lowest terms, we divide both numerator and denominator by 13, to obtain 5/2.

DEFINITION I.    *The* **absolute value** *of a positive number or zero is the number itself. The absolute value of a negative number is its negative.*

If $K$ is any real number, we use $|K|$ to represent the "*absolute value of K.*" Then

$$|K| = K \text{ if } K \text{ is zero or positive;} \tag{5}$$

$$|K| = -K \text{ if } K \text{ is negative.} \tag{6}$$

ILLUSTRATION 6.    $|0| = 0; \quad |6| = 6; \quad |-6| = -(-6) = 6; |-\tfrac{3}{5}| = \tfrac{3}{5}.$

On account of (5) and (6), if $x$ is any real number,

$$|-x| = |x|; \quad |x| \text{ is positive if } x \neq 0.$$

## 2.   Real number scale

We shall use the word *length*, or the unqualified word *distance* to refer to a nonnegative* number which is the measure of some distance, or straight line segment, between two points. On a line† as in Figure 1, we select a point

*Fig. 1*

* A nonnegative number is positive or zero.
† *Line* will mean *straight line*.

$O$, to be called the **origin**, and let it represent the number zero. Also, we choose a unit for length in measuring distances on the line $OX$. Then, if $p$ is any positive number, let it be represented by that point on $OX$ which is $p$ units to the *right* of $O$. Let the negative number $-p$ be represented by that point on $OX$ which is $p$ units to the *left* of $O$ on $OX$. Thus, each real number is represented by a point on $OX$. Conversely, if $H$ is any point, not $O$, on $OX$, then $H$ represents just one real number, $k$, which is *positive* if $H$ is to the *right* of $O$, and is *negative* if $H$ is to the *left* of $O$. Hereafter, if $r$ is any real number, sometimes we may refer to the *point r*, meaning the point on $OX$ representing $r$. We refer to $OX$ in Figure 1 as a **real number scale**.

DEFINITION II.   *To say that a is* **less than** *b or that b is* **greater than** *a, means that (b − a)* **is positive**.

We use the inequality sign "$<$" for "*is less than*" and "$>$" for "*is greater than.*" Thus,

$$a < b \qquad \textit{means that} \qquad (b - a) \textit{ is \textbf{positive}.} \tag{1}$$

We call "$a < b$" an *inequality*.

ILLUSTRATION 1.   $3 < 7$ because $(7 - 3) = 4$, which is *positive*.

$-8 < -5$ because $-5 - (-8) = -5 + 8 = 3$, which is *positive*.

$-9 < 0$ because $0 - (-9) = 0 + 9 = 9$, which is *positive*.

To state that "$p > 0$" means that $(p - 0)$ or $p$ is *positive*. To state that "$h < 0$" means that $(h - 0)$ or $h$ is *negative*.

$$p > 0 \qquad \textit{means that p is \textbf{positive}.} \tag{2}$$

$$h < 0 \qquad \textit{means that h is \textbf{negative}.} \tag{3}$$

In Illustration 1, we met special cases of the following fact, which we shall discuss more fully later in this chapter.

*The assertion a < b is equivalent to the statement that, on a number scale, the number a is located to the* **left** *of the number b.*

Know

## 3.   Integral exponents

By definition, if $m$ is a positive integer, then $a^m = a \cdot a \cdot a \cdots a$, to $m$ factors. We call $a^m$ the $m$th **power** of the **base** $a$, and $m$ the **exponent** of the power. By definition $a^1 = a$; as a rule, the exponent 1 is not written. We call $a^2$ the *square* of $a$, and $a^3$ the *cube* of $a$. Until later, any literal numeral appearing as an exponent will represent a positive integer. We recall the following theorems about exponents. These theorems are called the *laws of exponents.*

    (I)   *Law for multiplication:*    $a^m a^n = a^{m+n}$.

    (II)   *Law for finding a power of a power:*    $(a^m)^n = a^{mn}$.

  (III)   *Laws for division:*

$$\frac{a^m}{a^m} = 1; \qquad \frac{a^m}{a^n} = a^{m-n} \quad (if\ m > n); \qquad \frac{a^m}{a^n} = \frac{1}{a^{n-m}} \quad (if\ n > m).$$

  (IV)   *Laws for finding a power of a product or a quotient:*

$$(ab)^n = a^n b^n; \qquad \left(\frac{a}{b}\right)^m = \frac{a^m}{b^m}.$$

ILLUSTRATION 1.    $\dfrac{x^4}{x^4} = 1; \qquad \dfrac{x^{10}}{x^3} = x^7; \qquad \dfrac{a^3}{a^5} = \dfrac{1}{a^2}.$

$$\left(\frac{2}{5}\right)^3 = \frac{2^3}{5^3} = \frac{8}{125}; \qquad \left(\frac{3ax^2}{2h}\right)^3 = \frac{3^3 a^3 x^6}{2^3 h^3} = \frac{27 a^3 x^6}{8 h^3}.$$

Suppose that we wish to use 0 as an exponent, with base $a \neq 0$, and that $a^0$ is to obey the law of exponents in multiplication. Then, if $m$ is a positive integer,

$$a^m a^0 = a^{m+0} = a^m, \qquad or \qquad a^0 = \frac{a^m}{a^m} = 1.$$

Hence, **we define $a^0 = 1$.**

If a negative integral exponent $-n$ is to obey the law of exponents for multiplication, then, with $a \neq 0$, we should have

$$a^n a^{-n} = a^{n-n} = a^0, \qquad or \qquad a^n a^{-n} = 1.$$

Hence, we should have        $a^{-n} = \dfrac{1}{a^n}.$          (1)

We accept (1) as the *definition* of $a^{-n}$.

ILLUSTRATION 2.    $a^{-4} = \dfrac{1}{a^4}; \quad 5^{-1} = \dfrac{1}{5}; \quad 10^{-3} = \dfrac{1}{10^3} = \dfrac{1}{1000} = .001.$

Parentheses, ( ), brackets, [ ], braces, { }, or the vinculum, ——, may be used to enclose a sum which is to act like a single term in some algebraic operation. Let us continue by using the name *parentheses* to represent any one of the symbols of grouping. If a minus sign precedes parentheses, this indicates multiplication by $-1$. On removing the parentheses, this multiplication occurs, and hence each sign, $+$ or $-$, preceding a term within the parentheses must be changed. If a sign "$+$" precedes parentheses, this is equivalent to multiplication by $+1$, which does not alter signs if parentheses are removed.

ILLUSTRATION 3.    $-x^2(3x^3 + 5x - 7) = -3x^5 - 5x^3 + 7x^2.$

Suppose that one symbol of grouping encloses other symbols of grouping. Then, to remove them, it is best to start by removing the innermost symbol first, then the next innermost, etc.

ILLUSTRATION 4.

$-[2x - (3y - 5x + 2)] = -[2x - 3y + 5x - 2] = -7x + 3y + 2.$

In any sum, two products having the same literal parts are referred to as **similar terms**. In any term, such as $5xy$, the particular number, such as 5, which multiplies the other factors is called the *numerical coefficient*, or simply the *coefficient*. To collect similar terms in a sum, we add the coefficients of the terms.

ILLUSTRATION 5.    $-6xy + 3xy - 4xy = xy(-6 + 3 - 4) = -7xy.$

## Exercise 1

*Compute the expression as a simple fraction in lowest terms, if possible. Otherwise, remove any symbols of grouping and collect similar terms.*

1. $0(-4).$
2. $-(-2).$
3. $-4 + 5 - 9.$
4. $-(6 - 15) + 2.$
5. $-3(2 - 5).$
6. $(-1)(-1)(-2).$
7. $(-3)(+2)(-4).$
8. $(-2)^3.$
9. $3^4.$

10. $4^3.$
11. $(-2)^4.$
12. $(2^2)^3.$
13. $\dfrac{15}{18}.$

14. $\dfrac{40}{84}.$
15. $\dfrac{45}{24}.$
16. $\dfrac{39}{65}.$
17. $\dfrac{-5}{3}.$

18. $\dfrac{4}{-7}.$
19. $\dfrac{-4}{-12}.$
20. $\dfrac{15}{-35}.$
21. $\dfrac{5}{3}\dfrac{7}{4}.$

22. $\dfrac{5}{4}\dfrac{8}{3}.$
23. $\left(3\frac{1}{5}\right)\left(2\frac{1}{3}\right).$
24. $\left(2\frac{2}{3}\right)\left(4\frac{1}{5}\right).$
25. $14\left(\frac{2}{7}\right).$

26. $\dfrac{3}{7}\cdot\dfrac{2}{5}.$
27. $\dfrac{2}{3} \div 5.$
28. $\dfrac{6}{5} \div 3.$
29. $4 \div \dfrac{2}{3}.$

30. $3 \div \dfrac{2}{5}.$
31. $\left(4\frac{5}{9}\right) \div \dfrac{3}{2}.$
32. $\dfrac{15}{7} \div 2a.$
33. $-2xy - 3xy.$

34. $5cd + 9cd.$
35. $-11ax + 5ax.$
36. $4(2 - 5x) - 3(1 - 2x).$
37. $-2(x - 3 + y) - 3(y - x).$
38. $-[2x - (5 - 4x)].$
39. $-4[2y - (3x - y)].$

40. $\dfrac{\frac{2}{3}}{\frac{4}{5}}.$
41. $\dfrac{\frac{3}{7}}{\frac{9}{2}}.$
42. $\dfrac{\frac{3a}{5b}}{\frac{9b}{10a}}.$
43. $\dfrac{\frac{5x}{15x}}{4}.$

*44.* $\left(\dfrac{2}{3}\right)^2$.   *45.* $\left(\dfrac{5}{3}\right)^3$.   *46.* $(-10)^3$.   *47.* $-2^4$.

*48.* $6(3^0)$.   *49.* $(2^2)^3$.   *50.* $(3^3)(3^2)$.   *51.* $5^0(x^2)$.

*52.* $(a^2x)^3$.   *53.* $x^5x^4$.   *54.* $y^3y^h$.   *55.* $vv^5$.

*56.* $(2x^3)^5$.   *57.* $(y^2x)^4$.   *58.* $(d^3)^5$.   *59.* $(2x^2)^4$.

*60.* $\dfrac{x^5}{x^3}$.   *61.* $\dfrac{3x}{9x^4}$.   *62.* $\left(\dfrac{2}{xy}\right)^3$.   *63.* $\left(\dfrac{x^3y^5}{xy^7}\right)^2$.

*64.* $(-x^2y^3)^3$.   *65.* $(x^2y^4)^3$.   *66.* $(-2ab^2)^3$.   *67.* $(-3w^2)^3$.

*68.* State the absolute value of $15$; $-11$; $-\tfrac{3}{4}$; $0$; $-1.68$.

*69.* Read the symbol and tell its value: $|-17|$; $\left|-\tfrac{2}{5}\right|$; $|0{\cdot}5|$.

*Construct a real number scale. Read the given inequality and check it by use of* (1) *on page 4. Also, plot the two numbers on the scale.*

*70.* $3 < 5$.   *71.* $0 < 6$.   *72.* $-4 < 0$.   *73.* $-7 < -3$.

*Write the numbers with the proper sign,* $<$ *or* $>$, *placed between them.*

*74.* $3, 8$.   *75.* $-3, -5$.   *76.* $-2, 6$.   *77.* $-4, 0$.

*Read the statement. Check the inequalities by use of* (1) *on page 4.*

*78.* $|-3| < |-5|$ and $-5 < -3$.   *79.* $|-8| > |2|$ and $-8 < 2$.

*Express by means of positive exponents, and compute if possible.*

*80.* $5^{-2}$.   *81.* $10^{-1}$.   *82.* $10^{-2}$.   *83.* $10^{-4}$.   *84.* $3^{-2}$.

*85.* $x^{-3}$.   *86.* $2^{-1}a^{-2}$.   *87.* $x^{-2}y^3$.   *88.* $4^{-2}x$.   *89.* $2^{-1}6^{-2}$.

## 4.  Sets and variables

In speaking of a *set* of things, we take "*set*" as an undefined term. Each object in a set will be referred to as an *element* or a *member* of it. For any set, $T$, it is implied that we can recognize whether or not any specified object belongs to $T$. Or, we say that any set is *well defined*. A subset $S$ of a set $T$ is a set consisting of some (possibly all) of the elements of $T$. If a set $T$ has just $n$ members, where $n$ is a nonnegative integer, then $T$ is called a *finite set*. If $T$ is not a finite set, then $T$ is called an *infinite set*. In this case, corresponding to any positive integer $n$, there are more than $n$ members in $T$.

ILLUSTRATION 1.   The inhabitants of Chicago form a large but not infinite set of people. The positive integers form an infinite set of numbers. The real numbers form an infinite set of numbers.

If $S$ is a subset of a set $T$, it is said that $S$ is *included in* $T$, and we write "$S \subset T$," read "$S$ *is included in* $T$." Above, with $n = 0$, we implicitly introduced the empty set, or **null set**, consisting of no members, and to be represented by $\varnothing$. We agree to say that $\varnothing$ is a subset of every set. If $S$ and $T$ have the same members, we say that $S = T$. If $S \subset T$ and $S \neq T$, then $S$ is called a **proper subset** of $T$. In this case, there must be at least one element of $T$ which is *not* in $S$.

ILLUSTRATION 2.   If $R$ is the set of real numbers, and $I$ is the set of positive integers, then $I \subset R$ and $I$ is a proper subset of $R$. If $T$ is the set $\{2, 3, 4, 5, 6, 7, 8, 9, 10\}$, and if $S$ is the set $\{5, 6, 7, 8, 9, 10\}$, then $S$ is a proper subset of $T$.

To represent or describe a finite set of elements, we may write symbols for them enclosed within *braces*, which we shall use as a standard notation indicating that a set is involved. This device is referred to as the **roster method** for describing a set. The device was used in Illustration 2.

A **variable** is a symbol, such as $x$, which may represent any element of a nonempty set, $D$, of elements. We call $D$ the **domain** of $x$. Each element of $D$ is called a value of $x$. Unless otherwise specified, the domain of any variable met in this text will be a set of real numbers. However, on important occasions, the domain will consist of elements which are *not* numbers.

ILLUSTRATION 3.   We may use $x$ to represent any animal in the zoo of the city of San Diego. Then, each animal in the zoo is a value of $x$.

ILLUSTRATION 4.   Let $T$ be the set of all numbers $x < 3$. We could also define $T$ as the set of all numbers $h < 3$. Thus, the letter, $x$ or $h$, used as a symbol for the arbitrary member of $T$, is of no consequence.

In a given setting, a **constant** is a number symbol representing a fixed number. Any letter, such as $h$, which is a constant, also may be called a variable whose domain consists of just a single number. However, we agree that, when a symbol, $x$, is called a *variable*, it is *not* a constant unless otherwise stated.

In this text, unless otherwise implied, any literal number symbol such as $x$ will be understood to represent a variable. If $x$ is introduced in an algebraic expression, it will be inferred that the domain of $x$ consists of all real numbers for which the expression has meaning.

ILLUSTRATION 5.   If $x$ is introduced in $5/(x - 2)$, then $x$ is a variable whose domain consists of all real numbers except 2, because division by 0 has no meaning.

## 5.   Monomials and polynomials

A **monomial** in specified variables $x, y, z, \cdots$ is defined as the product of a nonzero constant, called the **coefficient** of the monomial, and powers of the variables, where the exponents are nonnegative integers. If each exponent is zero, the monomial is merely a constant, not zero.

ILLUSTRATION 1.   The expression $5x^2y^3$ is a monomial in the variables $x$ and $y$ with coefficient 5. The constant 7 is a monomial in any set of variables;

for instance, $7 = 7x^0z^0$ because $x^0 = z^0 = 1$. The constant 0 is never called a monomial.

A sum of monomials in certain variables is called a **polynomial** in them. A polynomial is named a **binomial**, or a **trinomial** according as the polynomial is the sum of *two*, or of *three* monomials, respectively. The *degree of a monomial* in a set of variables is the sum of the exponents of their powers which are factors of the monomial. The *degree of a polynomial* is the degree of the monomial of *highest degree* in the polynomial. Each monomial of a polynomial may be called a *term* of it. A polynomial of the *first degree* in any variables is said to be **linear** in them.

ILLUSTRATION 2.    If $a$ and $b$ are constants, not zero, while $x$, $y$, and $z$ are variables, the monomial $6abx^3y^2z^4$ is of degree $(3 + 2 + 4)$ or 9 in $x$, $y$, and $z$. If $x$ also is a constant, the monomial is of degree 6 in $y$ and $z$. The polynomial $(3b + ax^2y + 2z^4)$ is of degree 4 in $x$, $y$, and $z$, because the term of highest degree is $2z^4$, of degree 4. Any linear polynomial in a single variable $x$ is of the form $(a + bx)$ where $b \neq 0$. Any linear polynomial in $x$ and $y$ is of the form $(a + bx + cy)$, where at least one of $b$ and $c$ is not zero.

To find the product of two monomials, the law of exponents for multiplication of powers of the same base may be applicable. To obtain the product of two polynomials, multiply one of them by each term of the other polynomial, and add the results.

ILLUSTRATION 3.    $(5a^2x^3)(3ax^2) = 15a^2ax^3x^2 = 15a^3x^5.$

ILLUSTRATION 4.

$$(2x - 3)(4x + 5) = 8x^2 + 10x - 12x - 15 = 8x^2 - 2x - 15.$$

A polynomial of degree 2 is said to be a *quadratic polynomial* in the variables. Any **quadratic** in a single variable $x$ is of the form $(ax^2 + bx + c)$ where $a$, $b$, and $c$ are constants with $a \neq 0$.

ILLUSTRATION 5.    $(3x^2 - 5x + 2)$ is a quadratic in $x$.

## 6.  Square roots

If $H$ is any number and $R^2 = H$, then $R$ is called a **square root** of $H$. If $H = 0$, the only square root of $H$ is $R = 0$. If $H > 0$, then $H$ has two square roots, one positive and one negative, with equal absolute values. The positive square root of $H$ is represented by the **radical** $+\sqrt{H}$, or simply $\sqrt{H}$, read "*the square root of H*," which is understood to mean "*the positive square root of H*." The negative square root of $H$ is denoted by $-\sqrt{H}$. The only square root of 0 is 0, and we write $\sqrt{0} = 0$, read "*the square root of 0* *is* 0." In a radical $\sqrt{H}$, we call $H$ the **radicand**. At present, we shall consider square roots of only positive numbers and zero.

ILLUSTRATION 1.    The square roots of 9 are $\pm 3$, because $3^2 = (-3)^2 = 9$. The square roots of 25 are $\pm \sqrt{25}$, or $\pm 5$.

By the definition of $\sqrt{H}$,

$$(\sqrt{H})^2 = H. \tag{1}$$

Also, we observe that,

*if* $H \geq 0$ *and* $K \geq 0$,        $\sqrt{H}\sqrt{K} = \sqrt{HK};$        (2)

*if* $H \geq 0$ *and* $K > 0$,        $$\sqrt{\frac{H}{K}} = \frac{\sqrt{H}}{\sqrt{K}}. \tag{3}$$

We prove either (2) or (3) by squaring the two sides and noticing that equal results are obtained. Thus, in (2),

$$(\sqrt{H}\sqrt{K})^2 = (\sqrt{H})^2(\sqrt{K})^2 = HK = (\sqrt{HK})^2.$$

ILLUSTRATION 2.        $(\sqrt{167})^2 = 167.$

$$\sqrt{2}\sqrt{8} = \sqrt{16} = 4; \qquad \sqrt{\frac{9}{25}} = \frac{\sqrt{9}}{\sqrt{25}} = \frac{3}{5}.$$

In this text, to state that a rational number is a **perfect square** will mean that it is the square of a rational number. A monomial, or a quotient of monomials where each coefficient is a rational number, will be called a *perfect square* if it is the square of some expression of the same variety.

ILLUSTRATION 3.    $36x^2b^4$ is a perfect square because $36x^2b^4 = (6xb^2)^2$. $36x^4/49a^2$ is a perfect square because

$$\frac{36x^4}{49a^2} = \left(\frac{6x^2}{7a}\right)^2.$$

Until otherwise specified, in any radical $\sqrt{H}$, we shall suppose that all numerical coefficients are positive, and that all literal number symbols represent positive numbers such that the radicand is not negative.

If $n$ is any even integer and $a > 0$,

$$\sqrt{a^n} = a^{n/2}, \qquad because \qquad (a^{n/2})^2 = a^{2 \cdot n/2} = a^n. \tag{4}$$

As a consequence of (4), we reach the following conclusion: *To obtain the square root of a monomial where the exponents are even integers, divide each exponent by 2 and multiply by the square root of the numerical coefficient.*

$q\sqrt[4]{N} \equiv \sqrt[N]{a}$

ILLUSTRATION 4.    $\sqrt{4a^6} = \sqrt{4}\sqrt{a^6} = 2a^{6/2} = 2a^3.$

$$\sqrt{\frac{9x^2}{25y^4}} = \frac{\sqrt{9x^2}}{\sqrt{25y^4}} = \frac{3x}{5y^2}.$$

We use (2) and (4) to remove perfect square factors from radicands.

ILLUSTRATION 5.    $\sqrt{50} = \sqrt{25(2)} = \sqrt{25}\sqrt{2}$

$$= 5\sqrt{2} = 5(1.414) = 7.070,\; \textit{from Table I.}$$

Suppose that the radicand in $\sqrt{H}$ is a fraction whose denominator is not a perfect square. In such a case, we may arrange to make the denominator a perfect square by inserting a new factor in both terms of the fraction. Then, by use of (3), we obtain a result without a radical in the denominator. Such manipulation is referred to as *rationalizing* the denominator.

ILLUSTRATION 6.    $\sqrt{\dfrac{3}{5}} = \sqrt{\dfrac{3\cdot 5}{5\cdot 5}} = \dfrac{\sqrt{15}}{\sqrt{5^2}}$

$$= \frac{\sqrt{15}}{5} = \frac{1}{5}\sqrt{15} = \frac{1}{5}(3.873) = .775.$$

## 7.  Special products and factoring

The following formulas may serve either for rapid calculation of expressions like the left-hand members, or for factoring expressions such as appear on the right.

$$(a + b)^2 = a^2 + 2ab + b^2. \tag{1}$$

$$(a - b)^2 = a^2 - 2ab + b^2. \tag{2}$$

$$(a + b)(a - b) = a^2 - b^2. \tag{3}$$

On the right in (1) and (2), we observe trinomials which are *perfect squares*.

ILLUSTRATION 1.    By use of (2),

$$(3x^2 - y^3)^2 = (3x^2)^2 - 2(3x^2)(y^3) + (y^3)^2$$
$$= 9x^4 - 6x^2y^3 + y^6.$$

ILLUSTRATION 2.    From (3) with $a = 3x^2$ and $b = 5y^3$,

$$(3x^2 - 5y^3)(3x^2 + 5y^3) = (3x^2)^2 - (5y^3)^2 = 9x^4 - 25y^6.$$

In a trinomial which is a perfect square, as in (1) or (2), two terms are perfect squares, and the third term is *plus or minus twice the product of the square roots of the perfect squares.* To express the trinomial as a square, or to factor the trinomial, we first extract the square roots of the terms which are perfect squares, and then use (1) or (2).

ILLUSTRATION 3.   $(x^4 - 6x^2y^2 + 9y^4)$ is in the form of the right-hand side of (2). Since $\sqrt{x^4} = x^2$ and $\sqrt{9y^4} = 3y^2$,

$$x^4 - 6x^2y^2 + 9y^4 = (x^2 - 3y^2)^2.$$

ILLUSTRATION 4.   By use of (1),

$$4x^2 + 12xy + 9y^2 = (2x + 3y)^2.$$

When read from right to left, (3) states that *the difference of two perfect squares is equal to the product of the sum and the difference of the square roots of the squares.*

ILLUSTRATION 5.   By use of (3), with $\sqrt{16y^6} = 4y^3$ and $\sqrt{4x^2} = 2x$,

$$16y^6 - 4x^2 = (4y^3 + 2x)(4y^3 - 2x).$$

By trial and error, some trinomials of the form $(Ax^2 + Bx + C)$ can be factored, because

$$(cx + d)(hx + k) = chx^2 + x(dh + ck) + dk, \qquad (4)$$

which is of the second degree in $x$.

ILLUSTRATION 6.   To factor $(6x^2 - 11x - 10)$ by use of (4), we decide that $c$ and $h$ must be factors of 6, while $d$ and $k$ are factors of $-10$, with $d$ and $k$ of opposite signs. Hence, after various unsuccessful trials, we obtain

$$6x^2 - 11x - 10 = (3x + 2)(2x - 5),$$

which the student should check by multiplication.

## Exercise 2

1.  Let $S$ represent the set of integers $\{2, 4, 6, 8\}$. By the roster method, write symbols for all proper subsets of $S$ consisting of just two integers.
2.  If $S$ is the set $\{3, 5, 7\}$, write symbols for all proper subsets of $S$.
3.  Describe three sets whose elements are to be seen in the room where this text is being taught. Tell how many elements are in each of these sets.

*State the degree of each monomial or polynomial.*
4.  $5x^2y$.     5.  $3x^3y^2$.     6.  $x^2 + 3x - 1$.     7.  $x^2y^3 - 2x^5 + 4y^7$.

*Multiply and collect similar terms.*
8.  $2x^2(3x^3 - 5x)$.     9.  $(2 - 3x)(5 + x)$.     10.  $(2x - 3)(x + 7)$.
11.  $(a - k)(b - k)$.     12.  $(c - x)(c + x)$.     13.  $(x + y)^2$.
14.  $(2c - d)^2$.     15.  $(x^2 + 2y^3)^2$.     16.  $(5 - 3x^2)^2$.

17.  $(3 + x)(2 - 3x + x^2)$.   18.  $(y - 2)(2y - 5 - 3y^2)$.
19.  $(x^2 - y)(x^2 + y)$.   20.  $(c - 3d^3)(c + 3d^3)$.
21.  $(2x - 3y)(x + 5y)$.   22.  $(3a - 2x)(2a + 7x)$.
23.  $(a - 3b)^2$.   24.  $(2c + 3h)^2$.   25.  $(x - 2y)^2$.

Factor.

26.  $ax + bx$.   27.  $ab^2 + 3a^2 + a^3$.   28.  $2t^3 + t^2 - 3t$.
29.  $a^2 - x^2$.   30.  $4 - x^2$.   31.  $y^2 - 9x^2$.
32.  $a^2 - 4a + 4$.   33.  $b^2 + 6b + 9$.   34.  $x^2 - 2ax + a^2$.
35.  $4y^2 - 4xy + x^2$.   36.  $9x^2 - 12x + 4$.   37.  $121 - 4x^2y^2$.
38.  $x^2 + 8x + 15$.   39.  $x^2 + 7x + 12$.   40.  $6 - 5x + x^2$.
41.  $2x^2 + 3x - 5$.   42.  $3y^2 + 8y + 5$.   43.  $2 + 7y + 3y^2$.
44.  $9x^2 - 30xy + 25y^2$.   45.  $4y^2 + 12ay + 9a^2$.
46.  $5x^2 - 3xy - 2y^2$.   47.  $3x^2 + 7xy - 6y^2$.

Find the two square roots of the number or the specified root.

48.  36.   49.  49.   50.  121.   51.  $\frac{1}{4}$.
52.  $\sqrt{144}$.   53.  $\sqrt{\frac{36}{25}}$.   54.  $\sqrt{\frac{4}{9}}$.   55.  $\sqrt{\frac{49}{64}}$.
56.  $\sqrt{\frac{1}{49}}$.   57.  $\sqrt{9x^2}$.   58.  $\sqrt{4y^8}$.   59.  $\sqrt{49x^6}$.
60.  $\sqrt{9a^2b^4}$.   61.  $\sqrt{64x^4y^6}$.   62.  $\sqrt{36z^{10}}$.   63.  $\sqrt{49a^4b^6}$.
64.  $\sqrt{\frac{4}{x^2}}$.   65.  $\sqrt{\frac{y^4}{9}}$.   66.  $\sqrt{\frac{x^4}{4y^2}}$.   67.  $\sqrt{\frac{a^4x^2}{49y^6}}$.
68.  Square:  $\sqrt{147x}$;  $\sqrt{357y^3}$;  $\sqrt{\frac{1}{57}}$.

Calculate by use of Table I.

69.  $\sqrt{3}\sqrt{15}$.   70.  $\sqrt{2}\sqrt{14}$.   71.  $\sqrt{3}\sqrt{6}$.   72.  $\sqrt{175}$.
73.  $\sqrt{\frac{1}{2}}$.   74.  $\sqrt{\frac{2}{3}}$.   75.  $\sqrt{\frac{3}{5}}$.   76.  $\sqrt{\frac{6}{7}}$.

## 8.  Complex numbers

Assume that $p > 0$. Then, by definition, a number $R$ will be called a square root of $-p$ in case $R^2 = -p$. But, if $R$ were real, then $R^2 \geq 0$ and hence $R^2 \neq -p$. Thus, $-p$ has *no real number R as a square root*. Therefore, we decide to expand the system of real numbers by adjoining new numbers which will serve as square roots of negative numbers.

Let $i$ be introduced as a symbol for a new number, to be called an **imaginary number**, with the property that $i^2 = -1$. Let $T$ be the set of all real numbers. Let $H$ be the set of numbers consisting of all numbers in $T$ *together with i*. Then, if $a$ and $b$ are any real numbers, we join to $H$ the new number $bi$ to represent the *product* of $b$ and $i$, and the new number $(a + bi)$ to represent the *sum* of $a$ and $bi$. Let $C$ represent the resulting set of all numbers $(a + bi)$ where $a$ and $b$ are real. We call $C$ the system of **complex**

**numbers.** For any ordered* pair of real numbers $(a, b)$, $(a + bi)$ is called a complex number whose **real part** is $a$ and **imaginary part** is $b$.

If $b \neq 0$, then $(a + bi)$ is called an *imaginary number*. If $a = 0$ and $b \neq 0$, we usually write merely $bi$ instead of $(0 + bi)$, and call $bi$ a *pure imaginary number*. If $b = 0$, usually we write simply $a$ instead of $(a + 0i)$, and naturally call $(a + 0i)$, or $a$, a *real number*. That is, the real numbers now form a proper subset of the set of all complex numbers. In particular, the real number $(0 + 0i)$ is rewritten simply 0 as usual. To state that two complex numbers are *equal* means that they have *the same real and imaginary parts*. Or,

$$a + bi = c + di \quad \textit{means that} \quad a = c \textit{ and } b = d. \tag{1}$$

Sometimes 1 is called the *real unit* and $i$ is called the *imaginary unit* in the complex number system.

ILLUSTRATION 1.   $(5 - 6i)$ is an imaginary complex number with real part 5 and imaginary part $-6$. The real number 7 can be thought of as $(7 + 0i)$. $3i$ is a pure imaginary number.

In the system $C$, addition and multiplication are defined by the following statements where $a$, $b$, $c$, and $d$ are real.

$$(a + bi) + (c + di) = (a + c) + (b + d)i. \tag{2}$$

$$(a + bi)(c + di) = (ac - bd) + (bc + ad)i. \tag{3}$$

We shall not deal with division of complex numbers in this text although division can be defined conveniently. Instead of memorizing (2) and (3) as formulas, it is better to make the following observation.

> *To add or multiply two complex numbers, act as if they*
> *are polynomials in a variable i, which behaves as if it were*
> *a real number, and thus is subject to the laws of exponents*
> *in multiplication, with* $i^2 = -1.$    (4)

By use of (4), we obtain

$$\begin{aligned}
(a + bi)(c + di) &= ac + adi + bci + bdi^2 \\
&= ac + i(ad + bc) + bd(-1) \\
&= (ac - bd) + i(ad + bc),
\end{aligned}$$

which agrees with (3).

ILLUSTRATION 2.    $(3 + 4i)(5 - 7i) = 15 - 21i + 20i - 28i^2$
$$= 15 - i - 28(-1) = 43 - i.$$

---

* A *pair* of elements is an *ordered pair* if each element is assigned a specific place of two available places. Thus, an ordered pair $(a, b)$ is the same as an ordered pair $(c, d)$ if and only if $a = c$ and $b = d$.

If $W$ is any complex number, we use the same formal definition for a square root of $W$ as when $W$ is real. That is, to say that $R$ is a square root of $W$ means that $R^2 = W$. However, in this text, we shall deal with square roots of only *real numbers*. We have already considered square roots of 0 and positive numbers. Now we are prepared to discuss square roots of negative numbers.

By definition, $i^2 = -1$. Hence, $i$ was introduced as a square root of $-1$. It is interesting to notice, then, that the resulting expansion of the real number system to the set $C$ of complex numbers provides square roots (and, later, $n$th roots, where $n$ is a positive integer) *for all complex numbers.*

*& wow*

THEOREM I.   *If $p > 0$, then $-p$ has two square roots, $i\sqrt{p}$ and $-i\sqrt{p}$. In particular, $-1$ has two square roots, $i$ and $-i$.*

*Proof.*   The specified results are true because, by (4),

$$(i\sqrt{p})^2 = i^2(\sqrt{p})^2 = (-1)(p) = -p;$$
$$(-i\sqrt{p})^2 = i^2(\sqrt{p})^2 = -p.$$

Hereafter, if $p > 0$, we agree that $\sqrt{-p}$ will represent the particular square root $i\sqrt{p}$:

$$\sqrt{-p} = i\sqrt{p}. \tag{5}$$

Then, the two square roots of $-p$ are $\pm i\sqrt{p}$. With $p = 1$ in (5), we obtain $\sqrt{-1} = i$. To avoid a danger mentioned later, we emphasize that, *whenever a symbol $\sqrt{-p}$ is met, with $p > 0$, immediately the symbol should be changed to $i\sqrt{p}$.*

ILLUSTRATION 3.   The two square roots of $-7$ are $\pm \sqrt{-7}$, or $\pm i\sqrt{7}$.

On page 10, we met the result $\sqrt{H}\sqrt{K} = \sqrt{HK}$. This is true when $H \geq 0$ and $K \geq 0$. However, the result is NOT true if $H < 0$ and $K < 0$. This accounts for the caution above to use (5) immediately when it is applicable.

ILLUSTRATION 4.   To calculate $\sqrt{-2}\sqrt{-8}$, we use (5) to obtain

$$\sqrt{-2}\sqrt{-8} = i\sqrt{2}(i\sqrt{8}) = i^2\sqrt{2}\sqrt{8} = -1\sqrt{16} = -4.$$

If, incorrectly, we had failed to use (5) and had used $\sqrt{H}\sqrt{K} = \sqrt{HK}$, then

$$\sqrt{-2}\sqrt{-8} = \sqrt{(-2)(-8)} = \sqrt{16} = 4,$$

*which is wrong.*

## 9. Roots of any order, and rational exponents

If $H$ is any complex number, and $n$ is any positive integer, then $R$ is called an *n*th root of $H$ if $R^n = H$. In advanced algebra, it is proved that, if $H \neq 0$, there exist exactly $n$ distinct *n*th roots for $H$. We now restrict ourselves to the case where $H$ is a *real number*.

ILLUSTRATION 1.   3 is a third root (cube root) of 27 because $3^3 = 27$. $-2$ is a fifth root of $-32$ because $(-2)^5 = -32$.

If $H = 0$, the only *n*th root of $H$ is 0. If $H \neq 0$, the following results are proved at a more advanced level.

*If n is* **odd**, *every real number $H \neq 0$ has just* **one real *n*th root**, *which is positive when $H > 0$ and is negative when $H < 0$.*

*If n is* **even** *and $H < 0$, then all* *n*th *roots of H are imaginary.*

*If n is* **even** *and $H > 0$, then H has just two real* *n*th *roots, one positive and one negative, with equal absolute values.*

If $H > 0$, the *positive n*th root of $H$ is called its **principal *n*th root**. If $H < 0$ and *n is odd*, the *negative n*th root of $H$ is called its *principal nth root*. If $H = 0$, its *only* *n*th root is called the *principal nth root of H*. If $H < 0$ and *n is even*, no *n*th root of $H$ is called its principal *n*th root.

ILLUSTRATION 2.   The real 4th roots of 16 are $\pm 2$ because $2^4 = 16 = (-2)^4$; $+2$ is the principal 4th root of 16. The principal cube root of $-125$ is $-5$ because $(-5)^3 = -125$. The principal cube root of 125 is 5.

We use the **radical** $\sqrt[n]{H}$ to denote the *principal nth root of H*, when $H$ has a principal *n*th root. We read "$\sqrt[n]{H}$" as "*the nth root of H,*" or as "*the principal nth root of H.*" In $\sqrt[n]{H}$, we call $H$ the **radicand** and $n$ the **index** of the radical. When $n = 2$, the index is omitted and we use simply $\sqrt{H}$ instead of $\sqrt[2]{H}$. If $H$ has no principal *n*th root, and $n \neq 2$, sometimes $\sqrt[n]{H}$ is used to represent any one of the imaginary *n*th roots which appears convenient. If $n = 2$ and $H = -p$ where $p > 0$, we have already agreed that $\sqrt{H}$, or $\sqrt{-p}$, represents $i\sqrt{p}$.

$\sqrt[n]{H} > 0$   *if*   $H > 0$.

$\sqrt[n]{H} < 0$   *if*   $H < 0$ and *n is odd*.

$\sqrt[n]{H}$ *is imaginary if $H < 0$ and n is even.*

ILLUSTRATION   3.   $\sqrt[4]{16} = 2$;   $\sqrt[3]{-27} = -3$;   $\sqrt[3]{27} = 3$;   $\sqrt[4]{-9}$   is imaginary. The two real 4th roots of 81 are $\pm\sqrt[4]{81} = \pm 3$.

In this text, we shall have negligible use for $\sqrt[n]{H}$ when $n > 2$, and in all cases $\sqrt[n]{H}$ will be real. However, for completeness, we list the following properties of radicals, with the preceding limitation wherever it is essential. Also, $H > 0$ and $K > 0$ if $n$ is even.

$$(\sqrt[n]{H})^n = H; \qquad \sqrt[n]{H^n} = H; \qquad \sqrt[n]{HK} = \sqrt[n]{H}\sqrt[n]{K}.$$

$$\frac{\sqrt[n]{H}}{\sqrt[n]{K}} = \sqrt[n]{\frac{H}{K}}.$$

READ

*If $m$, $n$, and $m/n$ are positive integers, then*

$$\sqrt[n]{H^m} = H^{m/n}. \tag{1}$$

Powers with rational exponents are introduced as optional symbols instead of radicals in representing roots of numbers. Consider the possibility of using a power such as $a^{2/3}$. If the exponent $2/3$ is to obey the laws of exponents as met for integral exponents, then it should be true that

$$(a^{\frac{2}{3}})^3 = a^{\frac{2}{3}\cdot 3} = a^2.$$

Or, $a^{2/3}$ should represent a cube root of $a^2$. This illustrates the motivation for the definition which follows.

DEFINITION III.   *If $H$ is a real number, and $m$ and $n$ are positive integers where $m/n$ is in lowest terms, with\* $n$ odd when $H < 0$, then $H^{m/n}$ represents the principal $n$th root of $H^m$. Or,*

$$H^{m/n} = \sqrt[n]{H^m}. \tag{2}$$

Notice that (2) is consistent with (1) when $m/n$ is an integer. From (2) with $m = 1$,

$$H^{1/n} = \sqrt[n]{H}. \tag{3}$$

In algebra, it is shown that $\sqrt[n]{H^m} = (\sqrt[n]{H})^m$. Hence, instead of (2), we may use

$$H^{m/n} = (\sqrt[n]{H})^m. \tag{4}$$

ILLUSTRATION 4.   $8^{1/3} = \sqrt[3]{8} = 2.$   $(-8)^{1/3} = \sqrt[3]{-8} = -2.$   From (2),

$$64^{5/6} = \sqrt[6]{64^5} = \sqrt[6]{(2^6)^5} = \sqrt[6]{2^{30}} = 2^{30/6} = 2^5 = 32.$$

From (4), more easily,

$$64^{5/6} = (\sqrt[6]{64})^5 = (\sqrt[6]{2^6})^5 = 2^5 = 32.$$

If $-r$ is any negative rational number, and $A \neq 0$, then $A^{-r}$ is defined by

$$A^{-r} = \frac{1}{A^r}. \tag{5}$$

\* This agreement makes it certain that $H^m$ has a principal $n$th root.

On the basis of (2) and (5), it is proved in algebra that the laws for integral exponents, as on page 5, apply also when the exponents are *any rational numbers*. This fact, and certain results which arise in calculus, frequently make it desirable to use the exponential form $H^{m/n}$ instead of $\sqrt[n]{H^m}$ in analytic manipulation.

ILLUSTRATION 5.    $\sqrt[6]{x^5}\sqrt[3]{xy^2} = x^{5/6}(xy^2)^{1/3}$

$$= x^{5/6}x^{1/3}y^{2/3} = x^{5/6}x^{2/6}y^{4/6}$$

$$= x(x^{1/6}y^{4/6}) = x\sqrt[6]{xy^4}.$$

## Exercise 3

*Express in terms of i.*

1. $\sqrt{-9}$.    2. $\sqrt{-36}$.    3. $\sqrt{-100}$.    4. $\sqrt{-25}$.    5. $\sqrt{-\frac{1}{9}}$.
6. $\sqrt{-\frac{49}{36}}$.    7. $\sqrt{-\frac{25}{144}}$.    8. $\sqrt{-\frac{1}{4}}$.    9. $\sqrt{-\frac{81}{4}}$.    10. $\sqrt{-\frac{64}{49}}$.

*Find the two square roots of the number.*

11. $-49$.    12. $-\frac{25}{4}$.    13. $-25$.    14. $-\frac{49}{81}$.    16. $-\frac{9}{100}$.

*Each literal numeral except i represents a real number. Express the radical in terms of i.*

16. $\sqrt{-9x^2}$.    17. $\sqrt{-81y^4}$.    18. $\sqrt{-\frac{1}{9}a^2}$.    19. $\sqrt{-\frac{16}{81}x^4}$.

*Calculate the power of i by use of $i^2 = -1$.*

20. $i^3$.    21. $i^9$.    22. $i^5$.    23. $i^{17}$.    24. $i^{19}$.

NOTE 1.    Observe that $i^4 = 1$. Hence, any positive integral power of $i$ can be computed by use of the two convenient powers, $i^2 = -1$ and $i^4 = 1$.

*Perform any indicated operation, and simplify to the form $(a + bi)$.*

25. $\sqrt{-3}\sqrt{-9}$.    26. $\sqrt{-2}\sqrt{-10}$.    27. $\sqrt{-15}\sqrt{-6}$.
28. $(2 - 3i)(4 - 5i)$.    29. $(-2 + 5i)(4 - 3i)$.
30. $(1 + i)(3i - 1)$.    31. $(5 + 4i)(5 - 4i)$.
32. $(2 + 7i)(3i - 4)$.    33. $(6 - i)(4 - 3i)$.
34. $(2 + 3i)(4 - i + 3i^2)$.    35. $(2 + 3i)^2$.
36. $(3 - 4i)(3 + 4i)$.    37. $(5 - 6i)(5 + 6i)$.
38. $(2 - 5i)^2$.    39. $(1 + 6i)^2$.    40. $(3i - 5)^2$.
41. Specify the principal square root of 144;   4/81;   36/25.
42. Specify the principal cube root of $-27$;   8;   27/64;   $-216$;   1000; .001.
43. Specify the principal 4th root of 81;   625;   10,000;   .0001.

*Find the indicated principal root or power.*

44. $\sqrt{b^2}$ if $b > 0$.    45. $\sqrt{b^2}$ if $b < 0$.    46. $\sqrt[3]{x^3}$.
47. $\sqrt[3]{1000}$.    48. $\sqrt[3]{.001}$.    49. $\sqrt[4]{16}$.    50. $\sqrt{400}$.

$|x| = \begin{cases} x & \text{if } x > 0 \\ -x & \text{if } x < 0 \end{cases}$

51. $(\sqrt[3]{31})^3$.    52. $\sqrt[3]{x^3 y^6}$.    53. $\sqrt[4]{5^4}$.    54. $\sqrt[3]{27}$.

55. $\sqrt[3]{64}$.    56. $\sqrt[4]{81}$.    57. $\sqrt[4]{16}$.    58. $4^{1/2}$.

59. $16^{1/4}$.    60. $36^{3/2}$.    61. $(-8)^{1/3}$.    62. $216^{1/3}$.

## 10. Linear equations

An **equation** is a statement that two numbers, called the sides of the equation, are equal. If an equation is written without use of a variable, the equation may be true or false.

ILLUSTRATION 1.  The equation $3 = 1 + \sqrt{4}$ is a true statement, and $2 + \sqrt{9} = 7$ is false.

If at least one variable is involved in an equation, it is called an **open equation.**

ILLUSTRATION 2.  If $x$ is a variable, then $2 + 3x = 14$ is an open equation which is a true statement when $x = 4$, but is false if $x$ has any other value.

Hereafter, the unqualified word *equation* will refer to an *open equation* unless otherwise stated. A **solution of** an equation in a single variable $x$ is a value of $x$ for which the equation becomes a true statement, or is *satisfied*. A solution of an equation in $x$ also may be called a **root** of it.

ILLUSTRATION 3.  The solutions of the equation $3x^2 + 7x - 6 = 0$, or of $(3x - 2)(x + 3) = 0$ are $x = -3$ and $x = \frac{2}{3}$.

A solution of an equation in two variables $x$ and $y$ is a *pair* of their values $(x, y)$, for which the equation becomes a *true statement*, or is *satisfied*. A solution of an equation in more than two variables is defined similarly.

ILLUSTRATION 4.  The equation $x + 2y = 7$ has the solution $(x = 3, y = 2)$, as can be verified by substitution. For each value of $x$, or of $y$, a corresponding value of the other variable can be computed by use of the equation so as to obtain a solution $(x, y)$. Thus, if $x = 5$, then $5 + 2y = 7$, or $2y = 2$, or $y = 1$, so that $(x = 5, y = 1)$ is a solution. Hence, the equation $x + 2y = 7$ has infinitely many solutions.

The collection of all solutions of an equation is called its **solution set.** *To solve* an equation means to find all of its solutions.

ILLUSTRATION 5.  In Illustration 3, the solution set is $\{-3, \frac{2}{3}\}$, consisting of two numbers. In Illustration 4, the solution set has infinitely many members.

An equation is called **consistent** if it has at least one solution, and **inconsistent** if there are no solutions. A **conditional equation** is one which is *not* satisfied by *all* sets of values of the variables involved. If an equation, open or not, is satisfied by *all* values of any variables involved, the equation is referred to as an **identity**, or **identical equation**. Two equations are said to be **equivalent** if they have the same solutions.

ILLUSTRATION 6.    The equations $2x + 5 = 3$ and $x(2x + 5) = 3x$ are *not* equivalent. The second equation has the solution $x = 0$, not possessed as a solution by the first equation.

Let $F = G$ represent a given equation. Let $U$ and $V$ be number symbols which possibly involve any variable present in $F$ or $G$, with $V \neq 0$ for all values of the variable. Then, in the study of algebra, the student has had experience with the facts that $F = G$ is equivalent to

$$F + U = G + U, \quad \text{and to} \quad FV = GV. \tag{1}$$

Thus, in $F + U = G + U$, we note that the same number expression may be *added* (or *subtracted*) *on both sides* of $F = G$. In $FV = GV$, we recall that both sides of $F = G$ may be *multiplied* (or, *divided*) by the same number expression, provided that it is not equal to zero for any admissable values of the variables.

A **polynomial equation** is one where each member is a polynomial in the variables or is zero. A linear equation in one variable, $x$, is a polynomial equation equivalent to $cx = d$, where $c$ and $d$ are constants with $c \neq 0$. Hence, the equation has just one solution, $x = d/c$.

EXAMPLE 1.    Solve: $\dfrac{33}{10} + \dfrac{4x + 9}{5} = -\dfrac{6x - 5}{4}.$ $\tag{2}$

*Solution.*    Multiply both sides of (2) by the lowest common denominator, 20, to clear the equation of fractions:

$$2(33) + 4(4x + 9) = -5(6x - 5), \quad \text{or}$$
$$66 + 16x + 36 = -30x + 25;$$
$$46x = -77; \quad x = -\tfrac{77}{46}.$$

## 11.   Quadratic equations in one variable

A polynomial equation of degree 2 is called a **quadratic equation**. Any quadratic equation in a single variable $x$ is equivalent to an equation.

$$ax^2 + bx + c = 0, \tag{1}$$

where $a$, $b$, and $c$ are constants and $a \neq 0$.

To solve a quadratic equation in $x$ where no term, such as $bx$ in (1), of the first degree in $x$ occurs, solve for $x^2$ and extract square roots. The solutions may not be real numbers.

EXAMPLE 1.   Solve:                                   $5x^2 = 14 + 3x^2.$                     (2)

Solution.          $5x^2 - 3x^2 = 14,$     or     $x^2 = 7.$

Hence, $x = \pm\sqrt{7}.$

EXAMPLE 2.   Solve:                                   $3y^2 + 25 = -2y^2.$                    (3)

Solution.          $3y^2 + 2y^2 = -25,$     or     $y^2 = -5.$

Hence, $y = \pm\sqrt{-5}$, or $y = \pm i\sqrt{5}.$

Sometimes a quadratic equation may be solved by use of factoring, after terms in the equation are transposed, if necessary, to obtain 0 as one member.

EXAMPLE 3.   Solve:                                   $6x^2 - 5x = 6.$                        (4)

Solution.   *1.*  Arrange with one member zero, and then factor:

$$6x^2 - 5x - 6 = 0;\quad (3x + 2)(2x - 3) = 0.\qquad (5)$$

*2.*  Equation (5) is satisfied if and only if

$$3x + 2 = 0 \quad or \quad 2x - 3 = 0.$$

Hence, the solutions are $x = -\frac{2}{3}$ and $x = \frac{3}{2}.$

Recall that $(x + c)^2 = x^2 + 2cx + c^2$. Hence, if we wish to add a term to a polynomial $(x^2 + kx)$ to make it a *perfect square* (that is, *to complete a square*), we proceed as follows:

In $(x^2 + kx)$, *divide the coefficient of x by 2; then add the square of this result.* $\left.\right\}$     (6)

In arriving at (6), we thought of $k = 2c$ in $(x^2 + 2cx + c^2)$.

ILLUSTRATION 1.   To complete a square with $(x^2 + 7x)$, we add $(\frac{7}{2})^2$:

$$x^2 + 7x + \tfrac{49}{4} = (x + \tfrac{7}{2})^2.$$

EXAMPLE 4.   Solve the following equation by completing a square:

$$3x^2 + 2x + 4 = 0.\qquad (7)$$

Solution.   Subtract 4; divide by 3:

$$x^2 + \tfrac{2}{3}x = -\tfrac{4}{3}.\qquad (8)$$

Add $(\frac{1}{2} \cdot \frac{2}{3})^2$:                   $x^2 + \tfrac{2}{3}x + (\tfrac{1}{3})^2 = -\tfrac{4}{3} + \tfrac{1}{9};$

Write as a square on left:   $(x + \tfrac{1}{3})^2 = -\tfrac{11}{9}.\qquad (9)$

Extract square roots:        $x + \tfrac{1}{3} = \pm\sqrt{-\tfrac{11}{9}};$  *or*

$$x + \tfrac{1}{3} = \pm\tfrac{1}{3}i\sqrt{11};\qquad x = -\tfrac{1}{3} \pm \tfrac{1}{3}i\sqrt{11}.\qquad (10)$$

$(x+1)^2 = x^2 + 2x + 1 =$
*identity equation*

EXAMPLE 5. Solve by completing a square, where $a$, $b$, and $c$ are constants, and $a \neq 0$:

$$ax^2 + bx + c = 0. \tag{11}$$

*Solution.*  Subtract $c$; divide by $a$:

$$x^2 + \frac{b}{a}x = -\frac{c}{a}. \tag{12}$$

Complete a square on the left-hand side by adding $\left(\frac{1}{2}\cdot\frac{b}{a}\right)^2$ to both sides:

$$x^2 + \frac{b}{a}x + \frac{b^2}{4a^2} = \frac{b^2}{4a^2} - \frac{c}{a} = \frac{b^2 - 4ac}{4a^2};$$

Write as a square on left:  $\left(x + \frac{b}{2a}\right)^2 = \frac{b^2 - 4ac}{4a^2}.$

Extract square roots:  $x + \frac{b}{2a} = \frac{\pm\sqrt{b^2 - 4ac}}{2a};$  or

$$x = \frac{-b \pm \sqrt{b^2 - 4ac}}{2a}, \tag{13}$$

which is called the **quadratic formula** for the solution of (11).

ILLUSTRATION 2.  To solve $2x^2 + 4x + 5 = 0$, we use $a = 2$, $b = 4$, and $c = 5$ in (13):

$$x = \frac{-4 \pm \sqrt{16 - 40}}{4} = \frac{-4 \pm \sqrt{-24}}{4}. \tag{14}$$

Since $\sqrt{-24} = i\sqrt{4(6)} = 2i\sqrt{6}$, from (14) we find

$$x = \frac{-4 \pm 2i\sqrt{6}}{4}, \quad or \quad x = \frac{-2 \pm i\sqrt{6}}{2}.$$

Because of (13), it is seen that any quadratic equation (11) has exactly two solutions, which become *identical* when $b^2 - 4ac = 0$. We call $(b^2 - 4ac)$ the **discriminant** of (13). The solutions are *distinct real numbers* when $b^2 - 4ac > 0$; *equal real numbers* when $b^2 - 4ac = 0$; *imaginary numbers* when $b^2 - 4ac < 0$.

ILLUSTRATION 3.  To solve $4x^2 - 20x + 25 = 0$, we may factor, and obtain

$$(2x - 5)^2 = 0, \quad or \quad (2x - 5)(2x - 5) = 0.$$

Hence, from each factor we find $x = \frac{5}{2}$. Then, it is customary to say that the given equation has two equal solutions $\frac{5}{2}$ and $\frac{5}{2}$. Also, for $4x^2 - 20x + 25 = 0$, by use of the quadratic formula (13),

$$x = \frac{20 \pm \sqrt{(20)^2 - 4(4)(25)}}{8};$$

$$x = \frac{20 \pm \sqrt{400 - 400}}{8} = \frac{20 \pm 0}{8}.$$

Thus, both solutions as given by (13) are $\frac{5}{2}$.

## Exercise 4

*The variable in the equation is x, y, z, or u. Solve the equation.*

1.  $4x - 2 = x + 7$.
2.  $7 + 3z = 4 - 2z$.
3.  $3y + 7 = 4(3 - y)$.
4.  $4u + 3 = 6u - 5$.
5.  $\frac{2x}{3} - 4 = \frac{5x - 19}{2}$.
6.  $\frac{2x}{3} + 2 - \frac{3x + 9}{4} = 0$.
7.  $\frac{u + 5}{6} - \frac{u - 6}{9} = 2$.
8.  $\frac{8z - 11}{6} - \frac{7}{2} = \frac{2z - 5}{2}$.

9.  In the Fahrenheit–centigrade equation $5F - 9C = 160$, solve for $C$ in terms of $F$. Then, use the resulting formula to find the centigrade temperature corresponding to the following Fahrenheit temperatures: $0°$; $32°$; $212°$.

10. In Problem 9, find $F$ and $C$ when they are equal.

*Solve. Obtain decimal values of real results by use of Table I.*

11. $2x^2 = 3$.
12. $5x^2 + 3 = 0$.
13. $\frac{3}{2}x^2 - 2 = \frac{1}{3}x^2$.

*Solve by factoring.*

14. $x^2 - 3x = 10$.
15. $2x^2 - 5x - 3 = 0$.
16. $y^2 + 5y = 14$.
17. $3x^2 + 2x - 5 = 0$.
18. $5x^2 + 9x = 0$.
19. $3x^2 + 7x = 0$.
20. $16x^2 - 24x = -9$.
21. $25y^2 - 20y = -4$.

*Solve by completing a square, without using the quadratic formula.*

22. $x^2 + 6x - 7 = 0$.
23. $x^2 - 3x + 3 = 0$.

*Solve by use of the quadratic formula, or by use of factoring.*

24. $2x^2 - x = 3$.
25. $3x^2 - x = 10$.
26. $7y^2 - 4y = 3$.
27. $10 + 11x = -3x^2$.
28. $8x^2 + 2x = 3$.
29. $3z - z^2 = -10$.
30. $4x^2 + 12x = -9$.
31. $24x^2 + 2x = 15$.
32. $x^2 - 6x = -13$.
33. $3x^2 - 2x = 9$.
34. $9x^2 + 23 = -30x$.
35. $4x^2 + 5 = 8x$.
36. $9x^2 + 6x = 7$.
37. $5z - 3z^2 = 0$.
38. $24x^2 - 2x = 5$.

# 2 | LINEAR INEQUALITIES IN ONE VARIABLE AND SETS

## 12. The role of analytic geometry

In the year 1637, the French mathematician and philosopher RENÉ DESCARTES (1596–1650) established a landmark in the field of mathematics by publishing a book called *la Géometrie*. In it, he introduced the notion of the equation of a curve and corresponding analytic methods into the study of geometry in a plane. Similar methods were developed later for the study of geometry in space of three dimensions. This combination of analytic methods and geometry is referred to as *analytic geometry*. In contrast, the study of geometry by purely geometric means, as in standard Euclidean geometry at the high school level, is called *synthetic geometry*.

The achievements of Descartes provided fundamental assistance in the invention of the subject called *calculus* by SIR ISAAC NEWTON (1642–1727) and GOTTFRIED WILHELM LEIBNITZ (1646–1716). Calculus forms a corner-stone of modern mathematics and of our technological civilization. A few chapters on calculus will be met in this text.

Analytic geometry has applications apart from its use in calculus. We shall develop only certain aspects of analytic geometry, as needed for the purposes of this text.

## 13. Directed line segments on a number scale

Consider a number scale on a line, labeled as $OX$ in Figure 2. If $x$ is any real number, associate it with that point $P$ on $OX$ representing $x$, and call $x$ the **coordinate** of $P$. To indicate that $P$ has the coordinate $x$, write $P:(x)$, to be read simply "$P$, $x$" or, more elaborately if desired, "$P$ *with coordinate x*."

ILLUSTRATION 1.   In Figure 2, points on the scale are labeled above the line, with the corresponding coordinates below the line. Observe $A:(-3)$, $B:(2)$,   $C:(3)$,   and   $P:(x)$.

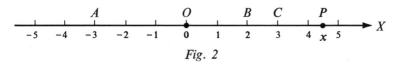

Fig. 2

Let* $P_1:(x_1)$ and $P_2:(x_2)$ be any two distinct points on a number scale $OX$, as in Figure 3. Then $P_1P_2$ will represent, or be the *name* of the line segment with $P_1$ as the initial point and $P_2$ as the endpoint. We shall refer to $P_1P_2$ as a *directed line segment*, directed *from* $P_1$ to $P_2$. The segment may be thought of as an arrow or vector with the initial point $P_1$ and arrowhead at $P_2$. $P_1P_2$ is said to have *positive direction*, and will be assigned a *positive value* later, if $P_1P_2$ is directed to the *right* on $OX$. $P_1P_2$ is said to have *negative direction*, and will be assigned a *negative value* if $P_1P_2$ is directed to the *left* on $OX$. If $P_1$ and $P_2$ are the same point, we let $P_1P_2$ represent the segment with no direction consisting of just that point.

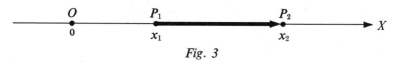

Fig. 3

For any points $P_1$ and $P_2$, we let $\overline{P_1P_2}$, read "*P one P two bar*," represent the *directed distance* from $P_1$ to $P_2$, or the *measure* of $P_1P_2$. We define $\overline{P_1P_2}$ as follows:

$$\textbf{(measure of } P_1P_2) = \overline{P_1P_2} = x_2 - x_1. \tag{1}$$

Thus $\overline{P_1P_2}$ is either *plus* or *minus* the number of units in the distance between $P_1$ and $P_2$. Then, with length meaning a nonnegative number,

$$(length\ of\ P_1P_2) = |\overline{P_1P_2}| = |x_2 - x_1|. \tag{2}$$

With the preceding agreements about *directed segments* on $OX$, we refer to $OX$ as a *directed line*.

ILLUSTRATION 2.   With $A:(-3)$,   $B:(2)$,   and   $C:(3)$ in Figure 2,

$$\overline{AB} = 2 - (-3) = 2 + 3 = 5; \quad |\overline{AB}| = |5| = 5; \tag{3}$$
$$\overline{BA} = -3 - 2 = -5; \quad |\overline{BA}| = |-5| = 5; \tag{4}$$
$$\overline{OC} = 3 - 0 = 3; \quad |\overline{OC}| = |3| = 3; \tag{5}$$
$$\overline{CO} = 0 - 3 = -3; \quad |\overline{CO}| = |-3| = 3. \tag{6}$$

* We shall read "$P_1:(x_1)$" as "$P$ one x one."

In (3) and (4), notice that $\overrightarrow{AB} = -\overrightarrow{BA}$. This illustrates the fact that, if the direction of a directed line segment on a number scale is *reversed*, the measure of the segment is *multiplied by* $-1$.

We use the number scale as a background for geometrical language where each *number* may be referred to as a *point*. Then, to remark that *b is close to a*, will mean that the scale distance $|b - a|$ is small.

On page 4, "$a < b$" was defined to mean that "$(b - a)$ is *positive*." Let $P:(a)$ and $Q:(b)$ be the corresponding points on a number scale, as in Figure 4. Then, by (1), $\overrightarrow{PQ} = b - a$. To state that $(b - a)$ *is positive* is equivalent to saying that *segment PQ is directed to the right*. Hence,

*a < b means that a is to the* **left** *of b on the number scale.*

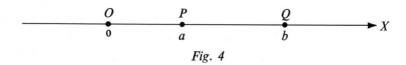

Fig. 4

ILLUSTRATION 3.    Since $A:(-3)$ is to the left of $B:(2)$ in Figure 2, the directed segment $AB$ has *positive* direction, which corresponds to the fact that $\overrightarrow{AB} = 2 - (-3) = +5$. Hence, $-3 < 2$ because $\overrightarrow{AB} > 0$. Similarly, $-1 < 6$ because $-1$ is to the *left* of 6 on a number scale, or $6 - (-1) = 7 > 0$.

ILLUSTRATION 4.    Let $A:(x_1)$, $B:(x_2)$, and $C:(x_3)$ be any three points on a number scale. Then

$$\overrightarrow{AB} + \overrightarrow{BC} = (x_2 - x_1) + (x_3 - x_2) = x_2 - x_1 + x_3 - x_2, \quad or$$
$$\overrightarrow{AB} + \overrightarrow{BC} = x_3 - x_1 = \overrightarrow{AC}.$$

That is, for any points $A$, $B$, $C$ on the scale,

$$\overrightarrow{AB} + \overrightarrow{BC} = \overrightarrow{AC}. \tag{7}$$

## Exercise 5

*1.*    Mark $R:(-3)$, $S:(2)$, $P:(-5)$, and $D:(6)$ on a number scale and calculate $\overrightarrow{RS}$; $\overrightarrow{SP}$; $\overrightarrow{DP}$; $\overrightarrow{DR}$; $|\overrightarrow{RP}|$; $|\overrightarrow{SP}|$.

*Plot the points on a number scale. Calculate* $\overrightarrow{AB}$, $\overrightarrow{BC}$, *and* $\overrightarrow{AC}$, *and check* $\overrightarrow{AC} = \overrightarrow{AB} + \overrightarrow{BC}$. *Also, compute* $(|\overrightarrow{AB}| + |\overrightarrow{BC}|)$ *and* $|\overrightarrow{AC}|$.

*2.*  $A:(-6)$; $B:(-2)$; $C:(-1)$.     *3.*  $A:(7)$; $B:(-4)$; $C:(-2)$.

*4.*  $A:(0)$; $B:(-5)$; $C:(6)$.      *5.*  $A:(7)$; $B:(4)$; $C:(0)$.

*Visualize the number as represented on a number scale. Then state the fact by use of an inequality.*

6.   *h* is positive; negative.
7.   *x* is to the right of $-3$.
8.   *x* is to the left of 5.
9.   *x* is to the left of $-2$.
10.  *k* is to the right of 3.
11.  *h* is to the left of $-6$.

*The inequality* $|a + b| \leq |a| + |b|$ *can be proved to be true for all real\* numbers a, b, and c. Verify the result for the indicated numbers.*

12.  $a = 4; b = 8$.
13.  $a = -9; b = -3$.
14.  $a = -16; b = -2$.
15.  $a = 9; b = -3$.
16.  $a = -6; b = 4$.
17.  $a = 0; b = -8$.

## 14.   Solution of linear inequalities

If $A$ and $B$ involve at least one variable, then "$A < B$" is called an *open inequality*. Hereafter, unless otherwise indicated, "*inequality*" will mean "*open inequality*." In the terminology for equations on page 19, if we merely change the word "*equation*" to "*inequality*," corresponding terminology is obtained for inequalities. Thus, two inequalities are said to be *equivalent* if they have the *same solution set*. An inequality is called an *absolute* or *identical inequality* if it is true for *all* values of the variables involved.

ILLUSTRATION 1.   The solution set of the inequality $x < 2$ consists of all numbers located to the left of 2 on a number scale. This illustrates the fact that an inequality may have *infinitely many solutions*.

ILLUSTRATION 2.   The inequality $x^2 < 0$ is *inconsistent* (has no solutions) because $x^2$ is positive or 0 for all real values of $x$. The inequality $x^2 \geq 0$ is an *identical inequality* because it is true for all values of $x$.

If $T$ is any set of real numbers, we define the **graph of $T$** on a number scale as the set of points on the scale representing the numbers of $T$. Thus, if $T = \{2, 3, 4\}$, the graph of $T$ would be the three points representing 2, 3, and 4 on the scale.

DEFINITION I.   *The graph on a number scale of an inequality involving a single variable, x, is the set of points on the scale which represent the solutions of the inequality. Or, its graph is the graph of its solution set.*

ILLUSTRATION 3.   In Figure 5 on page 28, the thick part of the scale, with the omission of the circled point for 2, is the graph of $x > 2$.

Since an inequality in a variable $x$, as a rule, will have infinitely many solutions, it is impossible to list them. Hence, *to solve* an inequality usually

---

\* The inequality also is true if $a$, $b$, and $c$ represent any complex numbers We shall not be concerned with this case.

will mean *to describe* the solutions in some simple fashion, so that as many solutions as desired can be computed easily. Frequently, such a description is made most conveniently by graphing the inequality, to exhibit the solution set.

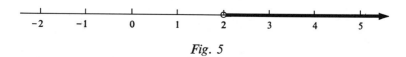

*Fig. 5*

From page 4, recall that

$$c < d \quad \text{means that} \quad (d - c) \text{ is positive.} \tag{1}$$

THEOREM I.   *Suppose that H, K, r, p, and N are number symbols involving the same variables, with p > 0 and N < 0 for all values of the variables. Then, the inequality H < K is equivalent to (has the same solutions as) each of the following inequalities:*

$$H + r < K + r; \quad pH < pK; \quad NH > NK. \tag{2}$$

*Proof of equivalence to* "$H + r < K + r$."   By (1),

$$\text{"} H < K \text{"} \quad \text{means that} \quad (K - H) \text{ is positive;} \tag{3}$$

$$\text{"} H + r < K + r \text{"} \quad \text{means that} \quad [(K + r) - (H + r)] \text{ is positive, or} \tag{4}$$

$$\text{that } (K - H) \text{ is positive.} \tag{5}$$

Since "$H < K$" and "$H + r < K + r$" have the same meaning, they have the *same solutions*, or are *equivalent*.

*Proof that* "$H < K$" *is equivalent to* "$NH > NK$."   By (1),

$$\text{"} NH > NK \text{"} \quad \text{means that} \quad (NH - NK) \text{ is positive, or} \tag{6}$$

$$N(H - K) \text{ is positive.} \tag{7}$$

Since $N$ is *negative*, (7) means that $(H - K)$ is *negative*, or $(K - H)$ is *positive*, which is the meaning for "$H < K$" in (3). Hence, "$H < K$" has the same meaning as "$NH > NK$," so that these inequalities are *equivalent*.

The student may prove that $H < K$ is equivalent to $pH < pK$, of (2), in a problem of the next exercise.

In Theorem I, if "$<$" is replaced by "$\leq$," the results remain valid. This is true because, when "$=$" applies, the results are a consequence of well known properties of equations.

In solving inequalities, frequently we shall proceed from a given inequality through successive equivalent inequalities leading to the final solution. In such a procedure, Theorem I justifies *addition of the same number* on both sides of an inequality, *multiplication of both sides by a positive number*, and *multiplication of both sides by a negative number with simultaneous* **reversal of the sign of inequality**. Also, we recall that *division* by any number means *multiplication* by its *reciprocal*.

ILLUSTRATION 4.   If $-2x < 5$, then $x > \frac{5}{2}$, where we multiplied both sides by $-\frac{1}{2}$.

If $H$ and $K$ are polynomials in a variable $x$, an inequality $H < K$ is said to be *linear* in $x$ when $H < K$ is equivalent to an inequality of the form $ax < b$ where $a$ and $b$ are constants and $a \neq 0$. *To solve* a linear inequality in $x$ will mean to obtain a description of the solution set in the form

$$x < w \quad \textit{or} \quad w < x. \tag{8}$$

We obtain (8) for any linear inequality by applying operations of types (2) leading to equivalent inequalities.

EXAMPLE 1.   Solve:
$$\frac{3}{2} - x < \frac{3}{4} - \frac{1}{10}x. \tag{9}$$

*Solution.*   Multiply both sides by the lowest common denominator, 20:

$$30 - 20x < 15 - 2x.$$

Subtract 15 and add 20x on both sides; then divide by 18:

$$15 < 18x; \quad \frac{5}{6} < x.$$

Thus, the solutions of (9) consist of all values of $x$ on a number scale to the right of $\frac{5}{6}$. The graph of (9) would consist of the part of the scale just described.

## Exercise 6

*Solve the inequality. That is, obtain an equivalent inequality of the form* $x < w$ *or* $w < x$. *Then, graph the inequality on a number scale.*

1.  $x - 3 < 0$.    2.  $-x < 4$.    3.  $2 - \frac{1}{3}x < 0$.    4.  $2x - 7 \leqq 0$.
5.  $3x + 8 < 18$.    6.  $7 - \frac{2}{3}x < 4$.    7.  $11 - 5x \leqq 0$.
8.  $5 - 2x < 3x$.    9.  $\frac{1}{3}x - 2 < 2x$.    10.  $3x - \frac{1}{3} > \frac{5}{2}x - 4$.
11.  $5x - \frac{2}{3} > 6x - 4$.    12.  $\frac{7}{2} - \frac{8}{3}x \leqq -\frac{5}{2} - \frac{20}{3}x$.
13.  $\frac{4}{5}x - \frac{2}{3} \leqq \frac{3}{2}x - \frac{17}{5}$.    14.  $\frac{3}{4} - \frac{1}{3}x + \frac{7}{2} \leqq \frac{5}{2}x$.
15.  $\frac{4}{5}x + 6(x - 1) \leqq \frac{3}{2}(2x + 1)$.

*Use* (1) *on page 28 in proving the specified result.*

16.  If $A < B$ and $B < C$, prove that $A < C$.
17.  If $A < B$ and $C < D$, prove that $A + C < B + D$.
18.  In Theorem I on page 28, prove that $H < K$ is equivalent to $pH < pK$.

## 15.  Some operations on sets

A set, $T$, of elements (not necessarily numbers) may be described by introducing a variable, say $v$, whose domain is $T$, and writing a condition on $v$ which is true if and only if $v$ is in $T$.

ILLUSTRATION 1.   The infinite set, $T$, of numbers greater than $-2$ can be represented by

$$T = \{x \mid -2 < x\}. \tag{1}$$

In (1), the vertical rule is read "*such that.*" Then, (1) is read as follows:

*T is the set of all numbers x such that $-2 < x$.*

When a symbol like that in (1) is used, we say that "*set builder,*" or "*set selector*" notation is employed. If $v$ is a variable whose domain is a certain set $T$, and if the nature of $T$ is well known, we may write simply $T = \{v\}$, to be read "*T is the set of elements v.*"

In the following discussion, we shall assume that all sets to be mentioned are subsets of a certain set $W$, called the *universe*, or the *universal set*, or the *basic space.*

DEFINITION II.   *If W is the universe, the complement, $S'$ (read "S prime"), of any set S is the set of all elements of W which are not in S.*

The elements of the universe $W$ are being thought of at present as *any* specified elements. Nevertheless, to appreciate Definition II, and later terminology, it is useful to act as if the elements of $W$ were points in a given plane. Thus, in Figure 6, let $W$ be thought of as all points of the plane inside the large circle. Let $S$ be the points of $W$ inside the small circle, left clear in the figure. Then, the complement $S'$ consists of those points of $W$ which are ruled. This representation of sets as points in a plane is extremely useful. A corresponding diagram like Figure 6 sometimes is called a **Venn diagram**. Such diagrams were first used by the mathematician JOHN VENN (1834–1923).

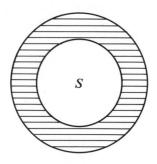

*Fig. 6*

ILLUSTRATION 2.    If the universe is the whole plane, and $R$ is the set of ruled points inside the circle in Figure 7, then the complement $R'$ of $R$ is the set of points indicated by radial lines.

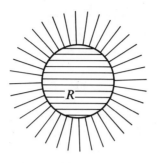

*Fig. 7*

DEFINITION III.    *The* **union** *of any number\* of sets is the set consisting of all elements which are in one or more of the sets.*

If $S$ and $T$ are sets, the "*union of S and T*" is represented by "$S \cup T$," read "*S union T.*"    By the wording of Definition III, the *order* in which the sets are mentioned is of no importance in referring to their union. Thus, $S \cup T = T \cup S$. Hence it is said that the operation of forming the *union* of two sets is *commutative.* The symbol "$\cup$" can be read "*union*" wherever met. The union of three sets ($S$, $T$, $V$) is represented by $S \cup T \cup V$, with the sets in any order. The language of Definition III, where the order of the sets is immaterial, shows that

$$S \cup T \cup V = S \cup (T \cup V) = T \cup (S \cup V) = etc.,$$

with any two of the sets associated as desired. Hence, it is said that the *union* operation is *associative.*

ILLUSTRATION 3.    Let the universe $W$ be all points in the plane of Figure 8 on page 32. Let $S$ be the ruled set of points inside the large circle, and $T$ be the ruled set inside the small circle. Then, $S \cup T$ is the set of all ruled points. This set includes some points, doubly ruled, which are in both $S$ and $T$. Thus, $S \cup T$ consists of points in $S$ alone, in $T$ alone, and in both $S$ and $T$.

DEFINITION IV.    *The* **intersection** *of any number† of sets is the set of elements belonging to all of the sets.*

* Possibly an *infinite* number, in advanced application of sets, but not in this text.
† Possibly an infinite number.

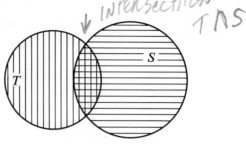

*INTERSECTION*
$T \cap S$

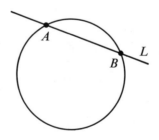

*Fig. 8*

If $S$ and $T$ are subsets of the universe $W$, the intersection of $S$ and $T$ is represented by "$S \cap T$," read "$S$ *intersection* $T$," where the order in which $S$ and $T$ are written is immaterial. That is, $S \cap T = T \cap S$; hence, the operation of *intersection* of sets is said to be *commutative*. The symbol "$\cap$" may be read "*intersection*" wherever met. The intersection of three sets $(S, T, V)$ is represented by $S \cap T \cap V$, with the sets in any order. The language of Definition IV shows that

$$S \cap T \cap V = S \cap (T \cap V) = V \cap (S \cap T) = etc.,$$

where any two of the sets may be associated. Hence, it is said the *intersection* operation is *associative*.

ILLUSTRATION 4.    In Figure 8, with sets $S$ and $T$ as described in Illustration 3, $S \cap T$ is represented by the points which are doubly ruled, and thus are in both $S$ and $T$. In Figure 9, let $S$ be the set of points on the circle and $T$ be the set of points on the line $L$. Then, $S \cap T$ consists of the points $A$ and $B$ where the line and the circle intersect. Thus, the concept of the intersection of sets is consistent with the meaning of intersections in elementary geometry, as applied to curves.

*Fig. 9*

DEFINITION V.    *To state that two sets $S$ and $T$ are* **mutually exclusive,** *or* **disjoint,** *means that they have no element in common, or that $S \cap T = \varnothing$,* *the empty set. To say that certain sets A, B, C, · · · are mutually exclusive means that the intersection of any two of them is the empty set.*

ILLUSTRATION 5.  In Figure 10 the ruled sets of points $S$ and $T$ are mutually exclusive sets.

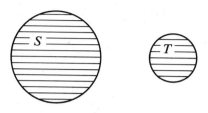

*Fig. 10*

NOTE 1.   Let $H$ and $K$ be meaningful statements. Then, we emphasize the following fact.*

*In this text, the statement " **H OR K is true**" means that one of the following three situations exists: (1) H is true and K is not true; (2) H is not true and K is true; (3) both H and K are true.*

With the preceding understanding, $A \cup B$ can be described as the set of elements in $A$ **OR** $B$, while $A \cap B$ is the set of elements in $A$ **AND** $B$.

ILLUSTRATION 6.   Let the universe $W$ be all points in the plane, $S$ be the set of points inside the large circle, and $T$ be the set inside the small circle in Figure 11. The various regions in the figure are numbered (I), (II), (III), and (IV), where (I) is ruled. To avoid complications, we shall omit mention of where boundary points on the circles belong in such a classification. Then (IV) = $S' \cap T'$; (II) = $S \cap T'$; (I) = $S \cap T$; (III) = $S' \cap T$.

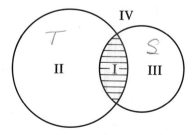

*Fig. 11*

* With "*or*" used as specified above, it may be said that the "*inclusive or*" is being employed. In the field of logic, sometimes "*exclusive or*" is used, where (3) above is not a possibility.

ILLUSTRATION 7. If the universe is $W = \{all\ positive\ integers\}$, and $A = \{1, 2, 3, 4, 5, 6, 7\}$, $B = \{5, 6, 7, 8, 9, 10, 11\}$, and $C = \{7, 8, 9, 10, 11, 12, 13, 14\}$, then we obtain

$$A' = \{all\ integers\ x \mid x > 7\}; \quad A \cup B = \{1, 2, 3, \cdots, 11\};$$
$$A \cap B = \{5, 6, 7\}; \quad A \cup B \cup C = \{1, 2, \cdots, 14\}; \quad A \cap B \cap C = \{7\};$$
$$(A \cap B) \cup C = \{5, 6, \cdots, 14\}; \quad A' \cap C = \{8, 9, 10, \cdots, 14\}.$$

ILLUSTRATION 8. Let the set of points inside each circle in Figure 12 represent one of sets $R$, $S$, and $T$, respectively. Then, each of the eight regions into which the plane is divided represents a set which can be expressed by use of $\cap$ applied to $R$, $S$, $T$, $R'$, $S'$, and $T'$. This will be done by the student in a later problem. For instance, the ruled region represents $(R \cap S) \cap T'$.

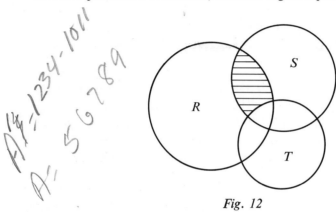

*Fig. 12*

## Exercise 7

In Problems 1 and 2, the universe is $W = \{all\ positive\ integers\}$.

1. If $A = \{4, 5, 6, 7, 8, 9\}$, $B = \{6, 7, 8, 9, 10, 11, 12\}$, and $C = \{8, 9, 10, 11, 12, 13, 14\}$, describe by the roster method or otherwise each of the following sets: $B'$; $A \cap B$; $A \cup B$; $A \cup B \cup C$; $A \cap B \cap C$; $(A \cap B) \cup C$; $A \cap (B \cup C)$; $C \cap A'$; $B' \cap (A \cup C)$; $A' \cap B'$; $A \cap B'$.

2. If $A = \{all\ even\ positive\ integers\}$, describe $A'$.

3. By the roster method, describe all proper subsets of children which can be selected from the set $\{John, Mary, Ruth\}$.

4. In a group of 100 children, let $S$ be the set having blond hair and $T$ be the set with blue eyes. There are 40 children in $S$, 30 with blue eyes and blond hair, and 20 who do not have blue eyes or blond hair. How many have blue eyes? To solve, draw a Venn diagram like Figure 11 on page 33 to represent $S$ and $T$. Then first indicate on the figure how many children are in the set for each region corresponding to the data.

5. In a group of 80 people, 40 have the antigen A in their blood; of these,

25 also have the antigen B, so that they are of AB blood type. Of the group, 30 do not have either A or B. How many of them have antigen B in their blood? Use a Venn diagram.

6. In a group of 200 men and women, there are 50 women who are Democrats, 60 men who are not Democrats, and 40 women who are not Democrats. How many men and how many Democrats are in the group? Use a Venn diagram.

7. In Figure 12, as described in Illustration 8 on page 34, number the eight regions. Then describe the region in the figure representing each of the following sets. $R \cap (S' \cap T')$; $(R \cap T) \cap S'$; $R \cap S \cap T$; $(S \cap T) \cap R'$; $T \cap (R' \cap S')$; $S \cap (R' \cap T')$; $R' \cap S' \cap T'$. Also, specify the regions represented by $S' \cup T'$; $R \cap (S' \cup T')$; $(R' \cup S') \cap T$.

8. Among 100 children, let $R$ be the set with blue eyes, $S$ be the set with blond hair, and $T$ be the set wearing braces to straighten teeth. Suppose that the number in $R$ is 26, in $S$ is 34, and in $T$ is 41. There are 10 with blue eyes and blond hair, 6 with blue eyes and braces, 9 with blond hair and braces, and 4 with blue eyes, blond hair, and braces. Draw a Venn diagram like Figure 12 on page 34, for representation of $R$, $S$, and $T$, and fill in the numbers of elements represented by various regions, as given data, or as derived from data. Then, find the number of children satisfying each of the following conditions: (1) no braces, not blue eyes, not blond hair; (2) blue eyes, not blond hair, no braces; (3) blond hair, not blue eyes, no braces; (4) braces, blond hair, not blue eyes; (5) blue eyes, braces, not blond hair.

9. A group of 100 children in a backward country are examined to learn the prevalence of the following diseases: (*a*) trachoma; (*b*) anemia; (*c*) rickets. Let $R$, $S$, and $T$ be the sets of children exhibiting (*a*), (*b*), and (*c*), respectively. It is found that there are 25 children with trachoma; 50 who are anemic; 8 who are anemic and have trachoma; 9 who have trachoma and rickets; 45 who are anemic and have rickets; 6 with all of the diseases; 20 who have none of the diseases. By use of a Venn diagram for $R$, $S$, and $T$, find how many are in each of the following sets: $R \cap S' \cap T$; $R \cap S \cap T'$; $S \cap T \cap R'$; $T$. Also, describe each of these sets in terms of the diseases present or absent.

10. A survey of 1000 heads of families in a neighborhood was carried out to check for the presence or absence of the following features: (*a*) political preference, Democratic party; (*b*) income above \$8000 per year; (*c*) graduate of a high school. Let $R$, $S$, and $T$ be the sets of heads of families with properties (*a*), (*b*), and (*c*), respectively. The survey reported the following results. Number in $R$ is 400; in $S$ is 600; in $T$ is 900; in $R \cap S \cap T$, 200; in $R \cap S$, 300; in $S \cap T$, 450; in $R \cap T$, 250. What should be the conclusion about this survey, and why is this decision proper? Use a Venn diagram.

★NOTE 1.    Let $S$ and $T$ be subsets of a universe $W$. Then, the **difference** of $S$ and $T$, denoted by "$S \setminus T$," read "$S$ *slash* $T$," is defined as the set of all elements of $S$ which are *not in T*. In Figure 13, if $T$ is the set of points inside the small circle, and $S$ is the set inside the outer circle, then $S \setminus T$ is the set of points which is ruled. In this case, if $W = S \setminus T$, then $S = W \cup T$, or $S = (S \setminus T) \cup T$, and thus "$\setminus$" and "$\cup$" act here like "$-$" and "$+$" in algebra. However, in Figure 14,

$$S \setminus T = S \qquad and \qquad (S \setminus T) \cup T = S \cup T \neq S.$$

Thus, "$\setminus$" in set operations does not always act like "$-$" does in algebra. The set definitions for *equality*, $=$, *inclusion*, $\subset$, the *empty set*, $\varnothing$, and the operations denoted by $\cup$, $\cap$, and $\setminus$, offer a basis for an *algebra of sets*. In this variety of "*algebra*," the roles played by the operations $\cup$, $\cap$, $\setminus$, $\subset$, and $\varnothing$ would resemble those of $+$, $\times$, $-$, $\leqq$, and 0 in ordinary algebra. We shall not be concerned with set algebra.

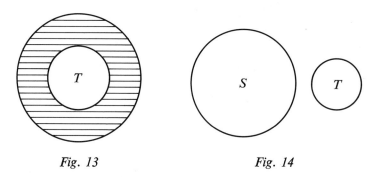

*Fig. 13*                    *Fig. 14*

## 16.  Intersections and unions of intervals

Any type of assertion about the *equality* or *inequality* of numbers may be called a *numerical statement*, or simply a *statement* when the context is clear. Such a statement may be a single equation or inequality, or a system of equations or inequalities. The terminology relating to solutions for a single equation on page 19 extends to numerical statements of any variety if the word *equation* on page 19 is changed throughout to *numerical statement*. Thus, the statement

$$2x - y = 3 \qquad and \qquad x + y = 9,$$

which is a system of two equations, is found to have just one solution $(x = 4, y = 5)$.

A statement such as

$$A < B < C \tag{1}$$

should be read        $A < B \qquad and \qquad B < C.$        (2)

Thus, (1) or (2) is a system of inequalities. If $A$, $B$, and $C$ involve just one variable, $x$, let

$$K \text{ be the solution set of } A < B; \tag{3}$$

$$M \text{ be the solution set of } B < C; \tag{4}$$

$$N \text{ be the solution set of } A < B < C. \tag{5}$$

A value of $x$ satisfies (1) when and only when $x$ is a solution of *both* inequalities in (2). Hence, $x$ is in the solution set of (1) when and only when $x$ is in *both* of the solution sets in (3) and (4). That is,

$$\left.\begin{array}{l} \textit{the solution set of } A < B < C \textit{ is the intersection of the} \\ \textit{solution sets for } A < B \textit{ and for } B < C. \textit{ Or, } N = K \cap M. \end{array}\right\} \tag{6}$$

We define the *graph* of any statement (1), in a single variable $x$, to be the *graph of the solution set* of the statement on a number scale. Thus, by (6), to graph (1) or (2), graph $K$ and $M$ from (3) and (4), and find $N = K \cap M$ on the number scale; then $N$ is the graph of (1).

EXAMPLE 1.   Graph                          $-3 \leqq x < 2.$ 　　　　　　 (7)

*Solution.*   *1.*   Statement (7) means that

$$-3 \leqq x \quad \textit{and} \quad x < 2. \tag{8}$$

*2.*   In Figure 15, the graph $K$ of $-3 \leqq x$ consists of the point $-3$ and the points to the right of $-3$ on the scale. The graph $M$ of $x < 2$ consists of the points to the left of 2. The graph, $N$, of (8) is the *intersection* of $K$ and $M$, or $N = K \cap M$, where $N$ consists of $-3$ and all points between $-3$ and 2 on the scale. In Figure 15, $N$ is the thick part of the scale. In set builder notation, $N = \{x \mid -3 \leqq x < 2\}$, which is read "$N$ *is the set of all $x$ such that* $-3 \leqq x < 2$." However, we shall prefer the more simple abbreviation $N = \{-3 \leqq x < 2\}$, to be read "$N$ *is the interval* $-3 \leqq x < 2$."

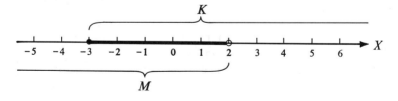

*Fig. 15*

An interval, $I$, of the number scale with endpoints $c$ and $d$ is called a *finite* interval of numbers. We refer to $I$ as a *closed* interval if $I$ includes its endpoints; an *open* interval if neither endpoint is included; a *half-open* or a *half-closed* interval if one endpoint is included and one is not included.

An interval, $S$, of the number scale including all numbers to the right (or, to the left) of a fixed number $c$ on the scale is called an *infinite interval*. The endpoint $c$ may or may not be included in $S$. The whole number scale also is referred to as an infinite interval.

ILLUSTRATION 1.    The set, $S$, of all numbers $x > 2$ is an infinite interval of numbers. We write

$$S = \{x > 2\}, \tag{9}$$

which is read "$S$ is the interval $x > 2$."

ILLUSTRATION 2.    Let $S$ be the set of solutions of "$c < x < d$," which means that $c < x$ AND $x < d$. Then, $S$ is the open interval of numbers $x$ on a number scale which are to the *right* of $c$, because $c < x$, and to the *left* of $d$, because $x < d$. Or, $S$ consists of all numbers *between* $c$ and $d$. We may write

$$\boldsymbol{S = \{c < x < d\}.} \tag{10}$$

ILLUSTRATION 3.    The whole number scale can be described as the infinite interval $R = \{all\ x\}$.

ILLUSTRATION 4.    The interval $\{-2 \leq x \leq 5\}$, or the solution set of the statement, is the closed interval with endpoints $-2$ and $5$. The interval $\{c < x \leq d\}$ is a half-open interval which is open at $c$ and closed at $d$.

Useful practice with the meaning of the intersection and union of sets is furnished by use of sets of points forming *intervals* on a number scale. We agree that the universe for numbers is the *whole number scale*.

EXAMPLE 2.    If $H = \{-3 \leq x < 2\}$ and $K = \{-1 < x \leq 4\}$, let $M = H \cup K$ and $N = H \cap K$. Show $H$, $K$, $M$, and $N$ on a number scale and describe $M$ and $N$ by use of inequalities.

*Solution.*    $H$ and $K$ are shown in Figure 16. Since $M$ is the set of numbers (points) in $H$ *or* $K$, we see that $M$ is the closed interval extending from $-3$ to $4$. Or, $M = \{-3 \leq x \leq 4\}$. If $N = H \cap K$, then $N$ consists of all $x$ in *both* $H$ *and* $K$, or $N$ is the interval where $H$ and $K$ *overlap*. Thus, $N = \{-1 < x < 2\}$.

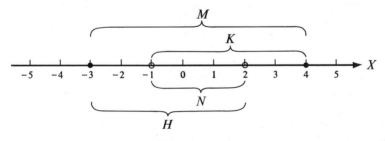

*Fig. 16*

EXAMPLE 3.   Obtain the graph of $S = \{|x| < 2\}$, and of the complement $S' = \{|x| \geq 2\}$.

*Solution.*   *1.*   With $P:(x)$ on the number scale as in Figure 17, we have $\overline{OP} = x$ and the length of $\overline{OP}$ is $|\overline{OP}| = |x|$. Hence, $S$ consists of all points $P$ on the scale with $|\overline{OP}| < 2$, or $S$ consists of all numbers between $-2$ and $2$. That is,

$$|x| < 2 \qquad \textit{is equivalent to} \qquad -2 < x < 2. \tag{11}$$

Or, $S$ is the open interval with endpoints $\pm 2$ in Figure 17.

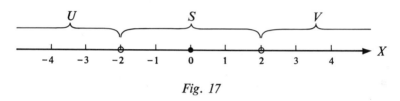

Fig. 17

*2.*   If $S' = \{|x| \geq 2\}$ and $P:(x)$ is in $S'$, then $|\overline{OP}| \geq 2$, or $P$ is at a distance of *at least* 2 units from 0. Hence, if $x$ is in $S'$, then $x \leq -2$ or $x \geq 2$. Let

$$U = \{x \leq -2\} \qquad \text{and} \qquad V = \{2 \leq x\},$$

as in Figure 17. Then $S' = U \cup V$.

Similarly as in Example 3,

$$|x| < p \qquad \textit{is equivalent to} \qquad -p < x < p; \tag{12}$$
$$|x| > p \qquad \textit{is equivalent to} \qquad x < -p \textit{ or } p < x. \tag{13}$$

ILLUSTRATION 5.   If $T = \{-3 \leq x < 5\}$, and $T'$ is the complement of $T$, then

$$T' = \{x < -3\} \cup \{5 \leq x\}. \tag{14}$$

The student should verify (14) on a number scale.

## Exercise 8

*On a number scale, let H be the graph of the first inequality and K be the graph of the second inequality. Show H ∩ K on the scale. Use a small open circle to indicate exclusion of any point, and a prominent dot to show inclusion. Then, write a statement of the form A < B < C whose graph is H ∩ K.*
*1.*   $-3 < x$; $x < 2$.      *2.*   $0 < x$; $x < 5$.      *3.*   $x < -2$; $-6 < x$.

*In any problem in this exercise, the universal set is understood to be all real numbers, or the whole number scale when each number is thought of as a point.*

4. If $H = \{x < 2\}$, describe $H'$.    5. If $H = \{x > -3\}$, describe $H'$.

*Obtain the graph, G, of the statement on a number scale. Also, by use of inequalities, define two intervals H and K so that $G = H \cap K$.*

6. $-2 < x \leq 3$.    7. $-4 \leq x < 0$.    8. $2 \leq x \leq 5.3 = G$
9. $-3 < x < 2$.    10. $|x| < 4$.    11. $|x| < 2$.

$G = \{2 \leq x \leq 5\}$

*Obtain the graph, G, of the inequality on a number scale. Also, define two intervals S and T by inequalities so that $G = S \cup T$.*

12. $|x| > 3$.    13. $|x| > 5$.    14. $|x| > 4$.

*Describe two intervals V and W by use of inequalities so that $S' = V \cup W$. Show S, V, and W on a number scale.*

15. $S = \{0 \leq x \leq 4\}$.    16. $S = \{-2 < x \leq 3\}$.    17. $S = \{-3 \leq x < -1\}$.

*Show the sets, or intervals, S and T on a scale. Then indicate $S \cup T$ and $S \cap T$ on the figure, if possible.*

18. $S = \{-2 \leq x < 4\};\quad T = \{1 \leq x < 6\}$.
19. $S = \{-5 < x \leq 2\};\quad T = \{0 < x \leq 4\}$.
20. $S = \{x \leq 4\};\quad T = \{2 < x\}$.
21. $S = \{x \leq -3\};\quad T = \{3 < x\}$.
22. $S = \{x \leq -4\};\quad T = \{4 \leq x\}$.
23. $S = \{-4 \leq x\};\quad T = \{x \leq 4\}$.
24. $S = \{-6 \leq x < -3\};\quad T = \{-4 < x \leq 8\}$.

25. If $S = \{|x| > 3\}$, describe $S'$ by inequalities.
26. If $A = \{-2 < x < 3\}$, describe $A'$ by use of inequalities.
27. If $A = \{x < -2\}$ and $B = \{4 < x\}$, describe the complement $(A \cup B)'$ by use of inequalities.

## 17.  Solution of a system of two linear inequalities in $x$

Suppose that a statement $A < B < C$ involves just a single variable, $x$. To find the corresponding solution set, usually it is best to express the statement as a system of two inequalities, and then to solve each of them separately. The intersection of their solution sets is the solution set of $A < B < C$. If the resulting solution set is the empty set, this will indicate that "$A < B < C$" is *inconsistent*.

EXAMPLE 1.   Solve:    $5 - 2x < 6x - 1 \leq 2x + 9$.    (1)

*Solution.   1.* Statement (1) means that

(a) $5 - 2x < 6x - 1$,    AND    (b) $6x - 1 \leq 2x + 9$.    (2)

2.  From (*a*),        $6 < 8x$,      *or*      $\frac{3}{4} < x$.                    (3)

3.  From (*b*),        $4x \leq 10$,      *or*      $x \leq \frac{5}{2}$.                    (4)

4.  Hence, (2) is equivalent to $\{\frac{3}{4} < x$   AND   $x \leq \frac{5}{2}\}$. Or, the solution set of (1) consists of all numbers $x$ on $S = \{\frac{3}{4} < x \leq \frac{5}{2}\}$.

Recall that, if $v$ is any variable, then

$|v| < p$      *is equivalent to*      $-p < v < p$;                    (5)

$|v| > p$      *is equivalent to*      $(v < -p$   OR   $p < v)$.                    (6)

EXAMPLE 2.   Solve:        $|3 - x| < 2$.                    (7)

*Solution.*   *1.*   $|3 - x| < 2$ means that $-2 < 3 - x < 2$, or

    (*a*)   $-2 < 3 - x$      AND      (*b*)   $3 - x < 2$.                    (8)

2.  From (*a*), $x < 5$. From (*b*), $1 < x$. Hence, (7) is equivalent to $(1 < x$   AND   $x < 5)$. Or, the solution set of (7) is the interval $S = \{1 < x < 5\}$, as shown in Figure 18. Notice that $S$ is an interval with center at $x = 3$, and length $2 \times 2$, or 4 units. With $P:(x)$ and $Q:(3)$ on the scale in Figure 18, $|3 - x| = |\overline{PQ}|$; (7) states that $|\overline{PQ}| < 2$.

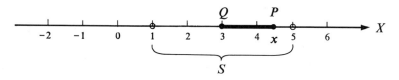

*Fig. 18*

EXAMPLE 3.   Solve:                    $|3 - x| \geq 2$.                    (9)

*Solution.*   *1.*   By (6), inequality (9) is equivalent to

    (*a*)   $3 - x \leq -2$      OR      (*b*)   $2 \leq 3 - x$.                    (10)

2.  From (*a*), $5 \leq x$. From (*b*), $x \leq 1$. Hence, the solution set, $W$, of inequality (9) is the *union* of the intervals $S = \{x \leq 1\}$ and $T = \{5 \leq x\}$, or $W = S \cup T$, as shown in Figure 19. With $P:(x)$ and $Q:(3)$ on the scale, $|\overline{PQ}| = |3 - x|$, and (9) states that $|\overline{PQ}| \geq 2$, which corresponds to the results for Example 3.

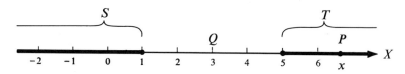

*Fig. 19*

## Exercise 9

*Solve the inequality statement algebraically.*

1. $2 < \frac{3}{2}x - 4 \leq 5$.

2. $3 - 2x < 6x - 1 \leq 2x + 3$.

3. $4 \leq 2 + \frac{2}{3}x < 6$.

4. $4 < x - 4 \leq -1 - \frac{1}{2}x$.

5. $4 < \frac{3}{2}x - 4 < 3 - x$.

6. $\frac{1}{3} + 3x < 4x - 5 < -4 + 2x$.

7. $\frac{5}{6}x - 3 < x + \frac{1}{3} < \frac{1}{3}x - \frac{3}{4}$.

8. $\frac{1}{5}x + 3 \leq \frac{3}{2}x + \frac{4}{3} < \frac{1}{2}x + 7$.

9. $\frac{2}{3}x - 4 < \frac{14}{3}x + 4 < -\frac{4}{3} - \frac{2}{3}x$.

10. $\frac{3}{4} + x < \frac{2}{3} + \frac{3}{2}x < \frac{5}{2} - \frac{1}{3}x$.

*Write an equivalent statement without use of an absolute value. Then, solve the statement and graph it on a number scale.*

11. $|x| < 4$.

12. $|x| > 5$.

13. $|x - 3| < 4$.

14. $|x - 3| > 4$.

15. $|x + 2| < 1$.

16. $|x + 2| > 1$.

★17. If $0 < A < B$ and $0 < U < V$, prove that $AU < BV$.

# 3 | FUNCTIONS AND GRAPHS IN A PLANE

## 18.  Coordinates in a plane

In this chapter, we shall be dealing with some of the elements of plane analytic geometry.

In a given plane, draw two perpendicular lines, intersecting at point $O$. Each of these lines will be called a *coordinate axis*, with one axis $OX$ horizontal and the other axis $OY$ vertical in the typical case, as illustrated in Figure 20. On $OX$, and also on $OY$, choose *arbitrarily* a unit for measuring distance, as the basis for number scales on $OX$ and $OY$, with their intersection, $O$, representing the number 0. The units on $OX$ and $OY$ need not be equal. Positive numbers will be to the *right* on $OX$, and *upward* on $OY$, with negative numbers to the *left* and *downward*, on $OX$ and $OY$, respectively.

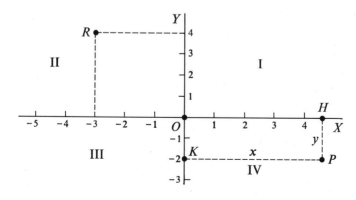

*Fig. 20*

We agree that any horizontal line segment will be *directed*, with the positive direction to the right and negative to the left, and will be measured in terms of the unit distance on $OX$. Vertical line segments will be *directed*, with the positive direction upward and negative downward, and will be measured in terms of the unit on $OY$. Let $P$ be any point in the plane of $OX$ and $OY$. Then, we define an ordered* pair of coordinates $(x, y)$ for $P$, as follows:

The **abscissa**, *or horizontal coordinate, of P is the directed distance, x, measured horizontally from the vertical axis OY to P.*

The **ordinate**, *or vertical coordinate, of P is the directed distance, y, measured vertically from the horizontal axis OX to P.*

The intersection of the axes $OX$ and $OY$ is called the **origin** of coordinates. The abscissa and ordinate of $P$ are called its **rectangular coordinates**, where the word *rectangular* is used because $OX$ and $OY$ are perpendicular.† The plane in which $OX$ and $OY$ lie is called the **coordinate plane**, or the *xy-plane*. We shall use "$P:(x, y)$" to mean "*P with coordinates* $(x, y)$." For each point $P$, there is just one pair of coordinates $(x, y)$, and each pair $(x, y)$ corresponds to, or locates, just one point. Coordinates as just defined are referred to as *a system of rectangular coordinates*. Frequently, with a duplicate of Figure 20 as a basis, we call the abscissa of $P$ its $x$-coordinate, and the ordinate of $P$ its $y$-coordinate. We may read $P:(x, y)$ as "$P, x, y$."

EXAMPLE 1.    Plot the point $R:(-3, 4)$.

*Solution.* At $-3$ on $OX$, in Figure 20, erect a perpendicular to $OX$. Go up 4 vertical units on this perpendicular to reach $R$. Or, at 4 on $OY$, erect a perpendicular to $OY$ and go 3 horizontal units to the left to reach $R$.

If an ordered pair of numbers $(a, b)$ gives the coordinates of a point, we may refer to it as "*the point* $(a, b)$."

The **projection** of a point $P$ on a line $L$ is defined as *the foot of the perpendicular from P to L*. Thus, the projection of any point $P:(x, y)$ on $OX$ is the point $H:(x, 0)$, and on $OY$ is the point $K:(0, y)$, as in Figure 20.

ILLUSTRATION 1.    In Figure 20, the projection of $R:(-3, 4)$ on the $y$-axis is the point $(0, 4)$, and on the $x$-axis is the point $(-3, 0)$. For $P:(x, y)$ in Figure 20, the projection of $P$ on $OX$ is the point $H:(4.6, 0)$, and on $OY$ is the point $K:(0, -2)$, so that $P$ has the coordinates $(4.6, -2)$.

The axes $OX$ and $OY$ divide the coordinate plane into four regions called **quadrants**, numbered I, II, III, and IV, counterclockwise as in Figure 20. A point on a coordinate axis is not said to lie in any quadrant.

* The pair $(x, y)$ is *ordered*, because $x$ is assigned to the *first position* and $y$ to the *second position*. Also, if $(a, b)$ and $(c, d)$ are the same ordered pair, then $a = c$ and $b = d$.

† Coordinates are used sometimes where the axes are not perpendicular.

## Exercise 10

*Give a figure on cross-section paper for each problem.*
*Plot the following points. A single coordinate system may be used.*

| | | |
|---|---|---|
| *1.* (3, 7). | *2.* (5, 9). | *3.* (−4, −8). |
| *4.* (−1, −5). | *5.* (−3, 0). | *6.* (0, −5). |
| *7.* (0, 6). | *8.* (3, −6). | *9.* (−5, 7). |
| *10.* (−3, −5). | *11.* (7, 0). | *12.* (5, −8). |

*13.*   Three corners of a rectangle are at the points (2, 2), (−1, 2), and (2, 5). Find the coordinates of the other corner.

*14.*   A square, with its sides parallel to the coordinate axes, has one corner at (−1, −2) in a coordinate system having the same unit for length on each axis. A side of the square is 5 units long. Find the coordinates of the other corners, if the square lies to the right of, and below (−1, −2).

*15.*   A line *L* passes through the point (3, −2) and is perpendicular to *OX*. What is true about the abscissa of each point on *L*?

*16.*   A line *L* passes through the point (5, −7) and is parallel to *OX*. What is true about the ordinate of each point on *L*?

*17.*   Where is *P*:(*x*, *y*) located if *y* = 0; if *x* = 0?

*18.*   Where is *P*:(*x*, *y*) located if *x* = 4; if *y* = −5?

*Find the coordinates of the projections of the point on OX and on OY.*

*19.* (3, −5).    *20.* (−2, −5).    *21.* (−4, 5).    *22.* (6, 4).

## 19.   Distance formula for a coordinate plane

If a line segment $P_1P_2$ is parallel to *OX* in an *xy*-plane, as in Figure 21, then $P_1$ and $P_2$ have the same *y*-coordinate. Thus, we may have $P_1:(x_1, b)$ and $P_2:(x_2, b)$ with $P_1P_2$ parallel to *OX*. The projections $M_1$ and $M_2$ of $P_1$ and $P_2$ on *OX* are seen in Figure 21. We have agreed that $M_1M_2$ is a *directed* segment and that $\overline{M_1M_2}$ and $\overline{P_1P_2}$ are measured in terms of the same unit for

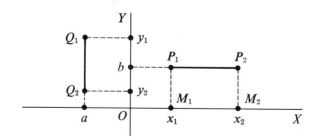

*Fig. 21*

distance. Hence $\overline{M_1M_2} = \overline{P_1P_2}$; or, from (1) on page 25, $\overline{M_1M_2} = x_2 - x_1$; hence

$$\overline{P_1P_2} = x_2 - x_1; \qquad |\overline{P_1P_2}| = |x_2 - x_1|. \tag{1}$$

Similarly, for the points $Q_1:(a, y_1)$ and $Q_2:(a, y_2)$ in Figure 21, with $Q_1Q_2$ parallel to $\overline{OY}$, we have

$$\overline{Q_1Q_2} = y_2 - y_1; \qquad |\overline{Q_1Q_2}| = |y_2 - y_1|. \tag{2}$$

Suppose that $P_1$ and $P_2$ are any points in an $xy$-plane, with segment $P_1P_2$ *not* parallel to either coordinate axis. Then we shall *not* consider segment $P_1P_2$ to be a directed segment. In this case, we let $\overline{P_1P_2}$ be the length of $P_1P_2$ as measured in terms of any unit which may be specified. We infer here that *length* is taken as a *nonnegative number*. Hence, $\overline{P_1P_2} \geqq 0$ if $P_1P_2$ is not horizontal or vertical.

NOTE 1.   Consider a right triangle situated in a plane for which a single unit for length has been assigned to measure distances in all directions. Then, for use below, we recall the *Pythagorean theorem* of geometry: *In a right triangle, the sum of the squares of the lengths of the perpendicular sides is equal to the square of the length of the hypotenuse.*

THEOREM I.   *Suppose that the scale units on the coordinate axes are equal in an xy-plane.\* Then, the distance d between $P_1:(x_1, y_1)$ and $P_2:(x_2, y_2)$, or the length of line segment $P_1P_2$, is given by*

$$d = |\overline{P_1P_2}| = \sqrt{(x_2 - x_1)^2 + (y_2 - y_1)^2}. \tag{3}$$

*Proof.   1.* In Figure 22, let $K$ be the intersection of perpendiculars to $OY$ through $P_1$, and to $OX$ through $P_2$. Then, in triangle $P_1KP_2$, by the Pythagorean theorem we obtain

$$d^2 = (\overline{P_1P_2})^2 = (\overline{P_1K})^2 + (\overline{KP_2})^2.$$

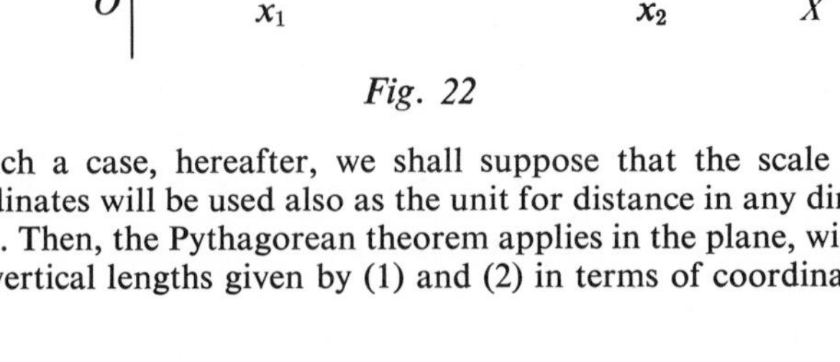

*Fig. 22*

\* In such a case, hereafter, we shall suppose that the scale unit for the coordinates will be used also as the unit for distance in any direction in the plane. Then, the Pythagorean theorem applies in the plane, with horizontal and vertical lengths given by (1) and (2) in terms of coordinates.

*2.* From (1) and (2), and Figure 22,

$$|\overline{P_1K}| = |\overline{S_1S_2}| = |x_2 - x_1|; \qquad |\overline{KP_2}| = |\overline{T_1T_2}| = |y_2 - y_1|.$$

Hence, $\qquad\qquad d^2 = (x_2 - x_1)^2 + (y_2 - y_1)^2.$

On extracting square roots, we obtain (3).

The lengths of $P_1P_2$ and $P_2P_1$ are the same, or $|\overline{P_1P_2}| = |\overline{P_2P_1}|$. Also, since the *squares* of $(x_2 - x_1)$ and $(y_2 - y_1)$ are involved in (3), the *order* in which we label the points $P_1$ and $P_2$ is immaterial. If $P_1P_2$ is not horizontal or vertical, we have agreed that $\overline{P_1P_2}$ is *nonnegative*. When this is the case, the absolute value bars with $|\overline{P_1P_2}|$ in (3) will be omitted.

ILLUSTRATION 1.  From (3), the distance between $A:(3, -5)$ and $B:(7, -2)$ is found by using $x_1 = 3$, $y_1 = -5$, $x_2 = 7$, and $y_2 = -2$:

$$\overline{AB} = \sqrt{(7 - 3)^2 + [-2 - (-5)]^2} = \sqrt{4^2 + 3^2} = 5.$$

The distance $d$ between $P:(x, y)$ and the origin $O:(0, 0)$ is found from (3) with $x_2 = x$, $y_2 = y$, $x_1 = 0$, and $y_1 = 0$:

$$d = \sqrt{x^2 + y^2}. \tag{4}$$

ILLUSTRATION 2.  If $P_1P_2$ is horizontal or vertical, then (1) or (2) can be used instead of (3) to find $|\overline{P_1P_2}|$. However, in such a case, (3) also can be used. Thus, with $P_1:(-3, 5)$ and $P_2:(6, 5)$, by use of (3) we obtain

$$|\overline{P_1P_2}| = \sqrt{[6 - (-3)]^2 + (5 - 5)^2} = \sqrt{9^2} = 9.$$

## Exercise 11

*If M represents the first point and N the second point, find* $\overline{MN}$ *and* $|\overline{MN}|$. *Plot M and N in an xy-plane. Notice that MN is a directed segment because it is parallel to a coordinate axis.*

1.  $(0, 7); (0, 11).$
2.  $(0, -3); (0, -8).$
3.  $(6, 0); (-2, 0).$
4.  $(3, 6); (7, 6).$
5.  $(-4, -2); (-8, -2).$
6.  $(3, -5); (3, 4).$
7.  $(5, 9); (5, -3).$
8.  $(-2, -3); (-8, -3).$
9.  $(-7, 0); (5, 0).$
10.  $(-4, 3); (-4, 8).$

*In the following problems, the units on the coordinate axes are equal. Find the distance between the points, or an expression for it. Table I may be used for square roots if necessary.*

11.  $(6, 1); (1, 13).$
12.  $(4, 8); (-5, 8).$
13.  $(-4, 1); (-8, -3).$
14.  $(1, -3); (4, 1).$
15.  $(-2, 0); (2, 7).$
16.  $(0, 2); (4, -1).$
17.  $(-3, 4); (-3, -2).$
18.  $(a, b); (2, 5).$

*An isosceles triangle is defined as a triangle having two sides of equal lengths. Prove that the triangle with the given vertices is isosceles.*

*19.*  $(-3, 9)$; $(-2, 2)$; $(2, 4)$.          *20.*  $(2, -2)$; $(2, -4)$; $(6, -3)$.

*An equilateral triangle is one whose sides have equal lengths. Prove that the triangle with the given vertices is equilateral.*

*21.*  $(-1, 0)$; $(9, 0)$; $(4, 5\sqrt{3})$.          *22.*  $(0, 3)$; $(0, -5)$; $(4\sqrt{3}, -1)$.

*If the sum of the squares of the lengths of two sides of a triangle is equal to the square of the length of the third side, then the triangle is a right triangle. (This result is the converse of the Pythagorean theorem.) Prove that the triangle with the given vertices is a right triangle.*

*23.*  $(0, -1)$; $(2, 0)$; $(-1, 6)$.          *24.*  $(2, 1)$; $(4, 2)$; $(-1, 7)$.

*25.*   Find $y$ if $(-2, y)$ is equidistant from $(-2, 2)$ and $(6, 6)$.

## 20.   A relation between two variables, and its graph

Let $x$ and $y$ be variables, and let $M$ represent a nonempty set of pairs of corresponding values of $x$ and $y$.

ILLUSTRATION 1.   Let $M$ be the set of 8 pairs of corresponding values of $x$ and $y$ given in the following table.

| $x =$ | $-3$ | $-3$ | $-2$ | $-1$ | $0$ | $1$ | $2$ | $4$ |
|-------|------|------|------|------|-----|-----|-----|-----|
| $y =$ | $2$  | $4$  | $2$  | $3$  | $4$ | $4$ | $3$ | $3$ |

(1)

DEFINITION I.   *A nonempty set M of pairs of corresponding values of two variables x and y is referred to as a* **relation** *between (or, in) x and y, and then they are called related variables.*

DEFINITION II.   *The* **graph of a relation** *M between two variables x and y is the set of points in an xy-plane whose coordinates (x, y) are number pairs in M.*

ILLUSTRATION 2.   The graph of the relation $M$ in (1) consists of $(-3, 2)$, $(-3, 4)$, $(-2, 2)$, etc., shown by black dots in Figure 23.

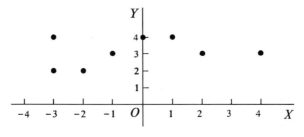

*Fig. 23*

## 21.  Equations in two variables

DEFINITION III.   *A* **solution** *of an equation in two variables, say x and y, is a pair of corresponding values of x and y for which the equation becomes a true statement. If the pair (x = a, y = b) is a solution, these values of x and y are said to satisfy the equation.*

The set of all solutions of an equation is called, for brevity, its **solution set**. If the equation has at least one solution, the equation is said to be *consistent*. If it has no solution, the equation is called *inconsistent*. Two equations in two variables are said to be *equivalent* if they have the same solutions.* We shall assume that the usual elementary operations on an equation lead to equivalent equations, with any number of variables involved.

The *solution set* of any consistent equation in two variables $x$ and $y$ is a *relation* between them. We shall find that a consistent equation in $x$ and $y$ usually has infinitely many solutions.

ILLUSTRATION 1.   In $3x - 4y = 12$, if $x = 0$ then $-4y = 12$ or $y = -3$, in order to satisfy the given equation. Thus, $(x = 0, y = -3)$ is a solution of it. If $y = 2$, we obtain $3x - 8 = 12$ or $x = \frac{20}{3}$, and $(x = \frac{20}{3}, y = 2)$ is another solution. Similarly, for each value of $x$, a corresponding value of $y$ can be found by substitution in $3x - 4y = 12$ so that the pair $(x, y)$ is a solution of it. Thus, the equation has infinitely many solutions.

DEFINITION IV.   *The* **graph of an equation** *in two variables x and y in an xy-plane is the set of points whose coordinates (x, y) form solutions of the equation.*

On comparing Definitions II and IV, we see that the graph of an equation in $x$ and $y$ can be described as *the graph of the solution set of the equation,* or of the relation between $x$ and $y$ which is defined by the equation. *To graph an equation* will mean to draw its graph. To obtain it, we may substitute values for either variable in the equation and compute the corresponding values of the other variable, to form a table of representative solutions $(x, y)$. The graph then is drawn through the points having the coordinates in the table. In graphing an equation in $x$ and $y$, usually we shall employ the horizontal axis for values of $x$.

ILLUSTRATION 2.   To graph $3x + 4y = 12$, we compute its following solutions by placing $x = 0$ and computing $y = 3$; placing $y = 0$ and obtaining $x = 4$; then placing $x = -2, 2$, and $5$ and computing corresponding values of $y$. The plotted points $(x, y)$ are shown in Figure 24 by black dots, and

* Similar terminology on page 19 about equations in only one variable should be recalled at this point.

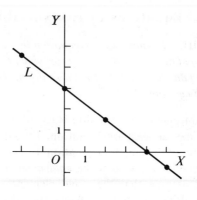

*Fig. 24*

are seen to fall on a line. Later, we shall prove that this line is the graph of $3x + 4y = 12$.

| $x =$ | $-2$ | 0 | 2 | 4 | 5 |
|-------|------|---|---|---|---|
| $y =$ | $\frac{9}{2}$ | 3 | $\frac{3}{2}$ | 0 | $-\frac{3}{4}$ |

ILLUSTRATION 3.   To graph $y - x^2 + 4x - 2 = 0$, solve for $y$ to obtain $y = x^2 - 4x + 2$. Then, assign values to $x$ and compute $y$, as in the following table. The graph through the corresponding points $(x, y)$ is in Figure 25, and is called a *parabola*. Sometimes we refer to an equation by giving it the name of its graph. Thus, in Figure 25, we see the *parabola* $y = x^2 - 4x + 2$.

| $x =$ | $-1$ | 0 | 1 | 2 | 3 | 4 | 5 |
|-------|------|---|---|---|---|---|---|
| $y =$ | 7 | 2 | $-1$ | $-2$ | $-1$ | 2 | 7 |

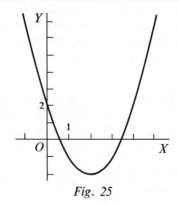

*Fig. 25*

An **equation of a curve** in an $xy$-plane is an equation in $x$ and $y$ whose graph is the given curve. If we can find *one* equation for a curve, then we can give infinitely many equations for it. It is customary to refer to any one of these as **THE** equation of the curve.

ILLUSTRATION 4.   The graph of $3x + 4y = 12$ is the line $L$ in Figure 24 on page 50. $L$ also is the graph of the equation $9x + 12y = 36$.

The *equation of a graph* in an $xy$-plane, or the *graph of an equation* in the variables $x$ and $y$, has the following properties.

(I)   *If $P:(x, y)$ is on the graph, the coordinates of $P$ satisfy the equation.*

(II)   *If $P:(x, y)$ is not on the graph, then the coordinates of $P$ do not satisfy the equation.*

NOTE 1.   Let $T$ be the solution set of $3x + 4y = 12$. Then, in set builder notation, as described on page 30, we may write

$$T = \{(x, y) \mid 3x + 4y = 12\}, \tag{1}$$

which is read "$T$ *is the set of all pairs of numbers* $(x, y)$ *such that* $3x + 4y = 12$." Instead of asking for "*the graph of* $3x + 4y = 12$," we could ask for "*the graph of* $\{(x, y) \mid 3x + 4y = 12\}$." The student may desire to make occasional use of set builder notation in discussing graphs of equations, and other sets. However, *the simple standard terminology about graphs*, as used up to this point, must be recognized as *the standard terminology of the field of analytic geometry*.

## 22.   Linear equations in two variables

Recall that a *polynomial* in two variables $x$ and $y$ is a sum of *monomials*, or terms, of the form $Sx^h y^k$, where $S$ is a constant and $h$ and $k$ are nonnegative integers. The degree of $Sx^h y^k$ is $(h + k)$. The *degree of a polynomial* is the degree of its term of *highest* degree. A polynomial of degree 1 in $x$ and $y$ is said to be *linear* in $x$ and $y$, and is of the form $(ax + by + c)$ where the constants $a$ and $b$ are not both zero.

ILLUSTRATION 1.   If $x$ and $y$ are variables, the polynomial

$$3x^2 y + x^3 - x + 2y - 6$$

is of degree 3 in $x$ and $y$ because $x^3$ and $3x^2 y$ are of degree 3. The polynomial $(4x + 5y - 7)$ is of degree 1, or is linear in $x$ and $y$.

A **polynomial equation** in $x$ and $y$ is an equation in which each side is a polynomial in $x$ and $y$ or is zero. The equation is said to be *linear* in $x$ and $y$ if the equation is equivalent to one of the form

$$ax + by + c = 0, \tag{1}$$

where the constants $a$ and $b$ are not both zero. Hence, the left-hand side of (1) is a polynomial of degree 1. Later, we shall prove that **the graph of any linear equation in $x$ and $y$ is a line.**

The **$x$-intercepts** of any graph in an $xy$-plane are the values of $x$ where the graph meets the $x$-axis. The **$y$-intercepts** are the values of $y$ where the graph meets the $y$-axis. The intercepts of the graph of an equation in $x$ and $y$ may be obtained as follows.

*To find the x-intercepts, place $y = 0$ and solve for $x$.*
*To find the y-intercepts, place $x = 0$ and solve for $y$.*

**To graph a linear equation $ax + by + c = 0$:**

*Obtain the intercepts by calculating the solution in which $x = 0$, and the solution in which $y = 0$, when such solutions exist.*

*Obtain an additional solution by substituting a value for $x$ or for $y$. (Obtain* **two** *additional solutions if both intercepts are 0.)*

*Draw the graph through the three\* points corresponding to the solutions obtained for the equation.*

ILLUSTRATION 2.   To graph $3x + 4y = 12$, place $y = 0$ to obtain the $x$-intercept $x = 4$; thus $(4, 0)$ is a point on the graph. Place $x = 0$ to obtain the $y$-intercept $y = 3$; thus $(0, 3)$ is on the graph. Place $x = 2$ to obtain $y = 1.5$, and the point $(2, 1.5)$. The graph is the line through these three points, as seen in Figure 24 on page 50.

ILLUSTRATION 3.   To graph $5x - 2y = 0$, place $x = 0$, to find $y = 0$; thus the $y$-intercept is 0; also the $x$-intercept is zero, or the graph is a line through the origin $O:(0, 0)$. To be assured of accuracy, two more solutions $(x = 2, y = 5)$ and $(x = -2, y = -5)$ should be obtained. The graph is the line through $(0, 0)$, $(2, 5)$, and $(-2, -5)$.

ILLUSTRATION 4.   The equation $x - 2 = 0$ is of the form $ax + by + c = 0$ where $b = 0$. The graph of $x - 2 = 0$, or $x = 2$, is a vertical line with $x$-intercept 2 and *no y-intercept*. The graph of $y - 3 = 0$ is the horizontal line with $y$-intercept 3 and *no x-intercept*.

## Exercise 12

*For the given equation, find the solution in which x has the specified value.*
1.   $3x - 5y = 30$; when $x = 5$.        2.   $2x + 9y = 36$; when $x = 4$.
3.   $2y - 3x^2 + 2x = 5$; when $x = 2$.
4.   $3y - 5x^2 - x^3 = 6$; when $x = 3$.

> \* A line is determined by *two points* on it. Use of three points is recommended above as a check on the work.

*Graph the relation between the variables x and y defined by the given set of pairs of values of x and y.*

5.

| x = | −3 | 2 | 1 | −3 | 0 | −2 | −3 |
|-----|----|----|----|----|----|----|----|
| y = | 4 | 4 | 3 | 5 | 6 | −1 | −4 |

6.

| x = | −2 | −1 | 0 | 1 | −2 | 3 | 4 |
|-----|----|----|----|----|----|----|----|
| y = | −2 | −3 | −4 | −3 | 2 | 1 | 0 |

*Graph each equation in the variables x and y.*

7. $x + 5y = 10$.
8. $3x − 2y = 6$.
9. $3y − 4x = 24$.
10. $2x + y = 6$.
11. $5x − 6y = 8$.
12. $4x − 3y = 0$.
13. $2x = −7y$.
14. $3x − 5 = 0$.
15. $15 + 2y = 0$.

*Graph the equation, with x = 2 used in the table of values (x, y).*

16. $y = 2x^2 − 8x + 5$.
17. $y − x^2 + 4x − 3 = 0$.

*Graph the equation, with y = 3 used in the table of values (x, y).*

18. $x = y^2 − 6y + 12$.
19. $x − 2y^2 + 12y = 15$.

*Write an equation of the line satisfying the condition.*

20. Parallel to the x-axis with the y-intercept 4.
21. Parallel to the y-axis with the x-intercept −5.
22. Perpendicular to the x-axis with the x-intercept 4.
23. If $(x = −1, y = 2)$ is a solution of $3x = 2k + ky$, find the value of the constant $k$.

## 23.  Slope of a line

Consider a nonvertical line $L$ in an $xy$-plane, where the units on the coordinate axes are *not necessarily equal*. Let $P_1:(x_1, y_1)$ and $P_2:(x_2, y_2)$ be any two distinct points on $L$. If we move on $L$ from $P_1$ to $P_2$, as in Figure 26, the ordinate changes from $y_1$ to $y_2$, and the total change is $(y_2 − y_1)$; the abscissa, or horizontal coordinate, changes from $x_1$ to $x_2$, and the total

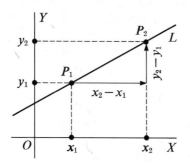

*Fig. 26*

change is $(x_2 - x_1)$. We accept the following property of $L$ as the defining property of any set of points, such as $L$, to which we shall apply the name "*nonvertical line*" in an $xy$-plane.

> The ratio of the change $(y_2 - y_1)$ in the y-coordinate to the change $(x_2 - x_1)$ in the x-coordinate is a constant for all distinct pairs of points $P_1:(x_1, y_1)$ and $P_2:(x_2, y_2)$ on L.    (1)

The important ratio referred to in (1) is given a name, as follows.

DEFINITION V.    The **slope** *of a nonvertical line L in an xy-plane is the ratio of the change in the vertical coordinate to the change in the horizontal coordinate as we move on L from any first point to a distinct second point.*

With $P_1:(x_1, y_1)$ and $P_2:(x_2, y_2)$ as distinct points on $L$, and $m$ representing the slope of $L$, from Definition V we obtain

$$m = \frac{y_2 - y_1}{x_2 - x_1}. \tag{2}$$

ILLUSTRATION 1.    To obtain the slope of the line through $M:(3, -6)$ and $N:(-2, 5)$, use (2) either with $M$ as $P_1$ and $N$ as $P_2$, or with $N$ as $P_1$ and $M$ as $P_2$. Then,

$$m = \frac{5 - (-6)}{-2 - 3} = -\frac{11}{5}; \quad or \quad m = \frac{-6 - 5}{3 - (-2)} = -\frac{11}{5}.$$

In colloquial phraseology, the slope of a line is *positive* if $L$ *slopes upward to the right*, and *negative* if $L$ *slopes downward to the right*. If $L$ is *horizontal*, its slope is 0. If $L$ is *vertical*, we have not defined the notion of slope for $L$, or *a vertical line is said to have no slope*.

We accept the following familiar facts about lines in an $xy$-plane. Thus, to say that two nonvertical lines are *parallel* means that they have the same slope. Also, only one line with a given slope passes through any given point in the plane. Any two distinct points lie on a line. To state that three or more points are *collinear* means that *they lie on a line*. Three points $R$, $S$, and $T$ are collinear if and only if the line through $R$ and $S$ is the same as the line through $S$ and $T$. Thus, we may state that $R$, $S$, and $T$ are collinear *when and only when the slope of line RS is the same as the slope of line ST*.

EXAMPLE 1.    Prove that $R:(-1, 7)$, $S:(1, 3)$, and $T:(3, -1)$ are collinear.

*Solution.*    From (2) with $R$ as $P_1$ and $S$ as $P_2$,

$$(slope\ of\ RS) = \frac{3 - 7}{1 - (-1)} = \frac{-4}{2} = -2.$$

From (2),    $(slope\ of\ ST) = \dfrac{-1 - 3}{3 - 1} = \dfrac{-4}{2} = -2.$

Hence, $R$, $S$, and $T$ lie on a line.

NOTE 1.   Hereafter, if $A$ and $B$ are given points, $AB$ will represent the *line* through $A$ and $B$, unless it is explicitly stated that $AB$ represents the *line segment* joining $A$ and $B$.

EXAMPLE 2.   With points $A:(1, 5)$, $B:(-1, 1)$, $C:(-2, -6)$, and $D:(3, 4)$, prove that $AB$ and $CD$ are parallel, or not parallel.

*Solution.*   From (1),

$$(\text{slope of } AB) = \frac{1 - 5}{-1 - 1} = 2; \quad (\text{slope of } CD) = \frac{4 + 6}{3 + 2} = 2.$$

Hence the lines are parallel because they have the same slope.

## Exercise 13

*In an xy-plane, draw the line through the points and compute its slope.*

1.   $(2, 2), (6, 9)$.
2.   $(-3, 4), (5, -3)$.
3.   $(-3, -6), (-2, -3)$.
4.   $(0, 4), (6, 5)$.
5.   $(-3, 0), (5, -2)$.
6.   $(-4, 6), (-3, 2)$.

*By use of slopes, prove that lines AB and CD are parallel, or that they are not parallel.*

7.   $A:(5, 3)$, $B:(1, 1)$, $C:(1, -2)$, $D:(3, -1)$.
8.   $A:(-2, -1)$, $B:(-4, -2)$, $C:(-5, 2)$, $D:(-2, 0)$.
9.   $A:(3, 4)$, $B:(2, 1)$, $C:(-1, -3)$, $D:(2, 6)$.
10.   $A:(3, 1)$, $B:(5, 3)$, $C:(7, -1)$, $D:(9, 1)$.
11.   $A:(1, 0)$, $B:(4, 1)$, $C:(2, 2)$, $D:(5, 3)$.

*A quadrilateral is a parallelogram in case opposite sides are parallel. Prove that the given points are the vertices of a parallelogram. Use a figure.*

12.   $(-1, 2), (0, -1), (3, 3), (4, 0)$.
13.   $(3, 3), (7, 1), (5, 5), (9, 3)$.

*A* **rhombus** *is a parallelogram with sides of equal length. Prove that the quadrilateral with the given vertices is a rhombus. Use a figure.*

14.   $(2, -3), (3, 1), (6, -2), (7, 2)$.
15.   $(2, 1), (4, 4), (5, 3), (7, 6)$.

*Prove that the given points are collinear.*

16.   $(3, 4), (4, 6), (2, 2)$.
17.   $(0, 3), (2, 4), (6, 6)$.

*If the points are known to be collinear, find the value of x or of y.*

18.   $(1, 6), (0, 8), (x, 5)$.
19.   $(4, -1), (2, -2), (3, y)$.

*Draw a line accurately to scale through the given point with the slope m.*

20.   Through $(3, 4)$; $m = 3$.
21.   Through $(-2, 5)$; $m = -2$.

## 24.  Standard equations of lines

If the $x$-intercept of a vertical line $L$ is $a$, the equation of $L$ is $x = a$. If the $y$-intercept of a horizontal line $L$ is $b$, the equation of $L$ is $y = b$. Hence, we have obtained the following standard forms.

*Line parallel to y-*axis:        $x = a.$                    (1)

*Line parallel to x-*axis:        $y = b.$                    (2)

THEOREM II.   *The line L through* $P_1:(x_1, y_1)$ *with slope m has the equation*

**(point-slope form)**          $y - y_1 = m(x - x_1).$          (3)

*Proof.   1.*   If $x = x_1$ and $y = y_1$, then (3) is a true statement because each side becomes 0. Hence $P_1:(x_1, y_1)$ is on the graph of (3).

*2.*   In Figure 27, let $L$ be the line through $P_1$ with slope $m$. Let $P:(x, y)$ be any point other than $P_1$ on $L$. Then, the slope of $P_1P$ is $m$ and, from (2) on page 54,

$$\frac{y - y_1}{x - x_1} = m, \quad or \quad y - y_1 = m(x - x_1). \qquad (4)$$

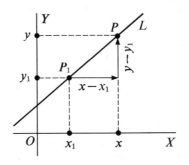

*Fig. 27*

*3.*   If $P:(x, y)$ is not on $L$, the slope of $P_1P$ is not $m$, and thus the pair of numbers $(x, y)$ does not satisfy (4). Hence, (3) is the equation of $L$, because (3) is true if $P:(x, y)$ is on $L$ and is *not* true if $P:(x, y)$ is *not* on $L$.

ILLUSTRATION 1.   The equation of the line with slope 2 through the point $(-3, 4)$ is

$y - 4 = 2[x - (-3)], \quad or \quad y - 4 = 2(x + 3), \quad or \quad y = 2x + 10.$

EXAMPLE 1.   Find an equation for the line $L$ through $(3, 5)$ and $(-2, 4)$.

*Solution.   1.*   From (2) on page 54, the slope of $L$ is

$$m = \frac{5 - 4}{3 + 2} = \frac{1}{5}.$$

2.  By use of (3) with (3, 5) as $(x_1, y_1)$, an equation for $L$ is

$$y - 5 = \tfrac{1}{5}(x - 3) \qquad or \qquad 5y - x = 22.$$

ILLUSTRATION 2.  The line $L$ through $P_1:(4, -3)$ and $P_2:(4, -7)$ is *vertical*, because $P_1$ and $P_2$ have the *same abscissa*. Hence, from (1), an equation for $L$ is $x = 4$.

NOTE 1.  By the method of Example 1, we find that an equation for the line $L$ through $P_1:(x_1, y_1)$ and $P_2:(x_2, y_2)$, where $x_1 \neq x_2$, is

$$y - y_1 = \frac{y_2 - y_1}{x_2 - x_1}(x - x_1). \tag{5}$$

In (5), the fraction is *the slope of L*. Although (5) could be used to solve Example 1, it is recommended that the student should *not* memorize (5) as an added result.

THEOREM III.  *The line L with slope m and y-intercept b has the equation*

**(slope-y-intercept form)**  $\qquad y = mx + b.$  $\qquad\qquad$ (6)

*Proof.*  Since the $y$-intercept is $b$, line $L$ passes through the point $P:(0, b)$ on the $y$-axis. Then, from (3) with $x_1 = 0$ and $y_1 = b$, line $L$ has the equation

$$y - b = m(x - 0), \qquad or \qquad y - b = mx, \qquad or \qquad y = mx + b.$$

ILLUSTRATION 3.  The line with slope $-3$ and $y$-intercept 2 has the equation $y = -3x + 2$.

ILLUSTRATION 4.  Since the equation $y = -5x + 3$ is in the standard form (6), the graph of the equation is the line with slope $-5$ and $y$-intercept 3.

If $A$, $B$, and $C$ are constants, with $B \neq 0$, we can change any equation $Ax + By = C$ to the form (6) by solving the equation for $y$ in terms of $x$. Then, as a consequence of Theorem III, the graph of the given equation is a line, whose slope and $y$-intercept can be obtained by inspection of the resulting *slope-y-intercept* form.

EXAMPLE 2.  Find the slope and $y$-intercept of the line $L$ which is the graph of the equation

$$3x + 4y = 8. \tag{7}$$

*Solution.*  Solve (7) for $y$ in terms of $x$, by subtracting $3x$ from both sides, and then dividing both sides by 4. This gives

$$4y = -3x + 8, \qquad or \qquad y = -\tfrac{3}{4}x + 2. \tag{8}$$

By comparing (6) and (8), we see that $L$ has the slope $-\tfrac{3}{4}$ and $y$-intercept 2.

NOTE 2.  *To find a line* usually will mean *to find its equation.*

## 25. General linear equation in two variables

A linear equation in the variables $x$ and $y$, or an equation of the 1st degree in $x$ and $y$, is a polynomial equation equivalent to one of the form

$$Ax + By + C = 0, \tag{1}$$

where $A$, $B$, and $C$ are constants with $A$ and $B$ not both zero. We shall call (1) the *general linear equation* in $x$ and $y$.

**THEOREM IV.** *The graph of any linear equation in $x$ and $y$ is a line.*

*Proof.*   *1.*   If $B = 0$ in (1), then $A \neq 0$, and (1) becomes

$$Ax + C = 0, \quad or \quad Ax = -C, \quad or \quad x = -C/A. \tag{2}$$

We recognize (2) as the equation of a vertical line.

*2.*   If $B \neq 0$ in (1), we may solve (1) for $y$ in terms of $x$ as follows:

$$By = -Ax - C, \quad or \quad y = -\frac{A}{B}x - \frac{C}{B}. \tag{3}$$

We recognize (3) as the equation of a line with slope $-A/B$ and $y$-intercept $-C/B$. Hence, in all cases, as seen in (2) and (3), we have proved that (1) is the equation of a line.

**THEOREM V.**   (*Converse of Theorem IV.*)   *Any line $L$ in an xy-plane has an equation which is linear in $x$ and $y$.*

*Proof.* If $L$ is vertical, with $x$-intercept $a$, then $L$ has the equation $x = a$. If $L$ is *not* vertical, it has a slope, $m$, and a $y$-intercept, $b$, because any nonvertical line has an intersection with the $y$-axis. Hence, $L$ has the equation $y = mx + b$. Thus, under all circumstances, $L$ has an equation which is linear in $x$ and $y$.

### Exercise 14

*Write an equation of the line satisfying the conditions of the problem.*

*1.*   Horizontal; $y$-intercept 4.      *2.*   Horizontal; $y$-intercept $-3$.
*3.*   Vertical; $x$-intercept $-6$.      *4.*   Vertical; $x$-intercept 5.
*5.*   Slope $-4$; $y$-intercept 2.      *6.*   Slope 3; $y$-intercept 4.
*7.*   Slope 6; $y$-intercept $-3$.      *8.*   Slope $-5$; $y$-intercept $-2$.

*Find an equation of the line through the points, or through the point with the given slope m. Also, draw the line.*

*9.*   $(3, -5)$; $m = 6$.      *10.*   $(-2, 3)$; $m = 0$.
*11.*   $(-5, -4)$; $m = -2$.      *12.*   $(6, 0)$; $m = -4$.

13.  $(0, 5); m = -3$.                    14.  $(0, -4); m = \frac{5}{2}$.
15.  $(3, -5); (-2, 6)$.                  16.  $(2, -3); (5, 7)$.
17.  $(0, 5); (-4, -5)$.                  18.  $(-4, 2); (-3, -5)$.
19.  $(0, 4); (6, 0)$.                    20.  $(0, 0); (4, -3)$.
21.  $(-3, -4); (0, 0)$.                  22.  $(0, -3); (-5, 0)$.
23.  $(0, 4); (-3, 0)$.                   24.  $(-2, -5); m = -.3$.

25.  If a line $L$ has the $x$-intercept 5 and $y$-intercept $-4$, tell the coordinates of two points on $L$, and obtain an equation for it.
26.  If a line $L$ has the $x$-intercept $a \neq 0$ and $y$-intercept $b \neq 0$, tell the coordinates of two points on $L$, and show that it has the following equation, called the **intercept form** for the equation of $L$:

$$\frac{x}{a} + \frac{y}{b} = 1. \tag{1}$$

*From (1), write an equation of the line with $x$-intercept $a$ and $y$-intercept $b$.*
27.  $a = 3; b = 5$.    28.  $a = -2; b = 4$.    29.  $a = -1; b = -5$.

*Write the equation of the line in the slope-$y$-intercept form, to obtain the slope and $y$-intercept of the line.*
30.  $3x - 2y = 6$.       31.  $2x + 5y = -4$.      32.  $4x = 9y - 3$.
33.  $5x - 3y = 15$.      34.  $6y + 9 = 5x$.       35.  $2x = 7y - 4$.

*Write an equation of the line through point $C$ parallel to line $AB$.*
36.  $A:(5, 2),\ B:(3, 1),\ C:(7, -2)$.
37.  $A:(2, -2),\ B:(5, 7),\ C:(6, 9)$.

*Prove that the points are collinear and find an equation for the line through them.*
38.  $(1, 2), (2, 4), (0, 0)$.            39.  $(2, -7), (-2, -6), (-6, -5)$.

*Write an equation for the line through the point parallel to the line.*
40.  Through $(-4, 3)$ parallel to the line $3x - 5y = 8$.
41.  Through $(2, -5)$ parallel to the line $2y + 7x = 5$.

★*Graph each equation.*
42.  $|x + 2y| = 3$.      43.  $|x| + 2|y| = 1$.      44.  $y + 3 = |x - 2|$.

## 26.  Function concept

In mathematics, frequently we meet situations where two related variables $x$ and $y$ are involved in such a way that, for each value of one variable, say $x$, *a single value of $y$ is specified by some rule*. In such a case, it is natural to say that "*$y$ is a function of $x$*," where we use "*function*" with a semi-colloquial meaning. We proceed to make precise the technical meaning of *function* in such a context.

DEFINITION VI.  *Let D be a set of numbers. Suppose that, for each number x in D, some rule specifies just one corresponding number y, and let R be the set of all of these values of y. Then, this whole set of ordered pairs of numbers (x, y) is called a* **function,** *F, whose* **domain** *is D and* **range** *is R.*

In Definition VI, we call each value of $y$ in $R$ a *value* of the function $F$; we refer to $x$ as the **independent variable** and to $y$ as the **dependent variable.** We may call $F$ "*a function of x*," to indicate that $x$ is to be used for the independent variable. Also, we call $F$ a function of a *single variable* because the domain $D$ consists of *single numbers.*

ILLUSTRATION 1.   Let $D$ be the set of numbers forming the first elements of the following ordered pairs of numbers, and let $R$ be the set of *distinct numbers* among those which are *second elements* of the ordered pairs:

$$(1, 2), \quad (1.5, 3), \quad (2, 2), \quad (3, -2), \quad (4, 6).$$

This set of ordered pairs *forms a function* whose domain is $D = \{1, 1.5, 2, 3, 4\}$, and range is $R = \{-2, 2, 3, 6\}$.

If a formula in a variable $x$ specifies a single number, $y$, corresponding to each value of $x$ in some set $D$, then the formula defines a *function* with the domain $D$ whose values are given by the formula.

ILLUSTRATION 2.   Let $D$ be the interval of numbers, $x$, where $2 \leq x \leq 5$, and let $y = 2x + 5$. If $x = 2$ then $y = 9$; if $x = 3$ then $y = 11$; if $x = 5$ then $y = 15$. Thus, for the values of $x$ in the domain $D$, the corresponding values of $y$ make up the interval $R$ from 9 to 15, or $9 \leq y \leq 15$, with exactly one value of $y$ assigned for each value of $x$. This correspondence between the numbers, or values of $x$, in $D$ and the numbers in $R$ is suggested by the sample broken-line arrows in Figure 28. There are infinitely many pairs of corresponding values of $x$ and $y$.

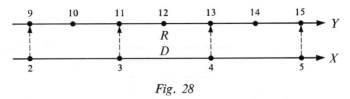

*Fig. 28*

In Definition VI, suppose that $D$ is a set of elements of any variety, with $R$ as another set of elements of any sort. Then, Definition VI, with the word *number* changed to *element*, describes a function whose domain, $D$, is the assigned set of elements and range, $R$, is another set of elements. Thus, $D$ might consist of the *people* in a certain group, and $R$ might be the *set of blood types* of these people. In later chapters, various important applications will employ functions of the type where one or both of $D$ and $R$ are *not sets of numbers.*

If a function is defined by a formula, the function frequently is named in accordance with the character of the formula. Thus, in algebra, we meet *algebraic functions*, which are given this name because their values are defined by algebraic formulas in the independent variable.

The literal number symbols used for arbitrary numbers in the domain and range of a function are of no significance. Thus, in Illustration 2, we could describe $D$ as the domain of a variable $u$, where $2 \leqq u \leqq 5$, and $R$ as the set of values of a variable $v$, where $9 \leqq v \leqq 15$.

ILLUSTRATION 3.    In Definition VI, if $y = h$, a constant, for all values of $x$, we say that the function $F$ is a *constant function.*

DEFINITION VII.    *In an xy-plane, the* **graph of a function** *of a single variable, x, is the set of points $P:(x, y)$ where the coordinates $(x, y)$ are a pair of corresponding values of x and the function.*

As a consequence of Definition VII, we present the following routine for graphing a function.

> **To graph a function,** $F$, *whose value, y, corresponding to each number x in the domain of F is defined by a formula in x, place y equal to the formula and graph the resulting equation in x and y.*     (1)

Usually, in graphing a function in a coordinate plane, the horizontal axis is used for plotting values of the independent variable (but this agreement is *not essential*).

ILLUSTRATION 4.    To graph the function, $F$, whose value is $(2x + 5)$ at any value for $x$, we would let $y = 2x + 5$ and graph this equation. The graph would be a line with slope 2 and $y$-intercept 5.

If $F$ is a function, it is very convenient if a formula in terms of the independent variable is available for calculating values of $F$. However, no formula of this nature may be available.

On page 48, we defined a *relation* between two variables $x$ and $y$ as a set of ordered pairs of values of $x$ and $y$. On inspecting Definition VI, we see that *a function is a particular kind of a relation*, where exactly **one value** of $y$ corresponds to each value of $x$.

NOTE 1.    In any algebraic formula in a variable $x$, unless otherwise specified, we agree that the domain of $x$ consists of all numbers for which the formula represents a real number.

ILLUSTRATION 5.    Let $F$ be a function whose value is $(2x^2 - 3)$ for each value of $x$. Then, the graph of $F$ is the graph of the equation $y = 2x^2 - 3$.

To obtain this graph, we substitute values for $x$ to obtain values for $y$, as below, and plot the resulting representative points of the graph. The curve through these points in Figure 29 is the graph of $F$, and is called a *parabola*.

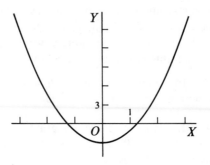

*Fig. 29*

| $x =$ | $-3$ | $-2$ | $-1$ | $0$ | $1$ | $2$ | $3$ |
|-------|------|------|------|-----|-----|-----|-----|
| $y =$ | $15$ | $5$ | $-1$ | $-3$ | $-1$ | $5$ | $15$ |

## Exercise 15

*A function F, with the value y corresponding to any value of x, is defined by the table. Graph F in an xy-plane.*

1.

| $x =$ | $-2$ | $-1$ | $0$ | $1$ | $2$ | $3$ |
|-------|------|------|-----|-----|-----|-----|
| $y =$ | $-4$ | $3$ | $3$ | $1$ | $-1$ | $-2$ |

2.

| $x =$ | $-3$ | $-1$ | $0$ | $2$ | $4$ |
|-------|------|------|-----|-----|-----|
| $y =$ | $-2$ | $2$ | $-2$ | $3$ | $5$ |

*Describe the range, R, of the function F and list the whole set of ordered pairs of numbers which form F. Construct a graph of F in an xy-plane.*

3. The domain of $F$ is the set $D = \{-4, -3, -2, -1, 0, 1, 2, 3\}$. The value of $F$ corresponding to any number $x$ in $D$ is $3x$.

4. The domain of $F$ is the set $D = \{-3, -2, -1, 0, 1, 2\}$. The value of $F$ corresponding to any number $x$ in $D$ is $x^2$.

5. The domain of $F$ is the set $D = \{1, 2, 3, \cdots, 12\}$. The value of $F$ corresponding to any number $x$ in $D$ is *the greatest integral multiple of 2 which is at most equal to x.*

*Graph the function whose value, corresponding to any value of the independent variable x, is given by the formula.*

6. $2x + 8$.     7. $-3x + 4$.     8. $x + 8$.     9. 5.

10. $x^2 - 6x + 6$, with $x = 3$ used in the table of values.

11. Let $D$ be the set of all positive numbers, $x$. Let a function $F$ be defined by stating that, for any value of $x$, the value of $F$ is the cost in cents of mailing a letter weighing $x$ ounces, at ten cents for each ounce or fraction of an ounce. Graph $F$ for the values of $x$ on the interval $0 < x \leq 6$, in an $xy$-plane.

12. For each value of $x$, let $|x|$ be the value of a function $F$. Draw a graph of $F$.

## 27. Functional notation

Let $F$ be a function with the domain $D$. Then, it may be convenient to represent the value of $F$ corresponding to the arbitrary number $x$ in $D$ by the symbol "$F(x)$," which is read "$F$ of $x$," or "$F$ at $x$." That is,

$$F(x) \text{ represents the } \textbf{value of } F \text{ corresponding to the} \atop \text{number } x \text{ in the domain } D \text{ of } F. \right\} \quad (1)$$

We refer to $F(x)$ as a symbol in *functional notation*. In $F(x)$, we call $x$ the **argument** of the symbol. Thus, we have introduced $F(x)$ instead of $y$, as in the previous section, to represent the value of $F$ described in (1). We may use both $y$ and $F(x)$ for this purpose, and then write $y = F(x)$. Either $y$ or $F(x)$ thus is the dependent variable, and $x$ is the independent variable.

ILLUSTRATION 1.   If we let $F(x) = 3x^3 + x - 5$, we thus assign $F$ as a symbol for the function, and simultaneously give a formula, $(3x^3 + x - 5)$, for the values of $F$. Then, the values of $F$ at $x = 2$ and at $x = -2$ are

$$F(2) = 3(2^3) + 2 - 5 = 21; \qquad F(-2) = 3(-2)^3 - 2 - 5 = -31.$$

A symbol $F(x)$ may be thought of as a *formula* from which we obtain particular values of $F$ by replacing $x$ by particular values in its domain. That is, if $x = a$ is a number in the domain of $F$, then

$$F(a) \text{ represents the value of } F \text{ when } x = a. \qquad (2)$$

ILLUSTRATION 2.   If $g(x) = 3x + 2/x$, then

$$g(3) = 9 + \frac{2}{3} = \frac{29}{3}; \qquad g(3b) = 9b + \frac{2}{3b}.$$

If $h(x) = x^2$, then

$$g(2)h(3) = (6 + 1)(9) = 63; \qquad \frac{g(1)}{h(2)} = \frac{5}{4};$$

$$g(h(x)) = 3h(x) + \frac{2}{h(x)} = 3x^2 + \frac{2}{x^2}.$$

In functional notation, routine (1) on page 61 may be restated as follows:

> *To graph a function F, with x as the independent variable,* $\left.\right\}$   (3)
> *in an xy-plane, graph the equation* $y = F(x).$

ILLUSTRATION 3.   If $g(x) = 4x - 5$, we would obtain a graph of the function $g$ by graphing the equation $y = g(x)$, or $y = 4x - 5$. The graph would be a line with slope 4 and $y$-intercept $-5$.

Let $x$ and $y$ be variables which are free to take on any ordered pair of values $(x, y)$ in a certain set, $D$, of *pairs of numbers*. Each *pair* in $D$ may be thought of as the coordinates of a point $P:(x, y)$ in an $xy$-plane. Thus, for illustration, $D$ might consist of all pairs $(x, y)$ giving the coordinates of the points in a rectangle in the $xy$-plane. Then, for each pair $(x, y)$ in $D$, suppose that some rule specifies *just one corresponding number z*, which produces a set of *ordered triples* of numbers, $(x, y, z)$. Then, the set of all of these ordered triples of numbers is referred to as a *function, F*, whose domain is $D$. The set, $R$, of all of the distinct corresponding values of $z$ is called the *range* of $F$. Also, $F$ is referred to as a function of the *two independent variables x and y*, because each element of $D$ is a *pair* of numbers. The variable $z$ is called the dependent variable. We extend functional notation to the case of functions of two independent variables. Thus, we would let $z = F(x, y)$, and refer to $z$, or to $F(x, y)$, as the dependent variable.

ILLUSTRATION 4.   If we let $F(x, y) = 3x + 2y - 5$, this defines a function $F$ of the two independent variables $x$ and $y$. Then,

$$F(2, -3) = 3(2) + 2(-3) - 5 = -5.$$

Similarly, we may introduce functions of three or more independent variables, and extend functional notation to such functions.

ILLUSTRATION 5.   If $G(x, y, z) = 2x - 3y^2 + 3z - 4$, we may let $w = G(x, y, z)$ and refer to $G$ as a function of the independent variables $x, y$, and $z$. Then, $w$ or $G(x, y, z)$ would be called the dependent variable.

NOTE 1.   To graph a function $F$ of two independent variables $x$ and $y$, we would graph the equation $z = F(x, y)$, where there are three variables. This would involve graphing in space of three dimensions, which is beyond the level of this text.

If $f$ is a function of a single variable, $x$, and if $y = f(x)$, sometimes we may refer to the dependent variable, $y$, as if it were the function, and say

**"$y$ is a function of $x$."**   (4)

In (4), we mean that "*y is the value of some function corresponding to the arbitrary number x in the function's domain.*" Also, we may refer to

**"a function $f(x)$,"**   (5)

as a brief way of stating that "*f is a function where an arbitrary number in the domain of f will be represented by x.*" Thus, in particular, we may refer to

$$\text{"} a \text{ function } ax^2 + bx + c, \text{"} \tag{6}$$

meaning that $(ax^2 + bx + c)$ is the *value* of the function corresponding to the number $x$ in its domain. The "elliptical" terminology of (5) and (6) is met with great frequency in many branches of advanced mathematics.

### Exercise 16

If $f(x) = 3x - 4$, find the value of the symbol.
1. $f(3)$.    2. $f(-2)$.    3. $f(\tfrac{3}{4})$.    4. $f(-\tfrac{1}{2})$.    5. $[f(-3)]^2$.

If $h(u) = u^2 - 2u + 5$, find the value of the symbol.
6. $h(2)$.    7. $4h(-1)$.    8. $h(2a)$.    9. $h(3c)$.    10. $[h(-3)]^2$.

If $f(x) = (x + 2)/(x - 3)$, find the value of the symbol or an expression for it.
11. $f(-4)$.    12. $[f(3)]^2$.    13. $5f(-1)$.    14. $f(2u)$.    15. $f(\tfrac{1}{2}x)$.

With $h$ defined as for Problem 6, and $f$ as defined for Problem 11, find the value of the symbol, or an expression for it in terms of the variables.
16. $h(3)/f(4)$.    17. $h(-2)f(4)$.    18. $f(h(u))$.    19. $f(3h(1))$.
20. If $f(x) = 3x + 5$, find $f(f(x))$.

If $F(x, y) = 3x + 2y + x^2$, find the value of the symbol.
21. $F(3, 5)$.    22. $F(-1, 4)$.    23. $F(2, \tfrac{1}{2})$.    24. $F(d, c^3)$.
25. If $f(u) = 5 - 2u$ and $h(v) = 3v + 4$, find $f(3)h(4)$; $f(-2)/h(3)$; $h(4)/f(-3)$; $f(x) + h(x)$; $f(2x)h(x)$.

Graph the function $f$, or $g$, whose values are defined.
26. $f(x) = 3x + 2$.    27. $f(x) = 5 - 3x$.    28. $g(x) = x^2$.

## 28.  Polynomial functions of degrees 0, 1, and 2

We recall the terminology about polynomials on page 9. Then, if $n$ is a nonnegative integer, a function $f(x)$ is called a **polynomial function** of degree $n$ if $f(x)$ is a polynomial of degree $n$ in $x$, that is, if

$$f(x) = a_0 + a_1 x + a_2 x^2 + \cdots + a_n x^n, \tag{1}$$

where $a_0, a_1, \cdots, a_n$ are constants and $a_n \neq 0$. If $n = 0$ in (1), then $f(x) = a_0 \neq 0$, and $f$ is a *constant function*. If $n = 1$ in (1), then $f$ is called a *linear function*, and $f(x)$ can be thought of in the form

(**linear function** $f$)    $f(x) = mx + b \quad (m \neq 0)$. $\tag{2}$

If $n = 2$ in (1), then $f$ is called a *quadratic function* of $x$, and $f(x)$ can be written in the form

(**quadratic function** $f$)    $f(x) = ax^2 + bx + c \quad (a \neq 0)$. $\tag{3}$

In (1), $f$ is called a cubic function if $n = 3$, and a quartic function if $n = 4$. We shall concern ourselves at present only with the graphs of constant functions, linear functions, and quadratic functions.

ILLUSTRATION 1.   If $f(x) = 5$ for all values of $x$, then $f$ is a constant function, whose graph in an $xy$-plane is the graph of the equation $y = 5$, which is a line parallel to the $x$-axis.

In Illustration 1, we met a special case of the fact that *the graph of any constant function of $x$ is a line parallel to the $x$-axis.*

ILLUSTRATION 2.   If $f(x) = 3x - 5$, then $f$ is a linear function, whose graph in an $xy$-plane is the graph of $y = 3x - 5$, which is a line with slope 3 and $y$-intercept $-5$.

In Illustration 2, we observe a special instance of the fact that, *if $f(x) = mx + b$, the graph of $f$ is the line with slope $m$ and $y$-intercept $b$,* which is the graph of the equation

$$y = f(x), \qquad or \qquad y = mx + b. \tag{4}$$

From (4) when $m \neq 0$, *the graph of the linear function $f$, where $f(x) = mx + b$, is a line whose slope is not zero.*

In complete treatments of analytic geometry, it is proved that the graph of any quadratic function of a single variable is a curve called a **parabola**.

EXAMPLE 1.   Graph the quadratic function

$$f(x) = x^2 - 2x - 6. \tag{5}$$

*Solution.   1.*   The graph of $f$ is the graph of the equation

$$y = x^2 - 2x - 6. \tag{6}$$

We select values of $x$ and compute $y$, as in the following table, to obtain representative points on the graph, which is the parabola in Figure 30, drawn through the points obtained from the table. The lowest point, $V$, of the parabola is called its **vertex**.

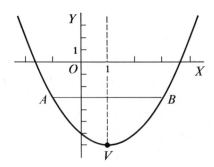

*Fig. 30*

| $x =$ | $-2$ | $-1$ | $0$ | $1$ | $2$ | $3$ | $4$ |
|-------|------|------|-----|-----|-----|-----|-----|
| $y =$ | $2$ | $-3$ | $-6$ | $-7$ | $-6$ | $-3$ | $2$ |

2. At $V$, we have $y = -7$ which is the *least*, or **minimum value** of $y$. That is, the minimum value of the function $f$ in (5) is $-7$. We may call $V$ the *minimum point* of the graph. The broken vertical line through $V$ is called the **axis** of the parabola. It is symmetric to its axis, because any chord of the parabola perpendicular to the axis (such as chord $AB$ in Figure 30) is bisected by the axis. The equation of the axis is $x = 1$. This parabola is said to be *concave upward* (open upward) because the curve bends counterclockwise if we travel on it from left to right. In more advanced texts, the following facts are proved.

**Concerning the graph of a quadratic function**

$$f(x) = ax^2 + bx + c. \tag{7}$$

(I)   *The graph of $f$, or of the equation*

$$y = ax^2 + bx + c, \tag{8}$$

*is a parabola with its axis perpendicular to the x-axis, where the parabola is* **concave upward** *if* $a > 0$, *and* **downward** *if* $a < 0$.

(II)   *The vertex of the parabola is the point on it where the abscissa is* $x = -b/2a$. *This value of $x$ gives the minimum value of $f(x)$ if $a > 0$, and the maximum value of $f(x)$ if $a < 0$.*[*]

(III)   *The equation of the axis of the parabola is* $x = -b/2a$.

To graph a quadratic function (7), first compute the abscissa of the vertex by use of (II). Then, to calculate values of $y$ from (8), use values of $x$ *symmetrically located by pairs* on the $x$-axis, to the right and the left of the vertex. Then, because of the symmetry of a parabola, the values of $y$ in the table will be equal in pairs.

ILLUSTRATION 3.   In (5), we have $a = 1$ and $b = -2$ for (II). This gives $x = -(-2)/2$, or $x = 1$ as the abscissa of the vertex. Then, in the table of pairs $(x, y)$, we may choose, for $x > 1$, the values 2, 3, and 4. The symmetrical values on the left are 0, $-1$, and $-2$, as seen in the table for Example 1, where we verify that the values of $y$ are equal in pairs.

ILLUSTRATION 4.   If $f(x) = -x^2 + 4x + 5$, from (I) we learn that the graph of $y = f(x)$ is a parabola concave *downward*. In this case, the vertex $V$ would be the *highest point* on the graph. From (II), the abscissa of $V$ is $x = -4/(-2)$, or $x = 2$. Then, at $V$, $y = -4 + 8 + 5 = 9$, which is the largest value of $f(x)$. The student will graph this function later.

[*] The existence of such a maximum or minimum value will be proved in a later chapter.

## 29.  Functions defined by equations

Any equation in two variables $x$ and $y$ is equivalent to an equation

$$h(x, y) = 0, \tag{1}$$

where we merely arrange to have 0 as one member. Sometimes, for each value of $x$, from (1) we find that there is *just one corresponding value for $y$* so that $(x, y)$ is a solution of (1). In such a case, we say that (1) *defines $y$ as a function of $x$.* If we let $f$ represent this function, then any solution of (1) can be represented as $(x, y = f(x))$, and we may call $f$ a *solution function for $y$ as a function of $x$.* Also, in some cases, for each value of $y$, from (1) we find that there is *just one corresponding value of $x$* so that $(x, y)$ is a solution of (1). Then, we say that (1) *defines $x$ as a function of $y$,* and we may let $x = g(y)$, where we call $g$ a *solution function of* (1) *for $x$ in terms of $y$.*

ILLUSTRATION 1.   Suppose that the variables $x$ and $y$ satisfy

$$3x + 5y = 12. \tag{2}$$

On solving (2) for $y$ in terms of $x$, we obtain

$$5y = 12 - 3x, \quad or \quad y = \tfrac{12}{5} - \tfrac{3}{5}x. \tag{3}$$

For each value of $x$ in (2) there is just one corresponding value of $y$, in (3); thus, (2) defines $y$ *as a function of $x$.* If we let $f(x) = \tfrac{12}{5} - \tfrac{3}{5}x$, then any solution of (2) is of the form $(x, y = f(x))$. Similarly, (2) defines $x$ *as a function of $y$,* with the value of $x$ for any $y$ obtained on solving (2) for $x$ in terms of $y$, which gives

$$x = 4 - \tfrac{5}{3}y. \tag{4}$$

If an equation $h(x, y) = 0$ defines one of the variables $x$ and $y$ as a function of the other variable, *the graph of the equation is the same as the graph of the function thus defined.*

ILLUSTRATION 2.   With $f(x) = \tfrac{12}{5} - \tfrac{3}{5}x$, from (3), the graph of $y = f(x)$ is the graph of (2).

ILLUSTRATION 3.   Let the domain, $D$, of a variable $x$ consist of all nonnegative real numbers. The graph of the equation

$$x = y^2 \tag{5}$$

is the parabola in Figure 31. We see that (5) defines $x$ *as a function of $y$,* because there is just one value of $x$ corresponding to any assigned real number $y$. From (5),

$$y = \sqrt{x} \quad or \quad y = -\sqrt{x}. \tag{6}$$

Let $f(x) = \sqrt{x}$ and $g(x) = -\sqrt{x}$. Then, the pairs $(x, y = f(x))$ are solutions of (5), so that we may call $f$ a solution function of (5) for $y$ as a function of $x$. The other solutions of (5) are the pairs $(x, g(x))$, with the solution $(0, 0)$ obtained by use of both $f$ and $g$. We *cannot* say that (5) defines $y$ as a function of $x$, because *two* values of $y$, in (6), correspond to each $x > 0$. However, all solutions of (5), with $(0, 0)$ repeated, can be grouped as in (6) by use of the *two solution functions* $f$ and $g$. In Figure 31, the graph of $y = \sqrt{x}$ is the part of the parabola from $(0, 0)$ above the $x$-axis. The graph of $y = -\sqrt{x}$ is the broken part of the parabola, also including $(0, 0)$.

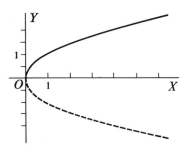

*Fig. 31*

EXAMPLE 1.   Obtain the graph of the equation

$$2y - 4x^2 + 12x - 5 = 0. \tag{7}$$

*Solution.*   Since (7) is of the first degree in $y$, we may solve (7) for $y$ in terms of $x$, to obtain

$$2y = 4x^2 - 12x + 5, \quad or \quad y = 2x^2 - 6x + \tfrac{5}{2}. \tag{8}$$

Hence, (7) *defines $y$ as a quadratic function of $x$.* The graph of (7), or (8), is a parabola, which could be obtained by use of (I)–(III) on page 67.

EXAMPLE 2.   Obtain the graph of the equation

$$3x + 6y^2 - 12y - 12 = 0. \tag{9}$$

*Solution.*   On solving (9) for $x$, we obtain

$$x = -2y^2 + 4y + 4. \tag{10}$$

Hence, (9) *defines $x$ as a quadratic function of $y$.* The graph of (9), or (10), is the parabola in Figure 32 on page 70. The parabola may be checked by using (I), (II), and (III) on page 67 with the roles of $x$ and $y$ interchanged.

Thus, the parabola is concave in the negative $y$-direction; the value of $y$ at the vertex is $y = (-4) \div (-4) = 1$, and then $x = 6$; etc.

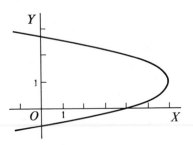

Fig. 32

## Exercise 17

Graph each function of x whose values are defined by the polynomial, or the symbol in functional notation.

1. $4x + 7$.  2. $-3 - 2x$.  3. $-5 + 7x$.  4. $3x$.
5. $6$.  6. $-5$.  7. $3 - 5x$.  8. $x^2$.
9. $f(x) = -x^2$.  10. $x^2 - 4x - 5$.
11. $-x^2 + 4x + 5$.  12. $2x^2 - 8x - 7$.
13. $g(x) = -2x^2 + 8x$.  14. $-2x^2 + 12x - 9$.

Find a formula for the values of the linear function of x, and for the linear function of y defined by the equation.

15. $3x - 2y = 18$.  16. $5x + 4y = 20$.  17. $2y - 7x = 15$.

18. Solve for $y$ to obtain a formula for the values of the function of $x$ defined by $2y - 2x^2 + 4x = 5$, and then graph the equation (or, the function defined by it).

19. Solve for $x$ to obtain a formula for the values of the function of $y$ defined by $7 + 2x - 4y^2 - 8y = 0$, and then graph the function with the $x$-axis horizontal in the coordinate system.

## 30.  Unions of graphs and special cases

As a consequence of Definition III on page 31, we observe that the *union* of two sets $S$ and $T$ of points $(x, y)$ consists of all points in only one or in both of the sets. We find an application for this fact where each of the sets is the graph of an equation.

ILLUSTRATION 1.  The equation

$$(x - y + 2)(2x + y - 4) = 0 \tag{1}$$

is satisfied by a pair $(x, y)$ if and only if

$$x - y + 2 = 0 \quad \textbf{OR} \quad 2x + y - 4 = 0. \tag{2}$$

Hence, the solution set, $T$, for (1) consists of all solutions of $x - y + 2 = 0$ *and* all solutions of $2x + y - 4 = 0$. Or, $T$ is the **union of the solution sets of the equations** in (2). Hence, the graph of (1) is the union of the graphs of the equations in (2), or consists of the two corresponding lines in Figure 33. The preceding details illustrate the following statement.

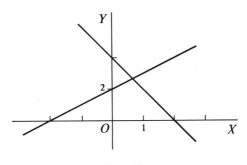

*Fig. 33*

**Summary.** *Suppose that a polynomial $F(x, y)$ is expressed as a product of polynomial factors. Then, the graph of $F(x, y) = 0$ is the **union** of the graphs of the equations obtained by placing each factor separately equal to zero.*

ILLUSTRATION 2.   An equation in $x$ and $y$ may have *no graph*. Thus, the equation $x^2 + y^2 = -5$ has no graph because $x^2$ and $y^2$ are not negative for any values of $x$ and $y$. Or, the graph of $x^2 + y^2 = -5$ is the *empty set*, $\varnothing$.

ILLUSTRATION 3.   The graph of $x^2 + 4y^2 = 0$ is a *single point*, the origin, because we must have $x^2 = 0$ and $y^2 = 0$, which requires $(x = 0, y = 0)$.

ILLUSTRATION 4.   To graph $4x^2 = 9y^2$, or $4x^2 - 9y^2 = 0$, we first factor, to obtain $(2x - 3y)(2x + 3y) = 0$. Hence, as in the Summary, the graph of $4x^2 - 9y^2 = 0$ consists of the *two lines*, through the origin, with the equations $2x - 3y = 0$ and $2x + 3y = 0$.

## 31.  Standard equations for a circle

In order that the distance formula of page 46 will be applicable, we agree that the scale units on the axes will be *equal* in any $xy$-plane involved in this section and in its later applications.

Let $T$ be a circle with center $C:(a, b)$ and radius $r \geqq 0$ in an $xy$-plane. Then, a point $P:(x, y)$ is on $T$ if and only if the distance $|\overline{PC}| = r$, as seen in Figure 34. From the distance formula on page 46, we have

$$\overline{PC^2} = (x - a)^2 + (y - b)^2.$$

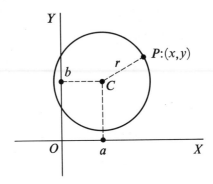

*Fig. 34*

Hence, an equation of the circle $T$ is $\overline{PC^2} = r^2$ or

$$(x - a)^2 + (y - b)^2 = r^2. \tag{1}$$

ILLUSTRATION 1.    From (1), an equation for the circle with radius 3 and center $C:(2, 5)$ is

$$(x - 2)^2 + (y - 5)^2 = 9, \quad or$$
$$x^2 - 4x + y^2 - 10y = -20.$$

From (1) with $a = b = 0$, an equation for the circle with radius $r$ and center at the origin $(0, 0)$ is

$$x^2 + y^2 = r^2. \tag{2}$$

ILLUSTRATION 2.    An equation for the circle with radius 4 and center at the origin is $x^2 + y^2 = 16$.

When $r = 0$, from (2) we obtain $x^2 + y^2 = 0$, whose graph then is just the single point $(0, 0)$, and is called a *point-circle*. If $r = 0$, the graph of (1) is the point $(a, b)$.

ILLUSTRATION 3.    The equation $x^2 + y^2 = -16$ has no graph, or its graph is the *empty set*. Since this equation is of the "*form*" (2) with $r^2 = -16$, sometimes $x^2 + y^2 = -16$ is said to represent an *imaginary circle* (because of the thought that $r^2 = -16$, which would yield $r = \pm 4i$). Similarly, if $r^2 < 0$ then (1) has no graph, and can be said to represent an imaginary circle.

Any equation of the second degree in $x$ and $y$ which is equivalent to

$$Ax^2 + Ay^2 + Bx + Cy + d = 0, \tag{3}$$

where $A \neq 0$, and the coefficients of $x^2$ and $y^2$ are equal, can be changed to the form (1). Hence, the graph of (3) is a circle, real or imaginary. To change (3) to the form (1), we complete a square, separately, with the terms in $x$, and then with the terms in $y$, after dividing both sides in (3) by $A$ when $A \neq 1$.

EXAMPLE 1.   Obtain the center and radius of the circle

$$4x^2 - 16x + 4y^2 + 24y + 27 = 0. \tag{4}$$

*Solution.*   *1.*   Divide both sides of (4) by 4:

$$(x^2 - 4x \quad) + (y^2 + 6y \quad) = -\tfrac{27}{4}. \tag{5}$$

2.   To complete squares in (5), add $[\tfrac{1}{2}(4)]^2$ to the terms involving $x$, and $[\tfrac{1}{2}(6)]^2$ to the terms involving $y$; hence add both of the numbers to the right-hand side:

$$(x^2 - 4x + 4) + (y^2 + 6y + 9) = 13 - \tfrac{27}{4}, \quad or$$
$$(x - 2)^2 + (y + 3)^2 = \tfrac{25}{4}. \tag{6}$$

On comparing (1) and (6), we note that (6), or (4), is the equation of a circle with center $(2, -3)$ and radius $\sqrt{\tfrac{25}{4}}$ or $\tfrac{5}{2}$.

## Exercise 18

*Graph the equation or state why it has no graph. Any circle may be drawn by use of compasses after its center and radius are recognized, without computing coordinates of points on the circle.*

1.  $(2x - y)(2x + y - 4) = 0.$    2.  $(x - 6)(x + 3y - 3) = 0.$
3.  $4x^2 - y^2 = 0.$    4.  $x^2 + 9y^2 = 0.$    5.  $4x^2 = 25y^2.$
6.  $x^2 - 4 = 0.$    7.  $y^2 + 16 = 0.$    8.  $x^2 + y^2 = 9.$
9.  $(x - 2)^2 + (y - 3)^2 = 16.$    10.  $(x + 1)^2 + y^2 = 9.$

*Write the equation of the circle with the specified center C and radius r.*

11.  $C:(4, 1); r = 2.$    12.  $C:(0, 0); r = 6.$
13.  $C:(2, 0); r = 5.$    14.  $C:(0, -4); r = 4.$
15.  $C:(-3, 2); r = 1.$    16.  $C:(-1, -2); r = 3.$

*Obtain the center and radius of the circle which is the graph of the given equation, or prove that its graph is the empty set.*

17.  $x^2 - 2x + y^2 - 4y = 4.$    18.  $x^2 + 4x + y^2 - 6y = 12.$
19.  $x^2 + 4x + y^2 + 1 = 0.$    20.  $x^2 + y^2 + 8y + 7 = 0.$
21.  $x^2 - 2x + y^2 + 4y + 7 = 0.$    22.  $x^2 + y^2 - 2y + 6 = 0.$

## ★32.  The conic sections*

In a plane, at the center of a circle $W$, let a line $M$ of indefinite extent be drawn perpendicular to the plane, $\tau$, of $W$. Let $V$ be any point on $M$ which is not on $\tau$, as in Figure 35. From any point $P$ on $W$, draw a line $L$ through $V$. With $V$ fixed, let $L$ be moved through all points $P$ on $W$. Then, the set of points thus swept out by $L$ is a surface of infinite extent called a (*complete*) **right circular cone**, $U$, whose **vertex** is $V$ and **axis** is $M$. Each position of $L$ is called a **ruling** of $U$. The vertex $V$ divides $U$ into two parts called **nappes**. In Figure 36, each nappe is cut above and below $V$ by a plane perpendicular to $M$.

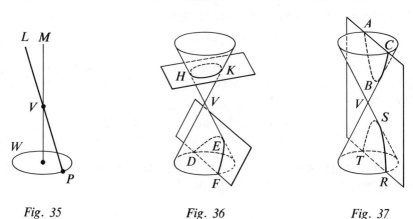

Fig. 35                 Fig. 36                 Fig. 37

If a plane cuts a cone (meaning a *complete* cone), the curve of intersection is called a **conic section**. First, assume that the plane does not pass through $V$. Then, if the plane cuts only one nappe and is not parallel to a ruling of $U$, the conic, or curve of intersection $HK$, is called an **ellipse**, as in Figure 36; the ellipse is a *circle* if the plane is perpendicular to the axis $M$. If the plane cuts just one nappe and is parallel to a ruling of $U$, as in Figure 36, the conic $DEF$ is called a **parabola**. If the plane cuts *both* nappes in any fashion, as in Figure 37, the conic consists of two parts, or branches, $ABC$, and $RST$, and is called a **hyperbola**. If the cone is cut by a plane through $V$, the only point of intersection with the cone may be $V$, so that the conic is just a *single point*. Or, the plane may pass through $V$ and intersect the cone only along a *single ruling* (or, be *tangent* to the cone); then the conic is this *single line*, thought of as *two coincident lines* because of the tangency. Or, a plane through $V$ may intersect the cone along *two rulings*, so that the conic consists of these *two lines intersecting at* $V$.

* The content of Sections 32 and 33 will not be needed in any future sections of this text.

Hereafter, we shall include under the name *conic section* all sets of points (curves) mentioned in (A) and (B) below. We include *two parallel lines* in (B) for algebraic reasons, even though two parallel lines cannot arise as the intersection of a plane and a cone, unless the lines coincide.

(A)   *The* **nondegenerate conics: parabola; ellipse,** *including a* **circle** *as a special case;* **hyperbola.**

(B)   *The* **degenerate conics: a single point; two parallel lines,** *possibly coincident;* **two intersecting lines.**

Recall that a polynomial function of two variables, $x$ and $y$, is said to be a **quadratic function** in case it is of degree 2 in $x$ and $y$. A polynomial equation in $x$ and $y$ is said to be a **quadratic equation** in $x$ and $y$ if the equation is equivalent to one of the form $F(x, y) = 0$, where $F(x, y)$ is of degree 2 in the variables. Any equation of this type is of the form

$$ax^2 + bxy + cy^2 + dx + ey + f = 0, \tag{1}$$

where $\{a, b, c, d, e, f\}$ are constants and at least one of $\{a, b, c\}$ is not zero. At a more advanced level, it is proved that *the graph of any equation* (1) *is a conic section,* or is the *empty set* (no graph). We shall consider various special cases of (1).

The following facts are proved in complete treatments of analytic geometry.

**Summary.**   *The graph of a quadratic equation in $x$ and $y$ has the indicated character under each of the specified conditions.*

(I)   *If A, B, and C are* **all positive or all negative,** *the graph of the equation* $Ax^2 + By^2 = C$ *is an* **ellipse** *symmetric to each coordinate axis, with the center of the ellipse at the origin. If $A = B$, the ellipse is a circle, provided that the same unit is used on the scales of the x-axis and y-axis.*

(II)   *If no one of A, B, and C is zero, while* **one of $(A, B)$ is positive and one is negative,** *the graph of $Ax^2 + By^2 = C$ is a* **hyperbola** *symmetric to each coordinate axis, and having two* **asymptotes*** *which are the graph of the equation*

(asymptotes)   $$Ax^2 + By^2 = 0. \tag{2}$$

(III)   *If $C \neq 0$, the graph of $xy = C$ is a* **hyperbola.** *If $C > 0$, the branches lie in quadrants* I *and* III; *if $C < 0$, the branches are in quadrants* II *and* IV. *The asymptotes in each case are the coordinate axes.*

(IV)   *If a quadratic equation* (1) *has* **no term in $y^2$ or $xy$,** *and $e \neq 0$, the graph of* (1) *is a* **parabola** *whose axis is parallel to the y-axis. If* (1) *has* **no term**

---

* To be described later.

in $x^2$ or $xy$, *and* $d \neq 0$, *the graph is a* **parabola** *whose axis is parallel to the* **x-axis**. *In either case the graph can be obtained as on page* 67.

ILLUSTRATION 1.   To graph the equation

$$2y - 4x^2 + 6x - 9 = 0, \tag{3}$$

we solve for $y$, to obtain

$$y = 2x^2 - 3x + \tfrac{9}{2}. \tag{4}$$

Hence, (3) defines $y$ as a quadratic function of $x$. The graph of (4) is a parabola, which could be obtained by the method of page 67.

EXAMPLE 1.   Graph:        $xy = 6.$                    (5)

*Solution.    1.*   By (III), the graph of (5) is a hyperbola. From (5), the values of $x$ and $y$ in a solution $(x, y)$ must be both positive or both negative, because $6 > 0$. Hence, all points on the graph are in quadrant I or in quadrant III, as stated in (III).

*2.    The intercepts.*   If $x = 0$ in (5), we obtain $0 = 6$, a *contradiction.* Hence, *no point of the graph is on the y-axis* and, similarly, *no point is on the* **x-axis**.

*3.*   From (5),                    $y = \dfrac{6}{x}.$                    (6)

We let $x = \pm 6, \pm 3, \pm 1,$ and $\pm.1$ and find the corresponding values of $y$ in the following table. Thus, if $x > 0$ and* $x \to 0$ in (6), we see that $y$ *grows large without bound*. To describe this behavior of $y$, we write "$y \to \infty$," which is read "*y approaches infinity*," meaning merely that "*y grows large without bound*." Hence, the corresponding point $(x, y)$ on the graph *rises beyond all bounds in the xy-plane and approaches the y-axis*, because $x \to 0$. The resulting nature of the graph is shown in Figure 38. Since the distance from a point on the graph to the $y$-axis approaches zero as we recede upward on the curve, in Figure 38, we say that the $y$-axis is an **asymptote** of the curve. Similarly, the $x$-axis is approached by the graph in quadrant I as $x$ grows large without bound, and hence the $x$-axis also is an asymptote of the graph. By letting $x$ take on negative values in (6) we obtain points on the graph in quadrant III, where we see that the $x$-axis and $y$-axis are asymptotes of the graph. The student should verify the following table of points on the graph. Naturally, points $(\pm.1, \pm 60)$ are not shown on the graph.

| $x =$ | no val. | $-6$ | $-3$ | $-1$ | $-.1$ | 0 | .1 | 1 | 3 | 6 | no val. |
|---|---|---|---|---|---|---|---|---|---|---|---|
| $y =$ | 0 | $-1$ | $-2$ | $-6$ | $-60$ | no val. | 60 | 6 | 2 | 1 | 0 |

* We use "$\to$" to abbreviate "*approaches*."

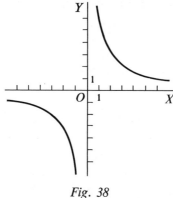

*Fig. 38*

## ★33.   Ellipse and hyperbola in simplest positions

If an ellipse or hyperbola has an equation as specified in (I) or (II) of Section 32, the corresponding conic in an $xy$-plane is referred to as being in *a most simple position.*

EXAMPLE 1.   Graph: $\qquad\qquad\qquad x^2 + 4y^2 = 25.$ $\qquad\qquad$ (1)

*Solution.   1.*   By (II) on page 75, the graph is an *ellipse.*

2.   *The intercepts.*   If $x = 0$ then $y^2 = \frac{25}{4}$; the $y$-intercepts are $y = \pm\frac{5}{2}$. Hence, points $(0, \frac{5}{2})$ and $(0, -\frac{5}{2})$ are on the graph, as seen in Figure 39. If $y = 0$ in (3), then $x^2 = 25$; the $x$-intercepts are $x = \pm 5$. Hence, points $(5, 0)$ and $(-5, 0)$ are on the graph.

COMMENT 1.   Later, after the student has learned by experience to appreciate the shape of an ellipse, he could draw a passable approximation to the graph, as in Figure 39, on the basis *merely of the four intercept points.* We continue otherwise at present.

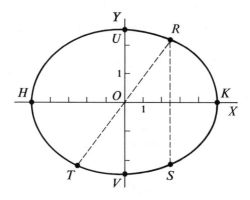

*Fig. 39*

*3.* To obtain more points on the graph, solve (1) for $y$:

$$4y^2 = 25 - x^2; \qquad y^2 = \tfrac{1}{4}(25 - x^2); \qquad y = \pm\tfrac{1}{2}\sqrt{25 - x^2}. \qquad (2)$$

If $x = \pm 2$ in (2), then $y = \pm\tfrac{1}{2}\sqrt{21} = \pm\tfrac{1}{2}(4.583) = 2.3$, by use of Table I. If $x = \pm 4$ in (2), then $y = \pm\tfrac{1}{2}\sqrt{25 - 16}$ or $y = \pm\tfrac{3}{2}$. Thus, we have obtained the pairs $(x, y)$ in the following table. These points were the basis for the graph in Figure 39.

| $x =$ | $-5$ | $-4$ | $-2$ | $0$ | $2$ | $4$ | $5$ |
|---|---|---|---|---|---|---|---|
| $y =$ | $0$ | $\pm\tfrac{3}{2}$ | $\pm 2.3$ | $\pm\tfrac{5}{2}$ | $\pm 2.3$ | $\pm\tfrac{3}{2}$ | $0$ |

COMMENT 2. We *avoid inserting black dots* for these points in Figure 39 because this would ruin the looks of the ellipse. The student, in his work, should insert dots with a pencil, draw any graph first with a pencil, and finally with ink, and then erase all pencil marks. Use of *too many points* (probably located slightly inaccurately) and then any attempt to make a graph go *exactly* through such points, would give a distorted curve. The final graph should be drawn *smoothly*, with *reasonably large scale units* on coordinate axes, to minimize the effects of slight errors in plotting points. The units on the axes *need not be equal.*

COMMENT 3. In Figure 39, the ellipse is *symmetric to each coordinate axis.* That is, any chord such as *RS* in Figure 39 perpendicular to an axis is *bisected* by it. Also, the ellipse is *symmetric to the origin,* called a **center of symmetry,** and in this case called the **center of the ellipse,** because any chord such as *RT* through the origin is bisected by it. We call segment *HK*, or its length, 10, the **major axis** and *UV*, or its length, 5, the **minor axis** of the ellipse because, with the chosen coordinate units, the length of *HK* is greater than the length of *UV*.

EXAMPLE 2.   Graph: $\qquad\qquad 4x^2 - 9y^2 = 36.$ $\qquad\qquad$ (3)

*Solution.* *1.* From (II) on page 75, the graph will be a hyperbola. We assume the facts in (II). They will be verified by the following "Supplementary Solution." Our first details will be arranged to offer a model for future rapid solutions by the student where (II) is involved.

*2. The intercepts.* If $x = 0$ in (3), then $-9y^2 = 36$ and $y^2 = -4$. Hence, $y = \pm\sqrt{-4} = \pm 2i$. That is, $y$ is *imaginary* when $x = 0$, or there is no $y$-intercept; the graph *does not meet the y-axis.* If $y = 0$ in (3), then $4x^2 = 36$ or $x = \pm 3$, the *x-intercepts*; this gives points $(\pm 3, 0)$ in the following table of values, and points *A* and *B* in Figure 40.

*3. The asymptotes.* By (II) on page 75, an equation for the two lines is

$$4x^2 - 9y^2 = 0, \qquad or \qquad (2x - 3y)(2x + 3y) = 0. \qquad (4)$$

Hence, the graph of (4) is the *union* of the lines (or, consists of the *two lines*) whose equations are

$$2x - 3y = 0 \quad \textit{and} \quad 2x + 3y = 0. \tag{5}$$

The graphs of (5) are the broken lines in Figure 40 through (0, 0). To graph (5), we let $y = 2$ and get $x = 3$ for $2x = 3y$; we let $y = 2$ and get $x = -3$ for $2x + 3y = 0$. The points (3, 2) and (−3, 2), together with (0, 0) on each line, give the broken lines through the origin.

    *4.   To draw the hyperbola.*   The branch at the right of the $y$-axis was drawn through the intercept point (3, 0) to approach the two asymptotes smoothly. The branch to the left of the $y$-axis was drawn similarly through the intercept point (−3, 0). With practice, the preceding method for graphing a hyperbola such as (3) will give results of sufficient accuracy for most purposes, as compared to the method of the following Supplementary Solution.

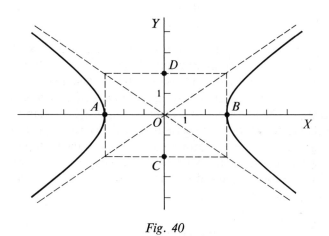

*Fig. 40*

*Supplementary Solution (by obtaining numerous points on the graph).*

    *1.*   From (3),        $9y^2 = 4x^2 - 36$;    $y = \pm\frac{2}{3}\sqrt{x^2 - 9}$.     (6)

In (6), we must use values of $x$ such that $|x| \geq 3$, because $(x^2 - 9)$ is negative if $|x| < 3$. That is, the *domain* for $x$ in order for $y$ to have a *real* value consists of *all* $|x| \geq 3$.

    *2.*   If $x = \pm 3$ in (6), then $y = 0$. If $x = \pm 4$ in (6), then

$$y = \pm\tfrac{2}{3}\sqrt{16 - 9} = \pm\tfrac{2}{3}\sqrt{7} = \pm 1.8.$$

This gives the points ($\pm 4$, $\pm 1.8$) in the following table. Similarly, we obtain other pairs in the table. On plotting the points from the table, we obtain a basis for the graph in Figure 40.

| $x =$ | $-5$ | $-4$ | $-3$ | $-3 < x < 3$ | $3$ | $4$ | $5$ |
|-------|------|------|------|--------------|-----|-----|-----|
| $y =$ | $\pm 2.7$ | $\pm 1.8$ | $0$ | *no val.* | $0$ | $\pm 1.8$ | $\pm 2.7$ |

COMMENT. In Figure 40, the hyperbola is symmetric to each coordinate axis, and has the origin $(0, 0)$ as a center of symmetry. Segment $AB$ of the $x$-axis, or the length, 6, of $AB$, is called the **transverse axis** of the hyperbola. The equation of any hyperbola, located as in Figure 40, is equivalent to the form

$$\frac{x^2}{a^2} - \frac{y^2}{b^2} = 1, \tag{7}$$

where we take $a > 0$ and $b > 0$. Thus, on dividing by 36 in (3), we obtain, as a special case of (7),

$$\frac{x^2}{9} - \frac{y^2}{4} = 1. \tag{8}$$

Then, for (7), the $x$-intercepts are $\pm a$; the transverse axis is $2a$; for (8), we have $a = 3$, and 6 as the transverse axis. In (8), $\sqrt{4} = 2$. Then, if we construct the rectangle in Figure 40, shown by broken lines, with vertices ($\pm 3$, $\pm 2$), the asymptotes of (8) are the *diagonals* of this so-called **fundamental rectangle**. The line segment $CD$, or its length $2(2)$ or 4, in Figure 40 is called the **conjugate axis** of the hyperbola. For the general hyperbola (7), the fundamental rectangle has the vertices ($\pm a$, $\pm b$), and the asymptotes are the diagonals of the rectangle. The student may desire to change any equation such as (3) to the form (7) and draw the fundamental rectangle as an aid in graphing the hyperbola.

## ★Exercise 19

*First name the graph of the equation. Then, obtain its graph in an xy-plane. If the graph is a circle, it may be drawn by use of compasses. Use equal scale units on the coordinate axes.*

1. $2y - 4x^2 + 12x = 5$.       2. $x - 2y^2 + 8y = 6$.
3. $xy = -6$.       4. $xy = 4$.       5. $x^2 - 4 = 0$.
6. $2x^2 - xy - 3y^2 = 0$.       7. $x^2 + x - 2 = 0$.
8. $9x^2 + 4y^2 = 36$.       9. $4x^2 - y^2 = 16$.       10. $4x^2 + 4y^2 = 9$.
11. $9y^2 - 4x^2 = 36$.       12. $4y^2 + x^2 = 4$.       13. $x^2 - y^2 = 9$.
14. $y^2 - 9x^2 = 9$.       15. $16x^2 + 9y^2 = 144$.       16. $y^2 - x^2 = 16$.
17. $25x^2 - 16y^2 = 0$.       18. $4x^2 + 81y^2 = 0$.       19. $x^2 + 9y^2 = -1$.

*20.* (*i*)   Graph $x^2 + y^2 = 16$, with equal scale units on the coordinate axes. (*ii*)   By use of only the $x$-intercepts and $y$-intercepts, graph the equation, with the scale unit for the $x$-axis *twice as long* as the scale unit for the $y$-axis.   (*iii*)   Repeat (*ii*) with the scale units interchanged. Notice that the preceding results emphasize the importance of "*equal scale units*" in reference to a circle in (I) on page 75. In (*ii*) and (*iii*), the graph is an ellipse which is not a circle.

*21.*   Graph the equation $4x^2 + y^2 = 16$, (*a*) with equal scale units used on the coordinate axes; (*b*) with the scale unit on $OX$ twice as long as the unit on $OY$. Thus, a graph which is an ellipse, with unequal axes, will become a circle if scale units on the coordinate axes are adjusted.

# 4 | LINEAR STATEMENTS*
## IN TWO VARIABLES

### 34.  Solution of a system of two linear equations

Suppose that $A$, $B$, $C$, $G$, $H$, and $K$ are constants where $A$ and $B$ are not both zero, and $G$ and $H$ are not both zero. Then, if $x$ and $y$ are variables, we refer to the statement

$$\text{“}Ax + By + C = 0, \quad and \quad Gx + Hy + K = 0\text{”} \qquad (1)$$

as a **system of two linear equations** in two variables. A *solution* of (1) is a pair of corresponding values of $x$ and $y$, say $(x = a, y = b)$, which is a solution of *both* equations in (1), and then $(a, b)$ is said to *satisfy* (1). To *solve* a system (1) means to find all of its solutions.

EXAMPLE 1.   Solve the system graphically:

$$x - y = 5, \; and \qquad (2)$$
$$x + 2y = 2. \qquad (3)$$

*Solution.*   In Figure 41, line $MN$ is the graph of (2) and line $ST$ is the graph of (3). Line $MN$ consists of all points whose coordinates form solutions of (2). Line $ST$ consists of all points whose coordinates form solutions of (3). Hence, the intersection, $W$, of $MN$ and $ST$ is the only point whose coordinates form a solution of both (2) and (3). The coordinates of $W$ are $(4, -1)$. Hence $(x = 4, y = -1)$ is the only solution of system [(2), (3)]. The student may check this solution by substitution in (2) and (3). We have illustrated the following method.

---

\* Both equations and inequalities are involved.

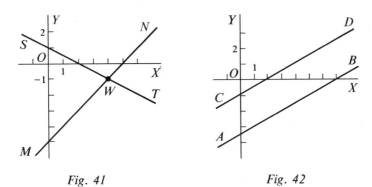

Fig. 41                    Fig. 42

**To solve a system of two equations in *x* and *y* graphically:**

*On one coordinate system, graph each equation. Measure the coordinates* $(x = a, y = b)$ *of each point of intersection, if any, of the graphs: these coordinates form a solution.*

Usually a graphical method will give only an approximate solution of (1), because we obtain the result by estimating the coordinates of a point. The graphical method applies also in the case of a system of two equations where one or both of them are not linear.

The graphical method of Example 1 emphasizes the following possibilites with respect to a system of two linear equations in two variables *x* and *y*.

(I)  *If the graphs of the equations in* (1) *are not parallel and hence intersect in a single point, system* (1) *has just one solution.*

(II)  *If the graphs of the equations are distinct parallel lines, they do not intersect and hence system* (1) *has no solution. In this case, the system and its equations are called* **inconsistent**.

(III)  *If the graphs of the equations are the same straight line, each solution of either equation also is a solution of the other equation, or the system has infinitely many solutions. In this case the equations are said to be* **dependent equations**.

Under circumstances (I) or (III), system (1) is called *consistent* because it has at least one solution.

EXAMPLE 2.   Solve graphically:

$$3x - 6y = 5, \quad and \tag{4}$$
$$x - 2y = 7. \tag{5}$$

*Solution.   1.*  The graph of (4) is *CD*, and the graph of (5) is *AB* in Figure 42. The graphs appear to be parallel, but this should be proved.

2.  In the slope-*y*-intercept form, (4) becomes $y = \frac{1}{2}x - \frac{5}{6}$, and (5) becomes $y = \frac{1}{2}x - \frac{7}{2}$. Each graph has slope $\frac{1}{2}$; thus the graphs are parallel.

They do not coincide because the $y$-intercepts $-\frac{5}{6}$ and $-\frac{7}{2}$ are different. The graphs are parallel lines which do not coincide, and thus have no point in common. Hence, system [(4), (5)] has *no solution*, or is *inconsistent*.

EXAMPLE 3.   Solve the system algebraically:

$$4x + 5y = 6, \quad and* \tag{6}$$
$$2x + 3y = 4. \tag{7}$$

*Solution.*   *1.*   Multiply by 3 in (6):    $12x + 15y = 18.$    (8)

Multiply by 5 in (7):                              $10x + 15y = 20.$    (9)

We now infer that system [(6), (7)] is equivalent to [(8), (9)], and continue by solving the new system.

*2.*   Subtract corresponding sides, in the order (9) from (8):

$$2x = -2; \quad hence, \quad x = -1. \tag{10}$$

Substitute $x = -1$ in (6):

$$-4 + 5y = 6, \quad or \quad 5y = 10, \quad or \quad y = 2. \tag{11}$$

Therefore, the solution of [(6), (7)] is $(x = -1, y = 2)$. The method just employed is referred to as a solution by *elimination of one variable by addition* (or, *subtraction*). This name is appropriate because our primary object was to obtain an equation [(10) in this problem] where one variable has been *eliminated*, and we can find the value of the other variable.

EXAMPLE 4.   Solve system [(4), (5)] algebraically.

*Solution.*   *1.*   Multiply in (5) by 3:

$$3x - 6y = 21. \tag{12}$$

Rewrite (4):                                         $3x - 6y = 5.$    (13)

Subtract corresponding sides, in the order (13) from (12):

$$0 = 16. \tag{14}$$

*2.*   *Discussion.*   In (14), we found that, **IF** system [(4), (5)] has a solution, then $0 = 16$, which is a contradictory statement. Hence, an assumption that [(4), (5)] has a solution is **FALSE**, or the system is *inconsistent*. This corroborates the graphical solution in Example 2.

### Algebraic solution of a system of two linear equations in $x$ and $y$:

(A)   *In each equation, multiply (if necessary) both members by a properly chosen number so as to obtain two equations in which the coefficients of one of the variables have the same absolute value.*

---

* Hereafter "*and*" will be omitted, but will be implied, in such places in systems of equations.

(B)  *If these coefficients are both positive or both negative, subtract each side of one equation from a corresponding member of the other equation; otherwise, add corresponding members. Thus, obtain an equation involving a single variable, to substitute for either of the given equations.*

(C)  *Solve the equation just obtained for the value of the variable in it.*

(D)  *Substitute the resulting value of this variable in one of the original equations, to obtain the value of the other variable.*

In (B) of the preceding method, a contradictory equation such as $0 = h$, where $h \neq 0$, will be obtained if and only if the given system is inconsistent. An identity $0 = 0$ will be obtained if and only if the given equations are dependent, and thus have the same graph (and hence have the same solutions).

Hereafter, *to solve* a system will mean to solve it *algebraically*, unless otherwise specified.

EXAMPLE 5.   Solve:
$$ax + by = e, \tag{15}$$
$$cx + dy = f. \tag{16}$$

*Solution.*   *1.*   Multiply by $d$ in (15):   $adx + bdy = de.$   (17)

Multiply by $b$ in (16):   $bcx + bdy = bf.$   (18)

*2.*   Subtract, in order (18) from (17):   $(ad - bc)x = de - bf.$   (19)

Assume that $(ad - bc) \neq 0$ and divide by $(ad - bc)$ in (19):

$$x = \frac{de - bf}{ad - bc}. \tag{20}$$

By a similar procedure, we obtain

$$y = \frac{af - ce}{ad - bc}. \tag{21}$$

## Exercise 20

*Solve graphically. If the equations are inconsistent, or dependent, prove the fact by obtaining slopes and y-intercepts of the lines. Also, solve algebraically.*

1.  $x + y = 3, \ 2x - 3y = 11.$      2.  $y - x = 4, \ 4y - 2x = 4.$
3.  $x + 2y = 3, \ 3x + 5y = 10.$     4.  $4x + 3y = 2, \ 5x + y = -3.$
5.  $2y - 3x = 8, \ 6x - 4y = 5.$     6.  $3x + 2y = 9, \ 4y - 18 = 6x.$
7.  $2x - 3y = 7, \ 2x - y = 1.$      8.  $5y - 4 = 0, \ 3x + 4y + 1 = 0.$
9.  $2x + 3y = 0, \ 5x - 2y = 0.$     10.  $y + 3x = 2, \ x - 5y = 0.$
11.  $3x - 5 = 0, \ 2x + 5y = 4.$     12.  $3x - y = 4, \ 2y - 6x = 9.$
13.  $6x - 5y = 3, \ 4y - 9x = 5.$    14.  $3x - 5y = 2, \ 2x + 3y = -5.$

*Clear of fractions if necessary and solve by any suitable method.*

15.  $3x - 4y = .5,$                  16.  $4x + 3y = 6.4,$
    $x + 2y = .8.$                           $3x - .5y = 1.5.$

*17.* $\frac{1}{2}x = 2 - \frac{5}{4}y,$                    *18.* $\frac{3}{2}x - \frac{4}{3}y = -1,$
    $\frac{1}{6}x = \frac{3}{2} + \frac{5}{3}y.$                         $\frac{2}{3}x - \frac{1}{4}y = \frac{7}{12}.$

*Solve for x and y, or for w and z. The other letters represent constants.*

*19.* $ax - 2y = 2 + b,$                 *20.* $2cx - dy = c^2 + d^2,$
    $ax + 4y = 2 - 2b.$                      $2x + y = 2c.$

*21.* $2bx + ay = a + b,$                 *22.* $aw + bz = a^2 + b^2,$
    $2abx - aby = a^2 - b^2.$                $bw - az = a^2 + b^2.$

## 35.  Linear demand and supply equations

Suppose that we are dealing with demand and supply in an economy where there is free competition among producers, and freedom of choice in buying by consumers. Then, a commodity may be such that its price, $p$, in dollars per unit may be considered as a function of only the number, $x$, of units which consumers demand. If $p$ is decreased, they will buy more of the commodity, or $x$ will increase. This is equivalent to stating that, *if x increases then p decreases.* Suppose that $p = h(x)$, where we call $h$ the **demand function**. Also, we refer to the equation $p = h(x)$, or any equivalent equation, as the **demand equation**. In this section, we shall assume that $h$ is linear,* say $h(x) = mx + b$, where $m$ and $b$ are constants and $m \neq 0$. Thus,

$$p = mx + b. \tag{1}$$

The graph of a special case of (1) in an $xp$-plane, as in Figure 43, is a line with slope $m < 0$, because $p$ decreases when $x$ increases. Only that part of the line in quadrant I, where $p \geqq 0$ and $x \geqq 0$, is significant for economic applications.

ILLUSTRATION 1.   Suppose that the demand equation is $p = -3x + 21$, whose graph is $AB$ in Figure 43. Even if the market demand, $x$, were small, the consumer would not have to pay a unit price $p > 21$, because 21 is the $p$-intercept of the graph of the demand equation. If $x$ "*approaches* 0," which we abbreviate by "$\to 0$," the price $p \to 21$. Also, the $x$-intercept in Figure 43 is 7, which is the least upper bound of the demand which can occur. If $p \to 0$ then $x \to 7$.

Suppose that consumers are willing to pay an increased price $p$ for a commodity. Then, it is natural to expect that producers, will increase the number of units $x$ supplied for sale. That is, *x increases when p increases.* If we think of *p as a function of x*, we restate the preceding fact by saying that *p increases when x increases.* Suppose that $p = g(x)$; then we call $g$ the **supply function**. Also, we refer to the equation $p = g(x)$, or any equivalent equation,

---

* Nonlinear cases will occur in sections on calculus.

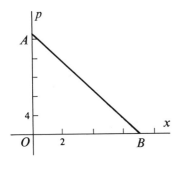

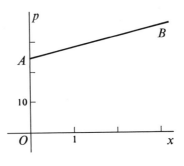

Fig. 43                    Fig. 44

as the **supply equation**. In our applications, we shall assume that $g$ is linear. Then the supply equation has the form

$$p = kx + c. \qquad (2)$$

The graph of a special case of (2) in an *xp-plane*, as in Figure 44, is a line with slope $k$, where $k > 0$ because *p increases when x increases.* In graphing (2), we consider only $x \geqq 0$ for economic applications. In (2), if $x \to 0$ then $p \to c$, where $c$ is the *p*-intercept of the graph of (2), and is the greatest lower bound of prices at which producers will supply the consumers.

EXAMPLE 1.   The supply equation for a commodity is

$$11x - 3p + 75 = 0. \qquad (3)$$

Find a lower bound for the price at which the commodity will be supplied, and obtain a graph of (3).

*Solution.*   In the slope-*p*-intercept form, (3) becomes

$$p = \tfrac{11}{3}x + 25. \qquad (4)$$

We obtain a graph, *AB*, of (4) in Figure 44 by use of the solutions ($x = 0$, $p = 25$) and ($x = 3$, $p = 36$); the *p*-intercept is 25. Hence, 25 is a lower bound of prices at which the commodity would be supplied by producers. Theoretically, no supply would be available at price $p = 25$. If $x \to 0$ then $p \to 25$. Or, if $p \to 25$ then $x \to 0$, and the producers let the supply tend to 0.

## 36.   Market equilibrium

In a competitive system, consider a certain commodity, with linear supply and demand equations, $p = g(x)$ and $p = h(x)$, respectively. If the price $p$ is increased, then certain consumers will no longer buy, or the demand will decrease. If the price $p$ is lowered, then the producers will reduce the supply. It can be assumed that, at any instant, the price $p_0$ per unit will be such that the corresponding number, $x_0$, of units *demanded* will equal the number of units which the producers will *supply*. That is, the pair $(x = x_0, p = p_0)$ will satisfy *both the demand equation $p = h(x)$ and the supply equation $p = g(x)$.* Or, $(x = x_0, p = p_0)$ is a solution of the system of equations

$$p = h(x) \quad and \quad p = g(x). \tag{1}$$

Hence, $(x_0, p_0)$ are the coordinates of the point of intersection of the graphs of the equations in (1). It is said that **market equilibrium** is established when $p = p_0$ and $x = x_0$. Also, $p_0$ is called the **equilibrium unit price**, and $x_0$ is referred to as the **equilibrium quantity** (both supplied and demanded).

EXAMPLE 1.    For a certain commodity, the demand equation is $5p + 8x = 40$, and the supply equation is $5p - 8x = 10$. Find the equilibrium price and equilibrium quantity for the commodity.

*Solution.*    The equilibrium price $p_0$ and equilibrium quantity $x_0$ form the solution $(x_0, p_0)$ of the system

$$5p + 8x = 40 \quad and \quad 5p - 8x = 10. \tag{2}$$

By the method of page 84, the solution of (2) is $(x = \frac{15}{8}, p = 5)$. The solution is exhibited graphically in Figure 45 as the coordinates of the point of intersection, $H$, of the graphs of the equations in (2).

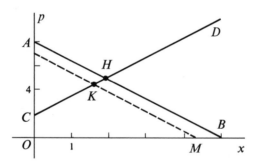

*Fig. 45*

EXAMPLE 2.    A government tax of $1 per unit is imposed on sales of the commodity in Example 1. Find the equilibrium price paid, in addition to the tax, and the equilibrium quantity.

*Solution. 1.*    Let $p$ be the price per unit which will be paid by the consumer *in addition to the tax.** Thus, $p$ is the price on which the producers

---

\* We may think of the tax being collected by the producer and then paid to the government.

will base their collective decision as to how large a supply they will provide. Hence, the supply equation of Example 1 remains in effect, or

$$5p - 8x = 10, \tag{3}$$

where $x$ units are supplied at price $p$.

2.   The consumers' demand equation is $5p_1 + 8x = 40$, where we let $p_1$ be the *actual price, including the tax*, which the consumer will pay. If the producer receives the price $p$, as in (3), then the consumer pays $p_1 = p + 1$. Hence, $p$ and $x$ satisfy the equation obtained by *replacing $p_1$ by $(p + 1)$* in the demand equation $5p_1 + 8x = 40$; thus

$$5(p + 1) + 8x = 40, \qquad or \qquad 5p + 8x = 35, \tag{4}$$

whose graph is the broken line $KM$ in Figure 45.

3.   The equilibrium price, $p_0$, for the producer and the equilibrium quantity, $x_0$, form the solution of the system

$$5p - 8x = 10 \qquad and \qquad 5p + 8x = 35. \tag{5}$$

The solution of (5), as obtained algebraically by the method of page 84, is $(x = \frac{25}{16}, p = 4.5)$. Hence, the producer receives $\$4.50$ per unit. The consumer pays $\$5.50$ per unit. This price is higher than the equilibrium price in Example 1. The equilibrium quantity sold, $x = \frac{25}{16}$, is smaller than that found in Example 1. Thus, the tax increases the price to the consumer and decreases the volume of sales. The equilibrium point $(\frac{25}{16}, 4.5)$ is $K$ in Figure 45.

To solve a problem like Example 2, the student should appreciate the following routine.

(I)   *A tax paid by the consumer does not alter the supply equation of the producer, where p is the price paid in addition to the tax.*

(II)   *In the demand equation, the price p should be replaced by $(p + tax)$.*

NOTE 1.   We could also solve a problem like Example 2 by leaving the demand equation unaltered, with $p$ representing the price *including* the tax, and altering the supply equation by replacing $p$ by $(p - tax)$. With this viewpoint, the producer pays the tax out of the price paid to him by the consumer. A government *subsidy* on sales of a commodity should be considered as a *negative tax*.

## Exercise 21

*In each problem, a certain commodity is involved, with p as the price in dollars and x as the number of units supplied or demanded. (a) Graph the demand and supply equations on the same xp-plane. (b) Find the largest demand which would exist at any price. (c) Find the greatest lower bound for the price at which producers would supply the commodity. (d) Find the equilibrium price and equilibrium quantity of the commodity when market equilibrium occurs.*

1.   Demand equation, $4p + 3x = 24$; supply equation, $4p - x = 8$.

2. Demand equation, $3p + 2x = 18$; supply equation, $3p - x = 9$.
3. Demand equation, $3p + 2x = 18$; supply equation, $6p - x = 6$.
4. Demand equation, $4p + x = 12$; supply equation, $8p - x = 12$.
5. Demand equation, $8p + x = 16$; supply equation, $16p - x = 8$.

*Find the equilibrium price paid to the producer, the equilibrium price paid by the consumer, and the equilibrium quantity of the commodity which is supplied (or, demanded) in the specified preceding problem, if the indicated tax or subsidy per unit is decreed by the government. Show the new equilibrium data as the coordinates of a point on a graph, with a new demand graph.*

6. In Problem 1; a tax of \$1 per unit of the commodity.
7. In Problem 3; a tax of \$2 per unit of the commodity.
8. In Problem 4; a tax of \$$\frac{1}{2}$ per unit of the commodity.
9. In Problem 5; a tax of \$$\frac{1}{4}$ per unit of the commodity.
10. In Problem 1; a government subsidy* of \$1 per unit of the commodity.
11. In Problem 4; a government subsidy of \$2 per unit of the commodity.

12. For a certain commodity, the demand equation is $x + 3p = 9$ and the supply equation is $6p - x = 9$, where \$$p$ is the price per unit and $x$ is the number of units of the commodity demanded or supplied. (*a*) Find the equilibrium price and equilibrium quantity when market equilibrium exists; solve both algebraically and graphically. (*b*) Solve the problem if a tax of \$1 per unit is imposed on the commodity.

## 37.   Inequalities in two variables

Let $g$ and $h$ be functions of two independent variables $x$ and $y$. Then, consider an inequality

$$h(x, y) < g(x, y), \qquad or \qquad h(x, y) \leq g(x, y). \qquad (1)$$

A *solution* of (1) is a *pair of numbers* $(x, y)$ for which (1) is true.

ILLUSTRATION 1.   Consider the inequality

$$3x - 2y < 6. \qquad (2)$$

If $x = 2$ and $y = 4$ in (2), we obtain $6 - 8 < 6$, or $-2 < 6$, which is true. Hence, $(x = 2, y = 4)$ is a solution of (2). If $x = 5$ and $y = 1$ in (2), we obtain $15 - 2 < 6$, or $13 < 6$, which is false. Hence, $(x = 5, y = 1)$ is *not* a solution of (2).

An inequality (1) may have no solutions, and then is said to be *inconsistent*. Or, its solution set is the empty set, $\varnothing$.

ILLUSTRATION 2.   The inequality $x^2 + y^2 < 0$ is inconsistent, because $x^2 + y^2 \geq 0$ for all real numbers $x$ and $y$.

---

\* We may think of the government paying \$1 to the producer who receives \$$p$, and thus the consumer pays only \$$(p - 1)$, as the "$p$" in his demand equation.

DEFINITION I.   *In an xy-plane, the* **graph** *of an inequality* $g(x, y) <$ $h(x, y)$ *is the set of points whose coordinates* $(x, y)$ *form solutions of the inequality. That is, its graph is the graph of the solution set of the inequality.*

EXAMPLE 1.   In an $xy$-plane where the scale units on the axes are equal, obtain the graph of

$$x^2 + y^2 - 4 > 0. \qquad (3)$$

*Solution.*   *1.*   First consider the graph of the related equation

$$x^2 + y^2 - 4 = 0, \qquad or \qquad x^2 + y^2 = 4. \qquad (4)$$

We recall that the graph of (4) is the circle, $C$, in Figure 46 with center $(0, 0)$ and radius 2.

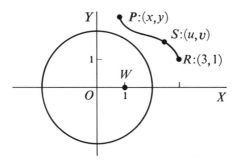

*Fig. 46*

*2.*   Let $f(x, y) = x^2 + y^2 - 4$. To each point $P:(x, y)$ in the plane, there corresponds a function value $f(x, y)$. Thus, at $R:(3, 1)$ outside $C$, $f(3, 1) = 9 + 1 - 4 = 6 > 0$. At all points on $C$, we have $f(x, y) = 0$. Let $T$ be any continuous curve lying outside $C$ and joining $R$ to an arbitrary point $P:(x, y)$ outside $T$. Let $S:(u, v)$ be any point on $T$. If $S$ moves continuously on $C$ from $R$ to $P$, then $f$ starts with the value $f(3, 1)$, or 6, at $R$ and changes continuously to the value $f(x, y)$ at $P$. We know that $f(x, y) \neq 0$ because $P$ is *not on* $C$. Since $C$ does not intersect $T$, then $f(u, v) \neq 0$ as $S$ moves from $R$ to $P$. Hence, $f(x, y) > \mathbf{0}$, because $f(u, v)$ could not change continuously from the *positive* value $f(3, 1)$ to a *negative* value $f(x, y)$ at $P$ without passing through the value 0, which has been ruled out. Therefore, $f(x, y) > 0$ at each point $P:(x, y)$ outside $C$, or the graph of (3) includes all of these points.

*3.*   The point $W:(1, 0)$ is *inside* the circle $C$. At $W$, we have $f(1, 0) = -3 < 0$. By the same type of reasoning as applied in the preceding paragraph, we conclude that $f(x, y) < 0$ at each point $P:(x, y)$ inside $C$, and hence $P$ is *not* in the graph of (3). Therefore,

> *the graph of* (3) *consists of all points outside the circle* $C$,
> *or the solutions of* (3) *consist of the coordinates* $(x, y)$     (5)
> *of all points* $P:(x, y)$ *outside of* $C$.

COMMENT.    In the preceding solution, we also showed that the graph of $f(x, y) < 0$ consists of all points *inside C*. Thus, the graph, $C$, of $f(x, y) = 0$ is the *boundary* between the graphs of $f(x, y) < 0$ and $f(x, y) > 0$.

In Example 1, we illustrated the fact that an inequality in two variables may have *infinitely many solutions*. As a rule, it would be unreasonable to expect that formulas could be obtained for the values of $x$ and $y$ in these solutions. Hence, instead of searching for such formulas, we obtain a graph of the inequality. Then, by calculating coordinates of points in this graph, we can obtain as many of the solutions as desired. In graphing an inequality in $x$ and $y$, we say that we have *solved* the inequality. In Example 1, the following method for graphing such an inequality was illustrated.

**Summary.**    *To graph an inequality $g(x, y) < h(x, y)$.*

(I)    *Draw the graph, $T$, of $g(x, y) = h(x, y)$, where $T$ will form the boundary between the graphs of $g(x, y) < h(x, y)$ and $g(x, y) > h(x, y)$. We assume that $T$ divides the plane into certain separated sets of points, say sets $U$, $V$, and $W$.*

(II)    *In set $U$, select arbitrarily a point $(x_0, y_0)$ and substitute $(x = x_0, y = y_0)$ in $g(x, y) < h(x, y)$. If $g(x_0, y_0) < h(x_0, y_0)$, then all of $U$ is a part of the graph of $g(x, y) < h(x, y)$. In case $g(x_0, y_0) > h(x_0, y_0)$, then all of $U$ is part of the graph of $g(x, y) > h(x, y)$.*

(III)    *Repeat the test (II) for each of the sets $U$, $V$, and $W$, to determine all parts of the desired graph.*

If the inequality $g(x, y) < h(x, y)$ is *linear*, then the graph of $g(x, y) = h(x, y)$ is a *line*, $L$, which divides the $xy$-plane into two sets of points, each called an **open half-plane**. Hence, in applying the Summary to any linear inequality, just two open half-planes $U$ and $V$ are involved in the testing procedure of (II).

EXAMPLE 2.    Solve graphically :     $3y - 2x < 6.$    (6)

*Solution.   1.*    The graph of     $3y - 2x = 6$    (7)

is the broken line, $L$, in Figure 47, dividing the $xy$-plane into two open half-planes.

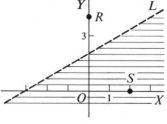

Fig. 47

2. Let $U$ be the open half-plane *below L. S*:(2, 0) is in $U$. With $(x = 2, y = 0)$ in (6), we obtain $0 - 4 < 6$, which is *true*. Hence, (6) *is satisfied at all points of U.*

3. The point $R$:(0, 4) is in the open half-plane, $V$, *above L.* With $(x = 0, y = 4)$ in (6), we obtain $12 < 6$, which is *false*. Hence (6) is *not* satisfied at any point in $V$, and $V$ is the graph of the inequality $3y - 2x > 6$.

In Example 2, we illustrated the fact that, for a linear inequality $g(x, y) < h(x, y)$, the line $L$ which is the graph of $g(x, y) = h(x, y)$ divides the $xy$-plane into two open half-planes where one is the graph of $g(x, y) < h(x, y)$, and the other is the graph of $g(x, y) > h(x, y)$. Hence, in graphing either one of these inequalities, it is necessary to use the testing procedure in (II) of the Summary *only for one of the open half-planes.* The result of this test provides information about *both* open half-planes.

ILLUSTRATION 3.   The graph of $3y - 2x \leq 6$ is the union of $U$, as found in Example 1, and the line $L$ which is the graph of the solution set of $3y - 2x = 6$.

We have defined an open half-plane as the graph of a linear inequality $g(x, y) < h(x, y)$. The *union of an open half-plane and its bounding line* is called a **closed half-plane**, which is the graph of $g(x, y) \leq h(x, y)$.

The method of the Summary applies to any inequality $g(x, y) < h(x, y)$ where we are able to obtain the graph of the equation $g(x, y) = h(x, y)$, if this graph divides the $xy$-plane into separated regions.

ILLUSTRATION 4.   To solve the inequality

$$(x - y + 2)(2x + y - 4) < 0, \tag{8}$$

first we obtain the graph of the equation

$$(x - y + 2)(2x + y - 4) = 0. \tag{9}$$

A graph, $T$, of (9) is in Figure 33, page 71, and divides the $xy$-plane into four regions. If the test (II) of the Summary is applied, it will be found that the graph of (8) consists of the points in *two* of the four regions just mentioned. The student should verify this fact.

## Exercise 22

*Graph the inequality in an xy-plane. Then, by inspection, obtain three solutions $(x, y)$ for the inequality. Show the graph by rulings or some other device.*

*1.* $2x + 3y < 6$.     *2.* $3x + 6y > 8$.     *3.* $x - 2y \leq 4$.
*4.* $5 \geq 3x - y$.     *5.* $x + y + 6 < 0$.     *6.* $y - x - 3 \geq 0$.
*7.* $x < 3$.     *8.* $x \leq 4$.     *9.* $y < -5$.     *10.* $y \geq 2$.
*11.* $(y - 2x)(y + 2x) \geq 0$.     *12.* $(x - y + 6)(x + y - 10) < 0$.

*13.* $(x + 2y - 4)(y - 3x - 2) \leqq 0.$        *14.* $x^2 - 9y^2 \leqq 0.$
★*15.* $4x^2 + 9y^2 < 36.$        ★*16.* $|x| + |y| \leqq 4.$

## 38.  Systems of inequalities in two variables

Consider the following system of two inequalities in the variables $x$ and $y$:

$$(a) \quad g(x, y) < h(x, y) \quad and \quad (b) \quad u(x, y) < v(x, y). \tag{1}$$

Let $S$ be the graph of $(a)$ and $T$ be the graph of $(b)$ in an $xy$-plane. A solution of (1) is a pair of numbers $(x, y)$ satisfying both inequalities. To solve (1) graphically will mean to describe the set of all solutions of (1) by obtaining the graph of its solution set. A point $P:(x, y)$ is in the graph, $W$, of (1) in case $P$ is in $S$ AND in $T$. Or, $W$ is the *intersection* of the sets $S$ and $T$. To obtain $W$, first we locate $S$ and $T$ and then determine $W = S \cap T$ from the figure. Observe that, in doing this, we are drawing a Venn diagram with $S$ and $T$ as given sets, defined by $(a)$ and $(b)$ in (1), and $W$ as the intersection of $S$ and $T$.

EXAMPLE 1.   Solve the system of inequalities:

$$\begin{cases} y - x \geqq 1, & and \tag{2} \\ y + 3x - 3 \geqq 0. \tag{3} \end{cases}$$

*Solution.   1.   To obtain the graph, S, of* (2): In Figure 48, line $L$ is the graph of $y - x = 1$. We substitute the coordinates of the point $(0, 0)$ in (2) and obtain $0 + 0 \geqq 1$, which is *false*. Hence, $S$ consists of the open half-plane *above L*, together with $L$ itself, because of the sign " $=$ " in (2). That is, $S$ is the *closed* half-plane consisting of $L$ and the open half-plane above $L$.

*2.*   Similarly, the graph, $T$, of (3) is the closed half-plane in Figure 48, consisting of the line $M$ and the open half plane above $M$.

*3.*   The graph, $W$, of [(2) *and* (3)] is the *intersection* of $S$ and $T$, or $W = S \cap T$, shown by the ruled points in Figure 48. $W$ includes the rays* of $L$ and $M$ which form the boundaries of $W$.

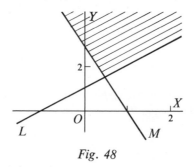

*Fig. 48*

* A *ray* is that part of a line $L$ in a specified direction on $L$ from some point on $L$.

EXAMPLE 2.   Solve the following system graphically:

$$(a) \quad x^2 + y^2 \leqq 9 \quad and \quad (b) \quad x - y \geqq 1. \tag{4}$$

*Solution.*   Let the graph of (a) be $S$, of (b) be $T$, and of (4) be $W$. By the method of page 92, in Figure 49, we verify that $S$ consists of the circle $x^2 + y^2 = 9$ and the points inside the circle; $T$ consists of the line $L$, $x - y = 1$, and the open half-plane below $L$. We have $W = S \cap T$. In Figure 49, $W$ is the ruled set of points, including their boundary, which consists of a segment of $L$ and an arc of the circle.

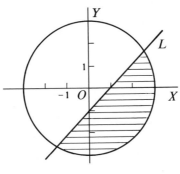

*Fig. 49*

## Exercise 23

*Solve the system graphically. Then find three solutions by reading co-ordinates for points in the graph, if the system is consistent.*

1. $x > 2$, *and*
   $y \leqq 2$.
2. $x + y - 1 \geqq 0$, *and*
   $x \leqq 2$.
3. $x - 2y + 2 \leqq 0$, *and*
   $x + y < 4$.
4. $x + 3 \geqq 2y$, *and*
   $2x + 3y + 2 > 0$.
5. $2x \leqq y$, *and*
   $y < 3$.
6. $x < y$, *and*
   $2y - 3x \geqq 2$.
7. $y - x \leqq 2$,
   $x + y > 2$, *and*
   $x \leqq 6$.
8. $x + y \leqq 7$,
   $x - 2y + 2 \leqq 0$, *and*
   $x \geqq 0$.
9. $x + y - 3 \geqq 0$,
   $y - x + 3 \geqq 0$, *and*
   $3y - x \geqq 6$.
10. $x + y - 2 \geqq 0$,
    $x + y - 4 \leqq 0$, *and*
    $y - 2x \leqq 2$.
11. $2x + y \leqq 2$, *and* $4x + 2y - 7 \geqq 0$.
12. $y - x \geqq 2$, $y - x \leqq 4$, $y \geqq 2$, *and* $y \leqq 5$.
13. $x^2 + y^2 \leqq 25$, *and*
    $2x - y - 2 \leqq 0$.
★14. $4x^2 + 9y^2 \leqq 36$, *and*
    $4y^2 - x^2 > 4$.

# 5 | LINEAR PROGRAMMING WITH TWO VARIABLES

### 39.  Convex sets of points in a plane

We recall the fact that any closed half-plane in an $xy$-plane is the graph of an inequality equivalent to

$$ax + by + c \leqq 0, \qquad (1)$$

where $a$, $b$, and $c$ are constants, and not both of $a$ and $b$ are zero. The line $L$ which is the graph of $ax + by + c = 0$ divides the $xy$-plane into two open half-planes with $L$ as their common boundary. The graph of (1) is the *union* of $L$ and one of the open half-planes just mentioned.

ILLUSTRATION 1.   The graph of $\qquad 2x + 3y - 6 \geqq 0 \qquad (2)$

is the *closed* half-plane which is ruled vertically in Figure 50.

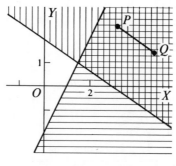

*Fig. 50*

96

DEFINITION I.  *A set, T, of points in an xy-plane is called a* **convex set** *of points in case T has the following property:*

*If P and Q are distinct points in T, then all points on the* $\left.\begin{array}{c} \\ \\ \end{array}\right\}$ (3)
*line segment PQ are in T.*

For convenience in stating results, we agree that, in an uninteresting sense, the empty set $\varnothing$ is a convex set of points.

ILLUSTRATION 2.  By geometrical appreciation of Definition I, we see that the set of points inside or on a circle form a convex set of points. Also, a half-plane, open or closed, is a convex set of points.

THEOREM I.  *If A and B are convex sets of points in an xy-plane, and if T = A ∩ B, then T is a convex set of points.*

NOTE 1.  The theorem is true for *any* convex sets $A$ and $B$. However, we shall be concerned with the result only when $A$ and $B$ are half-planes, open or closed. Hence, the following proof is illustrated for only this case.

*Proof of Theorem* I.  *1.*  Let $A$ and $B$ be half-planes, as in Figure 50, where we rule $A$ horizontally and $B$ vertically. With $T = A \cap B$, the doubly ruled points show $T$.

*2.*  Suppose that $P$ and $Q$ are in $T$. Then $P$ and $Q$ also are in $A$, and hence all points on segment $PQ$ are in $A$ because $A$ is convex. Since $T = A \cap B$, hence $P$ and $Q$ also are in $B$, and thus all points on $PQ$ are in $B$. Therefore, all points on $PQ$ are in *both A and B*, and thus are in $T = A \cap B$. Hence, $T$ is a convex set of points.

The reasoning used with Theorem I applies also when $T = A \cap B \cap C$ where $A$, $B$, and $C$ are convex sets; thus, $T$ is convex. Similarly, the intersection of any number of convex sets of points is a convex set.

DEFINITION II.  *The intersection, T, of two or more closed half-planes is called a* **polygonal set** *of points. If T has a finite\* area, then the boundary of T is called a* **convex polygon,** *and T is called a bounded, or finite polygonal set. Otherwise, T is called an infinite polygonal set.*

ILLUSTRATION 3.  In Figure 50, it can be verified that the set $A$ with horizontal rulings is the graph of the inequality at the left below. The set $B$ with vertical rulings is the graph of the inequality at the right. The intersection, $T$, of the closed half-planes $A$ and $B$ is the set of points with double rulings, and is the graph of the system

$$y - 2x + 2 \leqq 0 \quad and \quad 2x + 3y - 6 \geqq 0.$$

EXAMPLE 1.  Locate the polygonal set which is the graph of the system

* This means that $T$ lies entirely in some rectangle, however large.

$$y - x - 2 \leqq 0, \tag{4}$$
$$y \leqq 3, \tag{5}$$
$$x \leqq 3, \quad and \tag{6}$$
$$x + y - 2 \geqq 0. \tag{7}$$

*Solution.*    *1.*   We draw the four lines, in Figure 51, whose equations are obtained by using only the signs of equality in (4)–(7). These lines intersect at $A, B, C,$ and $D$. Let $M$ be the polygonal set of points which is the intersection of the graphs of (4)–(7).

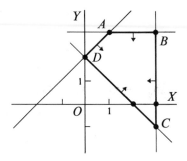

*Fig. 51*

*2.*   Temporarily disregard points on the lines in Figure 51. Then, because of (5), $M$ lies *below* $AB$, as indicated by a short arrow in the figure. Because of (6), $M$ lies to the *left* of $BC$. On substituting $(x = 0, y = 0)$ in (4), we obtain $-2 \leqq 0$, which is *true*; hence, the graph of (4) is the closed half-plane *at or below* $AD$. With $(x = 0, y = 0)$ in (7), we obtain $-2 \geqq 0$, which is *false*; hence the graph of (7) is the closed half-plane *at or above* $DC$. Thus, the graph $M$ of the system (4)–(7) consists of the sides and interior of polygon $ABCD$ in Figure 51.

## Exercise 24

*In an xy-plane, locate the polygonal set G, of points which is the graph of the system of inequalities, that is, the graph of the solution set of the system. Is G bounded by a polygon? The graphs for these problems should be retained for possible use in the next exercise.*

1.  $x \geqq 0, y \leqq x,$ and $y + x - 2 \leqq 0.$
2.  $x \geqq -2, y \geqq 2,$ and $y - x \geqq 0.$
3.  $x - y - 2 \leqq 0, x + y - 2 \geqq 0,$ and $x - 2y + 1 \geqq 0.$
4.  $x \leqq 6, x - y + 3 \geqq 0, x + y \geqq 3,$ and $x + 2y - 12 \leqq 0.$
5.  $2x + y \leqq 2, 2y + 1 \geqq x, 2y - x \leqq 4,$ and $3y - 4x \leqq 11.$
6.  $y - x - 2 \leqq 0, y + 5x \leqq 20, 3y + 8 \geqq 2x,$ and $y + 4x \geqq 2.$
7.  $2y - x \geqq 0, y + x \geqq 0, 4x + 7 \geqq 3y,$ and $2y + 3x \leqq 16.$

*A polygon in the xy-plane has the specified vertices. Find a system of inequalities whose graph is the polygonal set bounded by the polygon.*

8.  $(2, 0); (5, 0); (2, 4).$         9.  $(0, 4); (3, 1); (5, 6).$

HINT. First plot the vertices. Then find an equation for each side of the polygon. Finally, for each side, determine which inequality obtained from the equation is satisfied by points interior to the polygon.

10.  $(0, 6); (2, 6); (3, 0); (4, 1).$     11.  $(-2, 0); (0, 4); (0, -2); (3, 1).$

12.  Can a set of points in the $xy$-plane bounded by a triangle fail to be convex?

13.  Draw a quadrilateral which bounds a set of points $M$ where $M$ is *not* convex.

14.  A system of inequalities in $x$ and $y$ may be *inconsistent*. Show that no solutions exist, and hence no graph exists, for the system

$$y - x - 1 \geqq 0, \quad 2y - x - 2 \leqq 0, \quad and \quad x \geqq 2.$$

## 40.  Extremes of $(ax + by + c)$ on a bounded polygonal set

With $a$, $b$, and $c$ as constants, where $a$ and $b$ are not both zero, let

$$f(x, y) = ax + by + c. \tag{1}$$

For each point $P:(s, t)$ in the $xy$-plane, there is a corresponding number $f(s, t)$, which we shall call *the value of f at P*. If $T$ is any set of points in the plane, let $W$ be the corresponding set of values of $f$. If there is a *largest* number, $M$, in $W$, then $M$ is called the **maximum** of $f$ on $T$. If there is a *smallest* number, $m$, in $W$, then $m$ is called the **minimum** of $f$ on $T$. Either $M$ or $m$, if it exists, may be referred to as an *extreme (value)* of $f$ on $T$. We shall investigate the possibility of such extremes when $T$ is a polygonal set of points.

With $f$ as in (1), and $h$ as any constant, the graph of

$$f(x, y) = h, \quad or \quad ax + by + c = h, \tag{2}$$

is a line, $L(h)$. If $P:(s, t)$ is any point in the $xy$-plane, $L(h)$ will pass through $P$ if $h$ satisfies the equation obtained by substituting $(x = s, y = t)$ in (2), which gives $h = f(s, t)$. Or

$$L(h) \text{ passes through } P:(s, t) \text{ when } h = f(s, t). \tag{3}$$

ILLUSTRATION 1. Let $f(x, y) = 3x - 2y + 5$. Then $L(h)$ has the equation

$$3x - 2y + 5 = h. \tag{4}$$

To obtain $h$ so that $L(h)$ will pass through $P:(2, -3)$, substitute $(x = 2, y = -3)$ in (4):

$$h = 6 + 6 + 5, \quad or \quad h = 17.$$

Hence, $L(17)$ passes through $P:(2, -3)$, with the equation

$$3x - 2y + 5 = 17, \quad or \quad 3x - 2y = 12.$$

EXAMPLE 1. If $f(x, y) = y - 2x + 6$, show that $f$ has a maximum, $M$, and a minimum, $m$, on the polygonal set $T$ whose boundary is the pentagon $U$ with the following vertices:

$$A:(3, 0); \quad B:(5, 3); \quad C:(4, 6); \quad D:(2, 5); \quad E:(2, 2).$$

*Solution.* *1.* Let $W$ be the range (set of values) of the function $f(x, y)$ with $(x, y)$ on $T$; that is

$$W = \{all\ h \mid h = f(s, t)\ with\ P:(s, t)\ in\ T\}. \tag{5}$$

By (3), we may also describe $W$ as follows:

$$W = \{all\ h \mid L(h)\ intersects\ T\}. \tag{6}$$

*2.* With $f(x, y) = y - 2x + 6$, $L(h)$ has the equation

$$f(x, y) = h \quad or \quad y - 2x + 6 = h.$$

In the slope-$y$-intercept form, we obtain

$$L(h): \qquad\qquad y = 2x + (h - 6). \tag{7}$$

Now, let $h$ be a variable, whose domain is all real numbers. Consider the corresponding set of lines $V = \{L(h)\}$, where there is a line $L(h)$ for each value of $h$. Various members of $V$ are shown as broken lines in Figure 52. By (3), line $L(h)$ through $B:(5, 3)$ has $h = f(5, 3) = 3 - 10 + 6$, or $h = -1$. That is, $L(-1)$ passes through $B$. From (7), $L(-1)$ has the equation

$$y = 2x + (-1 - 6), \quad or \quad y = 2x - 7.$$

With $h = f(2, 5) = 7$, line $L(7)$ passes through vertex $D:(2, 5)$ in Figure 52. Line $L(2)$ is shown intersecting $T$, but not passing through a vertex of the boundary $U$. Similarly, we visualize a line $L(h)$ through each point $P:(s, t)$ of $T$. The corresponding numbers $h = f(s, t)$ form the set $W$ in (5) and (6).

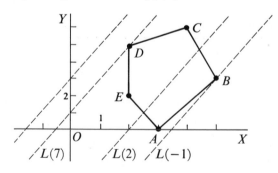

*Fig. 52*

3. For any value of $h$, line $L(h)$ of (7) has slope 2 and $y$-intercept $(h - 6)$. Suppose that $h$ has some value for which $L(h)$ is *below* $T$ in Figure 52. If $h$ increases, the $y$-intercept of $L(h)$ *increases* so that $L(h)$ *rises** in the $xy$-plane. Then, the *lowest* position of $L(h)$ (or, the *smallest* value of $h$) for which $L(h)$ intersects $T$ occurs when $L(h)$ passes through $B$. At this location of $L(h)$, we have $h = f(5, 3) = -1$; hence $-1$ is the *least* number in the set $W$ of (6). As $L(h)$ rises, the *highest* position (or, the *largest* value of $h$) for which $L(h)$ intersects $T$ occurs when $L(h)$ passes through $D$. Then $h = f(2, 5) = 7$; hence 7 is the *largest* number in the set $W$.

4. *Conclusion.* The function $f(x, y)$ has the maximum $M = 7$ and minimum $m = -1$ on $T$. Also, each of these is the value of $f(x, y)$ at a *vertex* of the polygon which is the boundary of $T$.

NOTE 1. When we refer to a *point* in an $xy$-plane, we shall consider this to be the equivalent of a reference to the *coordinates* $(x, y)$ *of the point.* Then, we may refer to a *set of points* as being the *domain* of a function $H(x, y)$.

The type of reasoning used in the solution of Example 1 will be employed to prove† the following fundamental result. The student may be willing to accept the theorem as intuitively evident, on the basis of the reasoning for Example 1, as a typical special case.

THEOREM II. *Let $T$ be a bounded polygonal set of points in an $xy$-plane, with $U$ as the polygon bounding $T$. Let*

$$f(x, y) = ax + by + c, \qquad (8)$$

*where $a$, $b$, and $c$ are constants.‡ Then, $f$ has a maximum value, $M$, and a minimum value, $m$, on $T$. Moreover, $f(x, y) = M$ at some vertex of $U$, and $f(x, y) = m$ at some vertex of $U$.*

*Proof.* (**When $b > 0$.**)   *1.* Let $L(h)$ be the line $f(x, y) = h$, or

$$ax + by + c = h, \qquad or \qquad y = -\frac{a}{b}x + \frac{h - c}{b}. \qquad (9)$$

Let $T$ be illustrated by the set of points with the pentagon $ABCDE$ as a boundary in Figure 52. Also, let $W$ be defined as in (5) or (6).

2. Let $V$ be the set of lines $\{L(h)\}$, for all real values of $h$. From (9), these lines are parallel. Also, $L(h)$ has the $y$-intercept $(h - c)/b$, which *increases* when and only when $h$ increases.

* The student may use the edge of a ruler as $L(h)$ in Figure 52, and simulate the actions being described.

† For an analytic proof, see Chapter 14 in *College Algebra, Fifth Edition*, by William L. Hart; D. C. Heath and Company, publishers.

‡ The theorem is trivial if $a = b = 0$. Hence, we shall assume that *not both* of $a$ and $b$ are 0.

*3.* If *L(h)* *rises* in the *xy*-plane from below *T*, and thus if *h increases*, there will be a *lowest position* for *L(h)* in which it intersects *T*, and hence a *smallest value of h* for which this happens. Since the boundary of *T* is a polygon, *U*, the lowest position just mentioned will occur when the variable line, in moving upward, first meets a *vertex\** *P*:(*s, t*) of *U*. Then, by (3), we have $h = f(s, t)$. Hence, we have proved that the set *W* described in (5) and (6) contains a *smallest number* $m = f(s, t)$, where *P*:(*s, t*) is a *vertex* of *U*.

*4.* Similarly, there is a *highest position* of the variable line *L(h)*, and hence a corresponding *largest value for h*, with *L(h)* intersecting *T*. As in the solution of Example 2, this gives a largest value of *h* with $h = f(s, t)$ where *P*:(*s, t*) is a *vertex* of *U*. Hence, we have completed the proof of Theorem II for the case where $b > 0$. A similar proof applies when $b < 0$, where the variable line *L(h)* would move *downward* in the *xy*-plane when *h* increases. A very simple similar proof would apply if $b = 0$.

As a consequence of Theorem II, we may obtain the extreme values of a linear function $f(x, y)$ on a bounded polygonal set *T* *by merely examining the values of f(x, y) at the vertices of T* (meaning the vertices of the polygon which is the boundary of *T*). The following routine is justified by Theorem II.

**Summary.**  *To obtain the extremes of $f(x, y) = ax + by + c$ on a bounded polygonal set T.*

(I)  *If T is defined as the graph of a system of inequalities, graph the lines whose equations are obtained by using equality signs in the inequalities. Verify the location of T as in Exercise 24 on page 98.*

(II)  *Find the coordinates of each vertex of T by solving the preceding equalities in pairs, as determined by inspection of the graph.*

(III)  *Substitute the coordinates of each vertex in f(x, y) to obtain the set of values of f at the vertices. Then, the maximum, M, of f on T is the largest, and the minimum of f is the smallest of the values of f at the vertices.*

In case a bounded polygonal set *T* is defined by giving the coordinates of the vertices of its boundary, only (III) of the preceding summary is involved.

ILLUSTRATION 2.  To obtain the extremes of $f(x, y) = y - 2x + 6$ in Example 1 by use of (III) of the Summary, we calculate $f(x, y)$ at the vertices of the polygon in Figure 52 on page 100:

$$at \ A:(3, 0), f(3, 0) = 0; \quad at \ B:(5, 3), f(5, 3) = -1;$$
$$at \ C:(4, 6), f(4, 6) = 4; \quad at \ D:(2, 5), f(2, 5) = 7;$$
$$at \ E:(2, 2), f(2, 2) = 4.$$

---

\* Possibly when *L(h)* meets a *whole side* of *U*, if such a side happens to be parallel to *L(h)*.

Hence, by Theorem II, the maximum of $f$ on the polygonal set $T$ is 7, attained at $D:(2, 5)$; the minimum of $f$ on $T$ is $-1$, attained at $B:(5, 3)$. The preceding results check with the solution of Example 1.

EXAMPLE 2.   If $f(x, y) = 2x + 3y - 5$, find the maximum and the minimum values for $f$ on the polygonal set $T$ which is the solution set of the system of inequalities

$$y - x \leqq 0, \qquad x - 2y + 1 \leqq 0, \qquad and \qquad y + x \leqq 8. \qquad (10)$$

*Solution.   1.*  With "$=$" used in each of inequalities (10), we find the following equations for the lines bounding the half-planes which intersect to form $T$:

$$y - x = 0; \qquad x - 2y + 1 = 0; \qquad y + x = 8. \qquad (11)$$

The graphs of (11) are seen in Figure 53. The student may verify that $T$ is bounded by $\triangle ABC$.

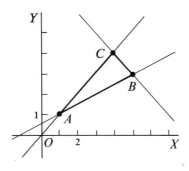

*Fig. 53*

2.   To obtain the vertices of $T$, we solve each of the following systems of two equations each, representing lines which intersect at a vertex. Thus, the solution of the system at the left below is the coordinates of $A$.

$$\begin{cases} y - x = 0, \ and \\ x - 2y + 1 = 0. \end{cases} \qquad \begin{cases} x - 2y + 1 = 0, \ and \\ y + x - 8 = 0. \end{cases} \qquad \begin{cases} y - x = 0, \ and \\ y + x - 8 = 0. \end{cases}$$

We obtain $A:(1, 1)$, $B:(5, 3)$, and $C:(4, 4)$ as the vertices.

3.   The values of $f(x, y)$ at the vertices are $f(1, 1) = 0$, $f(5, 3) = 14$, and $f(4, 4) = 15$. Hence, the maximum of $f(x, y)$ on $T$ is 15, attained at $C$; the minimum of $f(x, y)$ is 0, attained at $A$.

NOTE 2.   Let $P_1:(x_1, y_1)$ and $P_2:(x_2, y_2)$ be the endpoints of a line segment $P_1P_2$ in an $xy$-plane and suppose that $f(x, y)$ is a linear function. Let $H$ be the set of all points on $P_1P_2$. Then, it can be proved* that $f(x, y)$ has a

* See Chapter 14 in *College Algebra*, 5th *Edition*, by William L. Hart; D. C. Heath and Company, publishers.

maximum $M$ and a minimum $m$ for all points $(x, y)$ on $H$, and that $M$ and $m$ are attained at the *endpoints* of $P_1P_2$. That is, $f(x_1, y_1)$ and $f(x_2, y_2)$ are the values of $M$ and $m$, in *some order*. This fact can be used as a basis for a proof of Theorem II, to replace the geometrical reasoning which we employed. In particular, suppose that $f(x_1, y_1) = a$ at some vertex $P_1$ of a polygonal set $T$, and $f(x_2, y_2) = b$ at $P_2:(x_2, y_2)$, where segment $P_1P_2$ is a side of the polygon which is the boundary of $T$. If $R:(x, y)$ is any point on this side, then $f(x, y)$ is a number lying on the interval with endpoints $a$ and $b$ on a number scale.

## Exercise 25

*Find the maximum and the minimum values of $f(x, y)$ if the domain for $(x, y)$ is the specified polygonal set. Show the set in a figure. Also, draw lines of type $L(h)$, as discussed in Example 1 on page* 100, *corresponding to each extreme value of $f$.*

1. $f(x, y) = 5x - 2y + 3$; the polygonal set in Example 2 on page 103.
2. $f(x, y) = x + 2y - 5$; the polygonal set in Problem 1.
3. $f(x, y) = 2x - y + 8$; the polygonal set in Problem 3, page 98.
4. $f(x, y) = 4x + 2y + 7$; the polygonal set in Problem 3.
5. $f(x, y) = 2y - 3x + 6$; the polygonal set in Problem 4, page 98.
6. $f(x, y) = 9 - 2x - 2y$; the polygonal set in Problem 5. Also, describe, and show in the figure, all points at which $f$ attains its maximum value, and all points where $f$ attains its minimum value.
7. $f(x, y) = 3y - 7x$; the polygonal set in Problem 5, page 98.
8. $f(x, y) = 3x - 4y + 5$; the polygonal set in Problem 7.
9. $f(x, y) = 3x - 3y + 7$; the polygonal set in Problem 6, page 98. Also describe, and show in the figure, all points at which $f$ attains its maximum value, and all points where $f$ attains its minimum value in the polygonal set.
10. $f(x, y) = 3 - x - y$; the polygonal set of Problem 9.
11. $f(x, y) = 2x - 3y + 8$; the polygonal set in Problem 10, page 99.
12. $f(x, y) = 2y + 3x + 4$; the polygonal set in Problem 11, page 99.

NOTE 1.   Theorem II was proved for a *finite* polygonal set. However, a maximum, $M$, alone, or a minimum, $m$, alone, or neither or both $M$ and $m$ may exist for $(ax + by + c)$ in an *unbounded* polygonal set $G$. The existence or nonexistence of $M$ or $m$ would depend on the nature of $G$, and the values of $a$ and $b$. We shall not discuss any theorem covering the case of an unbounded set $G$. However, particular cases, as in the following problems, can be discussed by use of the geometrical method of Example 1 on page 100.

★*13.*   Let $f(x, y) = 6x + 2y - 4$, and let $G$ be the graph of the system

$$x \geqq 0, \quad y \geqq 0, \quad x + y - 2 \geqq 0, \quad and \quad x + 2y - 3 \geqq 0.$$

Prove geometrically, as in Example 1 on page 100, that $f(x, y)$ has a minimum, $m$, for all $(x, y)$ such that $P:(x, y)$ is in $G$, and that $f(x, y) = m$ at a vertex, or corner point of $G$. Does $f$ have a maximum in $G$?

★14. Let $f(x, y) = x + 2y + 4$, and let $G$ be the graph of the system

$$x \leq 4, \quad y \leq x, \quad and \quad x + y - 6 \leq 0.$$

Prove that $f(x, y)$ has a maximum or a minimum for all $(x, y)$ such that $P:(x, y)$ is in $G$, and find the extreme value which exists.

★15. Let $f(x, y) = 2y - 2x + 5$, and let $S$ be the solution set of the system

$$y - x \leq 1, \quad x - y \leq 1, \quad x \geq 0, \quad and \quad y \geq 0.$$

Prove that $f(x, y)$ has a maximum and a minimum for all $(x, y)$ in $S$.

## 41. Linear programming with two variables

Let us consider a problem which we shall call a *management problem* subject to the decision of an executive, $H$. Suppose that he is dealing with two variables, $x$ and $y$, which must satisfy a certain system of linear inequalities. Also, assume that he wishes to make a specified linear function $f(x, y)$ assume its maximum or its minimum value, subject to the given restrictions on $x$ and $y$. Then, a search for a satisfactory pair $(x, y)$ is referred to as a problem in *linear programming*. Such problems for the case of two or more variables arise in a wide range of applications, particularly in business affairs, in the fields of social science, and in military logistics. Theorem II is our basis for the solution of problems in linear programming involving just *two* independent variables. The consideration of such problems with more independent variables is beyond the level of this text.*

EXAMPLE 1. A manufacturer, $H$, will produce 200 trade units of bottles per week. His plant is geared to turn out bottles of three quality grades, (I), (II), and (III). He has a contract to sell 25 units of (I), and 50 units of (II) per week. He can sell all that he produces of (II), but can sell at most 100 units per week of (I), and 100 units of (III). His profit per unit on (I) is $40, on (II) is $25, and on (III) is $30. How much of each grade should he produce in order to obtain maximum profit? What production schedule would yield minimum profit?

*Solution. 1.* Let the number of units produced per week of (I) be $x$, and of (II) be $y$. Then $(200 - x - y)$ units of (III) are produced. The problem requires that

$$25 \leq x \leq 100; \quad 50 \leq y; \quad 200 - x - y \geq 0; \quad 200 - x - y \leq 100. \quad (1)$$

* For the case of three or more variables, efficient methods of solution are available involving use of electronic digital computing machines.

The inequalities in (1) are called the *constraints* of the problem. Let the profit of *H* per week be $f(x, y)$ dollars. Then

$$f(x, y) = 40x + 25y + 30(200 - x - y), \quad or$$
$$f(x, y) = 10x - 5y + 6000.$$

We wish to obtain *x* and *y* so as to *maximize* $f(x, y)$, and also so as to *minimize* $f(x, y)$, subject to the constraints (1). We simplify (1) to the following form:

$$25 \leqq x \leqq 100; \quad 50 \leqq y; \quad 200 \geqq x + y; \quad 100 \leqq x + y. \qquad (2)$$

2.    In Figure 54, the graph of the solution set of (2) is the polygonal set of points *T* bounded by the polygon *ABCDE*. The solutions of pairs of equations obtained from (2) was simple. The vertices of *T* are as follows:

$A$:(50, 50);    $B$:(100, 50);    $C$:(100, 100);    $D$:(25, 175);    $E$:(25, 75).

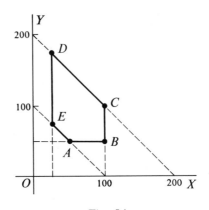

*Fig. 54*

3.    The values of $f(x, y)$ at the vertices are, respectively, as follows:

$$6250; \quad 6750; \quad 6500; \quad 5375; \quad 5875.$$

Hence, the maximum profit available is $6750 per week, resulting from production of 100 units of (I), 50 units of (II), and hence (200 − 100 − 50) or 50 units of (III). Minimum profit of $5375 per week would result from production of 25 units of (I), 175 units of (II), and no production of (III).

EXAMPLE 2.    A manufacturer, *E*, of dog food will prepare a food mixture, and considers using three compounds *R*, *S*, and *T*, which contain, by weight, the various percentages of the components carbohydrates, fats, and protein below. The mixture is to contain at least 25% of each component. The costs

| Compounds | Carbohydrates | Fats | Protein |
|-----------|---------------|------|---------|
| R | 45% | 20% | 35% |
| S | 45% | 45% | 10% |
| T | 5% | 25% | 35% |

per pound of $R$, $S$, and $T$ are six cents, eight cents, and four cents, respectively. Find how many pounds of $(R, S, T)$ should be used per 100 pounds of the mixture to minimize the cost.

*Solution.* 1. Let $(x, y, z)$ be the numbers of pounds of $(R, S, T)$, respectively, in 100 pounds of the mixture.

2. The values of $(x, y, z)$ are nonnegative, so that (3) below must be satisfied. The sum of the amounts is 100 pounds, as in (7). The number of pounds of carbohydrates is the sum of 45% of $x$ pounds, 45% of $y$ pounds, and 5% of $z$ pounds; this sum must be at least 25% of 100 pounds, as stated in (4). Similarly, (5) and (6) are obtained. Thus, we arrive at the constraints (3)–(7) below.

$$x \geqq 0; \quad y \geqq 0; \quad z \geqq 0; \tag{3}$$
$$.45x + .45y + .05z \geqq 25; \tag{4}$$
$$.20x + .45y + .25z \geqq 25; \tag{5}$$
$$.35x + .10y + .35z \geqq 25. \tag{6}$$
$$x + y + z = 100. \tag{7}$$

The cost, $f(x, y, z)$, in cents per 100 pounds is

$$f(x, y, z) = 6x + 8y + 4z. \tag{8}$$

We wish to obtain $(x, y, z)$ to satisfy the *constraints* (3)–(7), and to minimize $f(x, y, z)$.

3. From (7), $\quad z = 100 - x - y.$ \hfill (9)

When (9) is used in (3)–(6), the constraints take the following forms (10)–(13) after simplification, and $f(x, y, z)$ becomes $F(x, y)$ in (14). To simplify (4)–(6), both sides of each inequality were multiplied by 100.

$$x \geqq 0; \quad y \geqq 0; \quad 100 - x - y \geqq 0; \tag{10}$$
$$x + y \geqq 50; \tag{11}$$
$$x \leqq 4y; \tag{12}$$
$$y \leqq 40. \tag{13}$$
$$f(x, y, z) = 6x + 8y + 4(100 - x - y) = F(x, y), \quad or$$
$$F(x, y) = 400 + 2x + 4y. \tag{14}$$

4.   The polygonal set, $V$, in the $xy$-plane which is the graph of (10)–(13) is shown in Figure 55. The vertices of $V$ are as follows:

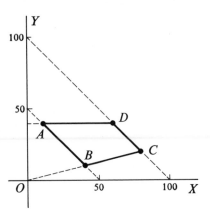

*Fig. 55*

$$A:(10, 40); \quad B:(40, 10); \quad C:(80, 20); \quad D:(60, 40). \qquad (15)$$

The values of $F(x, y)$ at the vertices are

$$F(10, 40) = 580; \quad F(40, 10) = 520; \quad F(80, 20) = 640; \quad F(60, 40) = 680.$$

Hence, the cost is a minimum if $E$ uses $x = 40$ and $y = 10$; then (7) gives $z = 50$.

COMMENT.   Notice the implication from having dealt with 100 pounds in Example 2. The results give percentages for *any* amount of the mixture. Thus, for minimum cost with *any* amount, 40% should be $R$, 10% $S$, and 50% $T$.

EXAMPLE 3.   A manufacturer of refrigerators has an inventory of 600 refrigerators of a certain variety at warehouse (I) and 600 at warehouse (II). Department stores A, B, and C order 300, 400, and 500 of these refrigerators, respectively. The costs of shipping one refrigerator to each of these stores from (I) and (II) are as follows:

|  | *To* A (300) | *To* B (400) | *To* C (500) |
|---|---|---|---|
| *From* (I), *per unit* | $45 | $15 | $65 |
| *From* (II), *per unit* | $65 | $15 | $15 |

How should the orders be filled if the manufacturer desires to minimize shipping costs?

*Solution.   1.*   Suppose that $x$ refrigerators are sent from (I) to A, and $y$ refrigerators from (I) to B. Then, the sources of supply for A, B, and C are as shown in the following table. The constraints limiting $x$ and $y$ are as follows, in addition to $x \geqq 0$ and $y \geqq 0$:

|  | *To* A | *To* B | *To* C |
|---|---|---|---|
| *From* (I) | $x$ | $y$ | $600 - (x + y)$ |
| *From* (II) | $300 - x$ | $400 - y$ | $500 - (600 - x - y)$ |

$600 - (x + y) \geqq 0$;    $300 - x \geqq 0$;    $400 - y \geqq 0$;    $x + y - 100 \geqq 0$.

The student should draw a figure showing the polygonal region which consists of all points $P:(x, y)$ where $x$ and $y$ satisfy the constraints.

2.  The cost $F$ of shipping the refrigerators is

$$F = 45x + 15y + 65(600 - x - y)$$
$$+ 65(300 - x) + 15(400 - y) + 15(x + y - 100), \quad or$$
$$F = -70x - 50y + 63,000.$$

The student will complete this solution in the next exercise, to find $x$ and $y$ so that $F$ will attain its minimum value.

## Exercise 26

*1.*  A corporation, E, produces two varieties of snowplows for use by home owners, a self-propelled blower type, *A*, and a riding pusher type, *B*. E can sell all snowplows which are manufactured. E uses two types, *H* and *K*, of skilled mechanics. To make one *A* snowplow requires 3 man-days of *H*-labor and 4 man-days of *K*-labor. To make one *B* snowplow requires 5 man-days of *H*-labor and 4 man-days of *K*-labor. The profit per *A* snowplow is $40, and per *B* snowplow is $50. E has available per month at most 2700 man-days of *H*-labor and 2400 man-days of *K*-labor. How many snowplows of each type should be produced per month in order to give E maximum profit?

*2.*  A farmer decides to raise a total of 1000 capons, geese, and turkeys, with not more than 200 geese included. His facilities require him to raise at least as many turkeys as capons, and at most 600 turkeys. He anticipates profits of $2 per capon, $1.50 per turkey, and $2.25 per goose. How many of each type of fowl should he raise in order to obtain the largest possible profit, and what is this profit?

*3.*  The manager of a theater has agreed to schedule performances for 150 nights of the season. He has three plays *A*, *B*, and *C* available for the performances, where each play will require a whole night. He is assured of a profit of $900 for each performance of *A*, and $500 for each performance of *B*. He considers it unwise to schedule more than 60

performances of $A$, or 75 performances of $C$. His profit per performance
of $C$ will be \$700. He is required to schedule at least 25 performances of
$B$. In order to obtain maximum profit, how many performances should
he schedule for each play?

4. A farmer wishes to mix three compounds, $R$, $S$, and $T$, to form fertilizer.
These compounds contain the various percentages of nitrogen, phos-
phate, and potash, by weight, as indicated in the following table. The
fertilizer is to contain at least 25% by weight of each chemical. The costs
per pound of $R$, $S$, and $T$ are 4 cents, 3 cents, and 5 cents, respectively.
How many pounds of each compound should be used per 100 pounds
of the mixture to minimize the cost?

| COMPOUND | R | S | T |
|---|---|---|---|
| NITROGEN | 30% | 30% | 20% |
| PHOSPHATE | 15% | 55% | 30% |
| POTASH | 35% | 15% | 35% |

5. Solve Problem 4 if the costs per pound of $R$, $S$, and $T$ are 4 cents, 5 cents,
and 3 cents, respectively.

6. Three foods, $A$, $B$, and $C$, are to be purchased for the basic diet of a
camp. These foods have calorie values per pound, and vitamin values per
pound, in appropriate units of measurement, as shown in the following
table, which also gives prices per pound. The diet provided by $A$, $B$, and
$C$ must have a minimum calorie value of 3 units, and a minimum vitamin
value of 3 units per pound. To make the diet palatable, at most 30% may
be of type $C$. Subject to the preceding conditions, how many pounds of
$A$, $B$, and $C$ should be used in 100 pounds of the food to obtain minimum
cost (or, what percentages of the diet should be provided by $A$, $B$, and
$C$)? Also, compute the minimum cost for 100 pounds.

| FOOD | A | B | C |
|---|---|---|---|
| CALORIE | 2 | 5 | 3 |
| VITAMIN | 3 | 4 | 2 |
| COST | \$.50 | \$.70 | \$.40 |

7. A manufacturer, M, of cosmetics will prepare a skin lotion by forming
a mixture of compounds ($A$, $B$, $C$) which contain, by volume, the various
percentages of the desirable ingredients *an aromatic oil, $\alpha$, an astringent,
$\beta$, and an antiseptic, $\gamma$,* as given in the following table. The costs in dollars

of *A*, *B*, and *C* per liter are 6, 10, and 4, respectively. The mixture is to contain at least 2% of each of the ingredients ($\alpha$, $\beta$, $\gamma$). Find how many liters of each of (*A*, *B*, *C*) should be used by M to minimize his cost for 1000 liters of the mixture.

| COMPOUNDS | $\alpha$ | $\beta$ | $\gamma$ |
|:---:|:---:|:---:|:---:|
| *A* | 2.5% | 1% | 3% |
| *B* | 2.5% | 6% | 1% |
| *C* | .5% | 2% | 3% |

8. A dietician in a hospital must decide on the percentages, by weights, of three foods *A*, *B*, and *C* which should be included in a given total weight of foods to be served. In order to include sufficient protein, at least 15% should be food *A*. To regulate the amount of carbohydrates eaten, at least 30% but not more than 60% should be food *B*. To provide suitable variety, the amount of *C* should not exceed the sum of the amounts of *A* and *B*. The costs of *A*, *B*, and *C* in cents per pound are 60, 70, and 50, respectively. (I) Find the percentages of the total food, by weight, which should be of types *A*, *B*, and *C*, respectively. (Consider the composition of 100 pounds of food.) (II) Find the minimum cost for 100 pounds under the specified conditions.

9. A drug company plans to produce a cough syrup containing in dilute liquid form an antihistamine, *A*, a barbiturate compound, *B*, and an aspirin compound, *C*. In the mixture, by weight, at least 20% but not more than 50% should be *A*; at least 30% should be *B*, and the amount of *B* should be greater than the amount of *A*; the amount of *C* plus the amount of *A* should exceed 30% of the mixture. The costs of *A*, *B*, and *C* per ounce are $5, $3, and $4, respectively. What percentages of the syrup by weight should be *A*, *B*, and *C*, respectively, to minimize the cost?

10. A drug manufacturer will prepare a compound *M* for use in a nation with an undesirable diet which has created deficiencies in the essential vitamins: thiamine, *T*, which aids children's growth; ascorbic acid, *A*, which prevents and cures scurvy, and *D*, which prevents rickets in children and aids utilization of calcium in building bones and teeth. To create *M*, a mixture will be made of components (*R*, *S*, *W*) containing the number of milligrams (mg) of each vitamin per gram (gm) as indicated in the following table. At most 40% of *M* by weight should be *W*. *M* must contain, per gm, at most 15 mg of *T*, at most 20 mg of *A*, and at least 10 mg of *D*. The costs in cents per gram of *R*, *S*, and *W* are

30, 20, and 10, respectively. What percentages of *M*, by weight, should be composed of *R*, *S*, and *W*, respectively, to minimize the cost of *M*? (One mg is .001 gm.)

| COMPONENTS | *R* | *S* | *W* |
|---|---|---|---|
| *T* (*mg per gm*) | 5 | 25 | 10 |
| *A* (*mg per gm*) | 15 | 10 | 30 |
| *D* (*mg per gm*) | 20 | 5 | 5 |

*11.* Complete the solution of illustrative Example 3 on page 108.

*12.* A manufacturer of dehumidifiers of a certain type has an inventory of 600 units at warehouse (I) and 700 at warehouse (II). Retailers A, B, and C order 300, 500, and 500 of these dehumidifiers. The costs, in dollars, of shipping one of them to each of the buyers from (I) and (II) are as follows:

|  | *To* A | *To* B | *To* C |
|---|---|---|---|
| *From* (I) | 15 | 10 | 20 |
| *From* (II) | 20 | 10 | 10 |

How should the orders be filled if the manufacturer desires to minimize the shipping costs?

# 6 | METHODS FOR COUNTING OUTCOMES

## 42. A preview of probability

In the next chapter, any probability will be described as the probability of an *"event"* when a certain *"random experiment"* is performed. *"Experiment"* will refer to any action or sequence of actions which either can be physically realized, or can be imagined as a logical process leading to various conclusions. The set of outcomes of the experiment will be called the *sample space* for the probability discussion, and the number of outcomes in the space will be *finite*. In any reference to a random experiment, use of the word *"random"* will imply that a companion definition of probability about the outcomes will be introduced. Any *event* for which probability is defined will be a *subset of the sample space.*

In developing a concept of probability for any sample space, it will be essential to have means for calculating the number of outcomes of the random experiment, and the number in any subset of it which is described. Methods in the present chapter will be designed to aid in such calculations.

ILLUSTRATION 1. Suppose that a factory has produced 1000 cabinets for television sets in a given month. For this output, we make the hypothesis that it involves exactly 20 defective cabinets, which have not been detected. Let the random experiment be the random selection of 25 cabinets for shipment to a customer. We ask: What is the probability that there will be 2 defective sets in the shipment? To answer this question, we must learn how to calculate the number of different ways in which we can be successful 23 times and unsuccessful 2 times in 25 plays of the *"game"* of selecting a perfect cabinet from the total production.

One elementary aid in counting outcomes of any action or sequence of actions is a *decision tree*, as met below.

ILLUSTRATION 2.   Suppose that a mouse will be given the opportunity to go through a maze starting in a room $R$ which has 3 exits to other rooms $R_1$; with 2 exits from each of these to other rooms $R_2$; with 2 exits from each of these to final terminals $T$, where there is food at only one terminal. We ask for the number of paths which are open for the mouse. The possibilities can be visualized by the tree in Figure 56, where each path is represented by a connected sequence of line segments leading to a terminal. Twelve paths are observed, corresponding to the twelve terminals. A method in the next section will yield this result without construction of the tree. However, a decision tree frequently is useful in clarifying the nature of an experiment, in checking results obtained by other means and, sometimes, in actually calculating desired results.

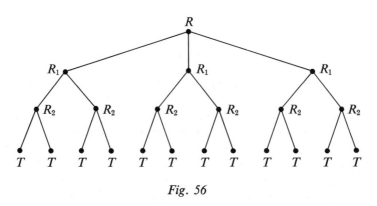

*Fig. 56*

## 43.   A multiplication method in counting

In the decision tree for Illustration 2 of the preceding section, we observe a setting where the following principle leads immediately to the result.

**Multiplication principle in counting.**   *For successive or simultaneous actions.*

*Suppose that an action $A_1$ has $h_1$ possible outcomes and, simultaneously with $A_1$ or after its performance, an action $A_2$ has $h_2$ possible outcomes. Then, performance of the compound experiment "$A_1$ and $A_2$" has $h_1 h_2$ possible outcomes.*

The preceding principle extends to the performance in succession, or in part simultaneously, of three or more actions.

ILLUSTRATION 1.   In Illustration 2 of the preceding section, the mouse has to make a first decision with three possible outcomes, a second decision with two outcomes, and a third decision with two outcomes. Hence, by the multiplication principle, he can choose a path in $3 \times 2 \times 2$ or 12 ways, as shown by the decision tree.

NOTE 1.   In this chapter and the next chapter, unless otherwise specified, *number* will refer to a *positive integer*.

EXAMPLE 1.   How many numbers of four different digits each can be formed by use of the digits $\{1, 2, 3, 4, 5, 6\}$?

*Solution.*   We can form numbers of four digits each by performing the following four actions in succession. $A_1$: *fill the first place (at the left) in the number;* $A_2$: *fill the second place;* $A_3$: *fill the third place;* $A_4$: *fill the fourth place.* We can perform $A_1$ in 6 ways, as indicated in the following diagram. Then, from the five remaining digits, $A_2$ can be performed 5 ways; then $A_3$ in 4 ways; then $A_4$ in 3 ways. Hence, by the multiplication principle, the final number can be formed in $6 \cdot 5 \cdot 4 \cdot 3$ or 360 ways.

| 6 | 5 | 4 | 3 |
|---|---|---|---|

EXAMPLE 2.   A teacher of mathematics will construct an examination of seven questions by use of three "*word*" problems and four problems involving only algebraic manipulation. In how many different orders can he arrange the questions if the first and the last are to be word problems?

*Solution.*   Let the boxes in the following diagram represent the places $\{1, 2, \cdots, 7\}$ on the examination. The first place can be filled in 3 ways, and then the last place in 2 ways. With five questions which then remain, the second place can be filled in 5 ways; then the third place in 4 ways, by selection from the remaining questions; then the fourth place in 3 ways; then the fifth place in 2 ways; then the sixth place in just 1 way. Hence, the examination can be arranged in $3 \cdot 5 \cdot 4 \cdot 3 \cdot 2 \cdot 1 \cdot 2$ or 720 ways.

| 3 | 5 | 4 | 3 | 2 | 1 | 2 |
|---|---|---|---|---|---|---|

In applying the multiplication principle to a complicated experiment, it is best to analyze it, if possible, into two or more successive actions of a more simple nature. Then, the principle may be applicable to each of these actions, and finally to their simultaneous performance.

EXAMPLE 3.   In Example 2, in how many ways could the examination questions be arranged with the three word problems in consecutive positions?

*Solution 1. Analysis.*  To arrange the questions with the three word problems occurring in succession, perform the following actions:

(*a*)  *Choose three consecutive positions from the seven positions on the examination. Then:*
(*b*)  *Fill the three chosen positions with word problems. Then:*
(*c*)  *Fill the remaining four places in any order with the manipulative problems.*

*2.*  Action (*a*) can be taken in 5 ways (all three positions at the extreme left; then another way if the chosen three move one place to the right; then another if the three move one place to the right; and so on, four times to the right).

*3.*  Action (*b*) can be taken in $3 \cdot 2 \cdot 1$ or 6 ways.

*4.*  Action (*c*) can be taken in $4 \cdot 3 \cdot 2 \cdot 1$ or 24 ways. Hence, [(*a*), (*b*), (*c*)] can be performed in succession in $5 \times 6 \times 24$ or 720 ways.

## 44.  Combinations, and arrangements or permutations

Recall that, if we refer simply to a *set* (or, *collection*) of elements, or to a *subset*, it is assumed that no question of order or arrangement of the elements is involved. Thus, in mentioning a set of six children, they are thought of as an *unordered group*. In referring to a subset of some universal set, frequently we shall call the subset a *combination* of the elements. The word *combination* will emphasize the fact that no ordering or arrangement of the elements is involved. In colloquial language, the word *group* may be used sometimes to mean combination.

ILLUSTRATION 1.   A combination of three digits selected from $\{1, 2, 3, 4, 5\}$ is a subset of three digits, for instance

$$\left\{ \begin{array}{cc} & 1 \\ 2 & 4 \end{array} \right\},$$

where we write them in this manner to emphasize that no relative order is assigned to them.

A particular order of precedence may be specified for the elements of a set by arranging them in a sequence, by locating them in earmarked positions with distinguishing labels, or in other ways. Thus, in Examples 1 and 2 of the preceding section, we dealt with the ordering of elements, digits in one case and examination questions in the other case. The assignment of relative order to the elements of a set will be called an **arrangement** of them. The technical word **permutation** also will be used in place of arrangement.

ILLUSTRATION 2.  From the combination, or subset

$$\left\{ \begin{matrix} & 1 & \\ 2 & & 4 \end{matrix} \right\}$$

in Illustration 1, the following six permutations, or arrangements, of the digits can be formed:

142;  124;  241;  214;  412;  421.

Notice that, with the place system for writing numerals, each *number symbol* is a *permutation of its digits,* as above.

**Summary.**  *In a combination of a set of elements, there is no question of relative order among them. A permutation of a set of elements consists of an arrangement of the elements in a definite order.*

ILLUSTRATION 3.  Let a set of students consist of {John, Harry, Grace, Helen}. From them, we can form the following six combinations, taken two at a time:

$$\left. \begin{array}{lll} \text{(John, Grace);} & \text{(John, Harry);} & \text{(John, Helen);} \\ \text{(Grace, Harry);} & \text{(Grace, Helen);} & \text{(Harry, Helen).} \end{array} \right\} \quad (1)$$

Now consider filling the positions of chairman and secretary of a club by appointments from the four students. With each combination in (1), two different choices of officers can be made. Thus, from the combination (John, Grace), we may have

$$(\textit{pres. John, secy. Grace}) \quad \textit{or} \quad (\textit{pres. Grace, secy. John}). \quad (2)$$

Hence, from the four students, we may form six combinations of two each, as in (1). From each of these combinations, we can form two permutations (choices for president and secretary). Therefore, by the multiplication principle, there are 6 × 2 or 12 permutations of the four students taken two at a time.

In Illustration 3, we met a special case of the fact that there are *more permutations* of a set of elements than there are *combinations* of them, taken any particular number at a time.

In this chapter, we shall be interested mainly in finding the numbers of combinations or of permutations of given elements under various conditions. The concept of a *combination* of a set of elements is more simple to describe than the concept of a *permutation* of them. However, it happens to be easier to learn how to calculate a number of permutations than a number of combinations. Hence, we shall start by dealing with permutations. Then, it will be found that the number of combinations in any case can be computed simply if a corresponding number of permutations is obtained first. A special case of this fact was met in Illustration 3.

ILLUSTRATION 4.   The combinations of the letters $\{g, h, k\}$ taken two at a time are $\{(g, h), (h, k), (g, k)\}$. The permutations of $\{g, h, k\}$ taken two at a time are $\{gh, hg, gk, kg, hk, kh\}$.

EXAMPLE 1.   Find the number of permutations of six different things taken four at a time.

*Solution.*   Regardless of the nature of the things, we may visualize the places in the permutation as the sequence of four boxes in the following diagram. Counting from the left, the first box can be filled in 6 ways, by selection of any one of the things; then the second box in 5 ways, by selection of any one of the five remaining things; then the third box in 4 ways; then the fourth box in 3 ways. Hence, by the multiplication principle, all of the boxes can be filled in $6 \cdot 5 \cdot 4 \cdot 3$, or 360 ways.

## 45.   Counting elements in the union of mutually exclusive sets

If $A$ and $B$ are sets of elements of some universal set, recall that the *union* of $A$ and $B$, or $A \cup B$, consists of all elements *in A or in B*. In case $A$ and $B$ are *mutually exclusive*, then $A \cap B = \varnothing$, the *empty set*, or $A$ and $B$ have *no common elements*. Hence, the number of elements in $A \cup B$ is equal to the sum of the number of elements in $A$ and the number in $B$. This simple fact is so convenient that we summarize the result:

**Addition principle,** *for mutually exclusive subsets.*
*If a set A has m elements and a set B has n elements, where A and B are mutually exclusive, then $A \cup B$ has $(m + n)$ elements.*

EXAMPLE 1.   The sales manager of a corporation has six different one-day exhibits available for conventions. He is told to present plans to the board of directors for a three-day *or* a four-day convention, with a different exhibit for each day, and associated publicity corresponding to the order in which the exhibits are presented. How many different convention plans could he offer?

*Solution.    1.    Analysis.*    Each plan will consist of a set of

(a)    *three exhibits designated for days* 1, 2, *and* 3; **OR**
(b)    *four exhibits designated for days* 1, 2, 3, *and* 4.

Sets (a) and (b) are mutually exclusive.

2.    The number of plans of type (a) is the number of permutations of six things taken three at a time, or $6 \cdot 5 \cdot 4$, or 120.

3.    The number of plans of type (b) is $6 \cdot 5 \cdot 4 \cdot 3$, or 360.

4.    By the addition principle, the number of plans of type (a) *or* type (b) is (120 + 360), or 480.

## Exercise 27

*1.*  In John's advance planning for an evening, he considers dating either Helen or Marie, and he will invite Marie first. Either girl may accept or decline. If a girl accepts, he will offer to take her to a dance, a movie, or a jazz concert. If he takes a girl to a movie or the concert, then he also will take her to one or other of two restaurants for a midnight snack. If they go to the dance, they will not have a midnight snack. Form a decision tree for John's evening, and find the number of possible outcomes.

*2.*  The executive vice-president in a company must decide which of two forms of a new product will be manufactured. If form $A$ is produced, he will decide in which one of three regions the product will be promoted for market testing. Then, for any region, he will decide whether to distribute the product by use of door-to-door salesmen, or by use of mail-order selling. If form $B$ is manufactured, he will decide in which one of two regions it should be test-marketed, and otherwise as for plan $A$. Make up a decision tree to learn how many decisions might be made by the vice-president.

*3.*  How many number symbols of three digits each can be written by use of $\{1, 3, 5, 6\}$, (a) if all digits in the symbol are different; (b) if any digit may be used as often as desired; (c) if the digits are all different and the symbol represents an odd number?

*4.*  In how many ways can six people be seated if seven seats are available?

*5.*  (a)  Find the number of permutations (numbers) of the digits $\{1, 2, 3\}$ taken two or three at a time. (b)  Write out all of these permutations.

*6.*  How many permutations are there of the letters $\{a, b, c, d, e\}$ taken either three, four, or five at a time?

*7.*  Each of the four aldermen of a city council requires a secretary and a chauffeur. Six women apply for the secretarial jobs and five men for the jobs as chauffeurs. (*a*) In how many ways can all of the positions be filled? (*b*) In how many ways can the positions be filled for a particular alderman?

8.  A multiple choice form of an examination gives three responses, of which only one is correct, for each of the eight questions. (*a*) How many sets of answers for all of the questions are possible? (*b*) If a student is sure to answer the first six questions incorrectly, how many sets of answers for all of the questions could he give?

9.  The manager of a boutique specializing in sportswear has available for window display four types of bikinis, five varieties of tennis dresses, three kinds of beach bags, and three styles of slacks. In how many ways can he decide on a window display exhibiting (*a*) one of each variety in his stock; (*b*) one of each variety, or one of each type of clothing, with a bikini considered as clothing?

10.  Three travelers arrive in a town with five hotels. In how many ways can they (*a*) take up quarters; (*b*) take up quarters with each in a different hotel?

11.  At a neighborhood meeting to consider means to reduce student unrest in a school, speeches will be made by two administrators, two teachers, and three parents, with each person talking just once. In how many ways can the order of speakers be arranged, (*a*) with an administrator opening and closing the program; (*b*) with the administrators in succession first, the teachers second, and the parents third; (*c*) with the parents talking consecutively?

12.  In a race where eight horses will run, two jockeys will be women and six will be men. In how many ways can the horses be assigned starting positions counting from the pole (the inside edge of the track) (*a*) with a woman jockey at each end; (*b*) with the women consecutive; (*c*) with a woman jockey at each end, or with the women in consecutive positions?

13.  In how many ways can three students choose sections in registering for a course where five sections are available?

14.  How many numbers without repeated digits can be written by use of the digits {1, 2, 3, 4, 5}?

15.  By use of six flags of different colors, how many flag signals can be shown by a battleship if the signal mast has six positions, and any signal with less than six flags uses the top positions on the mast?

16.  If a cubical die* is tossed, in how many ways can it fall? If two dice are tossed together, in how many ways (*a*) can they fall; (*b*) can they fall showing a total of 2; 3; 4; 5; 6; 7; 8; 9; 10; 11; 12?

17.  A chemist is forming a liquid mixture of six compounds, {*A, B, C, D, E, F*}, by adding one at a time. He knows that *A*, and also *B*, must be added

---

* The die has faces numbered {1, 2, 3, 4, 5, 6}, as usual.

either first or last. He wishes to test the result for each order of adding components. How many different mixtures must he prepare?

18. A psychologist is experimenting on the effect on blood pressure if a subject is shown pictures, projected on a screen, designed to cause *anger*, *disgust*, or *nausea*. Also, he plans to observe the possible effect of quick repetition of such a stimulus. For each reaction emotion, he has three different pictures designed to produce it. For control, to check normal blood pressure for the subject, he has six different pictures of neutral interest. In how many sequences can he arrange his pictures for projection with the three for each emotion consecutive, and with two neutral pictures in succession preceding those for each emòtion?

## 46.   Formulas for numbers of permutations

Let $_nP_r$ represent the number of permutations of $n$ different things taken $r$ at a time. We read $_nP_r$ briefly as "*the number of permutations of n things taken r at a time.*"

THEOREM I.   $_nP_r = n(n - 1)(n - 2) \cdots [(n - (r - 1)]$.        (1)

We remember (1) as follows: "$_nP_r$ *is the product of r factors commencing with n and decreasing* 1 *at a time.*"

ILLUSTRATION 1.   $_7P_3 = 7 \cdot 6 \cdot 5 = 210$.

*Proof of* (1).   In any permutation of the $n$ things, we can fill the 1st place by any one of the $n$ things; then the 2d place by any one of the $(n - 1)$ things remaining after the 1st place is filled; then the 3d place by any one of the $(n - 2)$ remaining things; $\cdots$. Finally, when the last or $r$th place is to be filled, $(r - 1)$ places already have been filled so that only $[n - (r - 1)]$ things remain. Hence, the $r$th place can be filled in $[n - (r - 1)]$ ways. By the multiplication principle, the number of ways of filling the $r$ places in the permutation is the product of the numbers of ways which have been mentioned, as given in (1).

NOTE 1.   The symbol $n!$, called "$n$ **factorial**," is defined as the product of all positive integers from 1 to $n$ inclusive. Hence,

$$n! = 1 \cdot 2 \cdot 3 \cdots n.$$

Also, it proves convenient to define $0! = 1$. Thus,

$$5! = 1 \cdot 2 \cdot 3 \cdot 4 \cdot 5 = 120.$$

COROLLARY 1. *The number of permutations of n different things taken n at a time is n!*

$$_nP_n = n(n - 1)(n - 2) \cdots 3 \cdot 2 \cdot 1 = n!\qquad(2)$$

*Proof.* For $_nP_n$, the product in (1) has $n$ factors (one for each place to be filled). Hence, in filling the last or $n$th place, previously $(n - 1)$ things have been used so that only one remains, and the last factor in (1) is simply 1.

ILLUSTRATION 2.    $_5P_5 = 5 \cdot 4 \cdot 3 \cdot 2 \cdot 1 = 120$.

NOTE 2.    The student should remember that the multiplication principle of page 114 has much wider application than formulas (1) and (2), which were obtained by use of the principle.

EXAMPLE 1.    Protocol, or the necessity of taking account of seniority of service and assumed relative importance, requires that six ambassadors should be arranged in a certain order in the receiving line at a reception. If an uninformed social secretary neglects protocol, in how many different orders could he arrange the ambassadors?

*Solution.*    The result is $_6P_6 = 6! = 720$.

EXAMPLE 2.    In how many relative orders can six men be seated at a round table?

*Solution.*    Think of any one of the men as being seated first. Then, the number of relative orders is the number of distinct ways in which the five remaining men can be seated in five different places, or $_5P_5$, which is 120.

In Example 2, we were concerned with **circular permutations**, where the places to be filled are "*numbered*" only after a fixed basis location for observation of these places has been chosen. In ordinary permutations, to which formulas (1) and (2) apply, we may think of the places to be filled as being located in a *line*. Hence, such arrangements may be called **linear permutations**. By the method of Example 2, we obtain the following result.

THEOREM II.    *The number of cyclical permutations of n different things taken n at a time is $(n - 1)!$.*

EXAMPLE 3.    In how many relative orders can we seat three men and their wives around a table, with men and women alternating?

*Solution.    1.    Analysis.*    Think of any one of the men as seated. This specifies seats for the other men and for the women. Then:

(*a*)    *Seat the two remaining men in the seats for men.*

(*b*)    *Seat the three women in the seats for women.*

*2.*   Action (*a*) can be performed in $_2P_2$ or 2! ways, and action (*b*) in $_3P_3$ or 3! ways. Hence, by the multiplication principle, the number of relative orders for seating the men and women is (2!)(3!) or 12.

EXAMPLE 4.   A corporation decides to arrange a succession of publicity television programs for three hair sprays and four varieties of hair colorings on seven successive days, with only one item mentioned per day and the days for the hair sprays to be consecutive. In how many ways could the publicity department arrange the sequence of programs?

*Solution.   1.   Analysis.*   The days for the programs may be chosen by performing the following actions in succession:

(*a*)   *Select three successive days out of days* {1, 2, 3, 4, 5, 6, 7}.

(*b*)   *Specify one of these three days for each hair spray.*

(*c*)   *Specify one of the four other days for each hair coloring.*

*2.*   For action (*a*), we represent the seven days by the boxes in the following diagram. Three successive places may be picked at the extreme left; then these places may be altered, still successive, by moving the block of three

| 1 | 2 | 3 | 4 | 5 | 6 | 7 |
|---|---|---|---|---|---|---|

by one place to the right; then by another place to the right; etc. so that there are seen to be 5 ways of selecting three successive days.

*3.*   Action (*b*) can be performed in $_3P_3$ or 3! ways, and action (*c*) in $_4P_4$ or 4! ways. Hence, by the multiplication principle, (*a*), (*b*), and (*c*) can be performed in 5(3!)(4!), or 5(6)(24), or 720 ways.

EXAMPLE 5.   Find the number of distinct permutations of the letters {*a, a, a, b, c*} taken all at a time.

*Solution.   1.*   Let *P* be the desired number of permutations.

*2.*   First, consider {$a_1, a_2, a_3, b, c$} where the letters are all different. The number of permutations of these letters all at a time is 5! These permutations can be obtained as a result of the following successive actions:

(*i*)   *Take in turn each distinct permutation of* {*a, a, a, b, c*}.

(*ii*)   *In the locations occupied by the three identical letters* {*a, a, a*}, *place the three different letters* {$a_1, a_2, a_3$}.

*3.*   Action (*i*) can be performed in *P* ways. The number of ways of performing action (*ii*) is $_3P_3$ or 3! ways. Hence, actions (*i*) and (*ii*) can be performed in succession in $P \cdot (3!)$ ways, which we know is equal to 5! Therefore,

$$(3!)(P) = 5!, \quad or \quad P = \frac{5!}{3!} = \frac{120}{6} = 20.$$

The method of solution for Example 5 yields the following result.

THEOREM III.  *Let P be the number of distinct permutations of n things of which u are alike, v others are alike, etc. Then*

$$P = \frac{n!}{u! \, v! \cdots}.$$  (3)

In (3), the numerator is the number of permutations which would exist if all of the things were different. The divisor $u!$ is a consequence of the fact that permutations of the $u$ like things in their places would not give other distinguishable permutations, and similarly for the $v$ like things, etc. for other like things if present.

ILLUSTRATION 3.   The number of different numbers of seven digits each that can be written by use of {4, 4, 5, 5, 5, 3, 8} is

$$\frac{7!}{2! \, 3!} \quad or \quad \frac{1 \cdot 2 \cdot 3 \cdot 4 \cdot 5 \cdot 6 \cdot 7}{(1 \cdot 2)(1 \cdot 2 \cdot 3)} = 420,$$

because there are two 4's and three 5's.

## Exercise 28

*Read the symbol and calculate its value.*

*1.*  $_5P_2$.       *2.*  $_7P_3$.       *3.*  $_6P_6$.       *4.*  $_8P_4$.       *5.*  $_9P_3$.

*Find the number of distinct permutations of the digits or letters taken all at a time.*

*6.*  {2, 2, 4, 4, 4, 5}.              *7.*  {b, b, b, c, c, c, d, d}.

*8.*  The manager of a bookstore wishes to exhibit seven recent books in a row on a shelf. In how many ways can he display the books?

*9.*  Three Democrats and four Republicans who are candidates for local offices will speak at a women's club. In how many orders can the speakers be arranged, with the Democrats consecutive and the Republicans consecutive?

*10.*  How many distinct permutations are there of the letters in the word *illusion*?

*11.*  In how many ways can three apples and five oranges be distributed among eight children, with each child receiving a piece of fruit?

12. In how many ways can four men and four women be seated in a row of seven seats with men and women in alternate seats?

13. In an experiment to test the accuracy of preferences as to cigarettes of varieties $\{A, B, C\}$, each person of a group will be asked to smoke nine cigarettes in succession while blindfolded, and tell which of them he considers the best. The first three will be any permutation of $\{A, B, C\}$. The next three will be some other permutation of $\{A, B, C\}$. The last three will be a third permutation of $\{A, B, C\}$. In how many orders can the nine cigarettes be arranged?

14. A lazy teacher has read the examinations of fifteen students and has graded five A, five B, and five C. He decides to give the same proportion of A's, B's, and C's at random to the examinations of the nine remaining students, without reading their papers. In how many ways could he assign the grades?

15. Six girls are to be seated around a table, and then a boy will be assigned to stand behind each girl. In how many different ways can couples thus be arranged, if only their relative order around the table is of importance?

16. In how many ways can three men and three women be assigned positions as the first three couples in a grand march?

17. In how many ways can the hats of three men be handed back to men at a checkroom so that no man will receive his own hat? (No formula applies.)

    NOTE 1. A *complete permutation* of the integers $\{1, 2, 3, 4, \cdots, n\}$ is defined as a permutation in which *no integer remains in its place in the natural order*. Let $\eta_n$ represent this number of complete permutations. In Problem 17, the result is $\eta_3$.

★18. Prove that, if $n \geq 3$, $\eta_n$ of Note 1 satisfies the recursion formula

$$\eta_n = (n - 1)\eta_{n-1} + (n - 1)\eta_{n-2}.$$

Also, show that $\eta_1 = 0$, and $\eta_2 = 1$. Then find $\eta_3$, $\eta_4$, and $\eta_5$.

★19. In how many ways can six men and their wives be matched by lot as partners for a dance so that no man obtains his wife for a partner?

## 47. Formulas for the number of subsets of a set

Frequently we shall refer to any subset of a given set of elements as a *combination* of the elements. Recall that, in referring to a subset or combination of elements, no relative order is assigned to the elements.

ILLUSTRATION 1. The different combinations of the set of letters $\{t, u, v, w\}$ taken three at a time are

$$\{t, u, v\}; \quad \{t, v, w\}; \quad \{t, u, w\}; \quad \{u, v, w\}. \tag{1}$$

From each combination in (1), we can form 3! or 6 permutations of the four letters taken three at a time. Since there are 4 combinations in (1), we thus obtain 4 × 6 or 24 permutations of the letters taken three at a time. If we let $C$ be the number of combinations in (1), and $P$ be the number of permutations just mentioned, then we have seen that $P = C \cdot 6!$, or $C = P/6!$ This illustrates the following result, which is used to calculate numbers of combinations.

THEOREM IV.   *The number of combinations of n elements taken r at a time, or $_nC_r$, is equal to the number of permutations of these elements taken r at a time divided by r!.*

*Proof.   1.*   All *permutations* of the $n$ elements taken $r$ at a time can be formed by carrying out the following actions in all possible ways.

(*a*)   *Form a combination of r elements selected from the n elements.*

(*b*)   *Form a permutation of the selected r elements taken r at a time.*

2.   The number of ways of performance for action (*a*) is $_nC_r$, and for action (*b*) is $r!$. We know that the number of ways of performing "(*a*) *and* (*b*)" is $_nP_r$. Hence, by the multiplication principle,

$$_nP_r = {_nC_r} \cdot r!, \qquad or \qquad _nC_r = \frac{_nP_r}{r!}. \tag{2}$$

EXAMPLE 1.   From the twelve members of the board of directors of a corporation, in how many ways can the chairman of the board appoint (*a*) a committee of five members; (*b*) fill the positions of treasurer, legal director, and vice-presidents in charge of finance, sales, and foreign subsidiaries?

*Solution.   (a)*   A *committee* is a *subset* of the board. The number of subsets of the specified size is $_{12}C_5$. We use (2) and obtain

$$_{12}C_5 = \frac{_{12}P_5}{5!} = \frac{12 \cdot 11 \cdot 10 \cdot 9 \cdot 8}{1 \cdot 2 \cdot 3 \cdot 4 \cdot 5} = 792, \tag{3}$$

where cancellation indicates division by common factors. Thus, 792 choices are possible.

(*b*)   The number of ways is the number of permutations of 12 things taken 5 at a time, or $_{12}P_5$. From the numerator in (3), we obtain $_{12}P_5 = 95{,}040$.

If a subset of $r$ elements is *chosen* from a set of $n$ elements, then a subset of $(n - r)$ of the elements is *left*. Hence, the number of ways of specifying subsets of $r$ elements each is the same as the number of ways of specifying subsets of $(n - r)$ elements each, or

$$_nC_{(n-r)} = {_nC_r}. \tag{4}$$

Relation (4) is convenient for use if $r$ is near $n$, and $n$ is large. We could also prove (4) by use of (5) below. The student may do this later as an exercise.

ILLUSTRATION 2.   The number of ways in which a subset of 498 people can be selected from a group of 500 people is (because $500 - 498 = 2$),

$$_{500}C_{498} = {}_{500}C_2 = \frac{_{500}P_2}{2!} = \frac{(500)(499)}{2} = 124{,}750.$$

THEOREM V.    $\qquad {}_nC_r = \dfrac{n!}{r!\,(n-r)!}.$    (5)

*Proof.*   From (2), and then (1) on page 121,

$$_nC_r = \frac{_nP_r}{r!} = \frac{n(n-1)(n-2)\cdots(n-r+1)}{r!}.$$    (6)

In (6), multiply both numerator and denominator on the right by the product $1\cdot2\cdot3\cdots(n-r)$, or $(n-r)!$. We obtain

$$_nC_r = \frac{1\cdot2\cdot3\cdots(n-r)(n-r+1)\cdots(n-2)(n-1)n}{r!\,(n-r)!}.$$    (7)

Observe that the numerator in (7) is $n!$. Hence (5) is true.

ILLUSTRATION 3.   From (5),

$$_7C_3 = \frac{7!}{(3!)(4!)} = \frac{1\cdot2\cdot3\cdot4\cdot5\cdot6\cdot7}{1\cdot2\cdot3\cdot1\cdot2\cdot3\cdot4} = 35,$$

where preliminary cancellation of common factors simplified the arithmetic.

EXAMPLE 2.   If six coins are tossed, in how many ways can it result that four coins fall heads and two fall tails?

*Solution.*   To obtain any case where exactly four fall heads, we conceive of performing the following successive actions:

(a)   *select a combination of four coins from the six coins;*

(b)   *place the selected four coins on a table with their heads up;*

(c)   *place the other two coins on the table with tails up.*

Action (a) can be performed in $_6C_4$ ways; action (b) in one way; action (c) in one way. Hence, by the multiplication principle, the number of ways for performing (a), (b), and (c) is $_6C_4 \cdot 1 \cdot 1$ or $_6C_4$, or 15.

The symbol $\binom{n}{r}$ is used frequently instead of $_nC_r$. We shall use $\binom{n}{r}$ as well as $_nC_r$, which is more convenient in printing. For future reference, we note that

$$_nC_r = \frac{n!}{r!\,(n-r)!} = \binom{n}{r}. \tag{8}$$

In place of $_nP_r$, sometimes $P_{n,r}$ or $P_r^{(n)}$ is used.

## 48.  Problem Analysis

In any complicated problem involving preceding methods of this chapter, a preliminary analysis of the problem into simple stages is desirable. In particular, the key words **AND** and **OR** in various verbal statements should be recognized as implying use of the multiplication principle and the addition principle, respectively.

ILLUSTRATION 1.   Suppose that a room contains 6 men, 5 women, and 4 children. By the addition principle, we can select a woman **OR** a child in $(5 + 4)$ or 9 ways. By the multiplication principle, we can select a woman **AND** a child in $5 \times 4$ or 20 ways. The key words AND and OR led to use of the corresponding principles.

EXAMPLE 1.   From a set of 5 women and 7 men, in how many ways can we select a subset of (*a*) 4 men alone OR 3 women alone; (*b*) 4 men AND 3 women?

*Solution.   1.*   The number of ways of selecting a subset of 4 men is $_7C_4$, and for a subset of 3 women is $_5C_3$.

*2.*   By the addition principle, a group of 4 men alone or 3 women alone can be selected in $(_7C_4 + _5C_3)$ ways, or $(35 + 10)$ or 45 ways.

*3.*   By the multiplication principle, the number of ways of selecting a subset of 4 men AND 3 women is $(_7C_4)(_5C_3)$ or $(35)(10)$ or 350 ways.

EXAMPLE 2.   How many numbers of five different digits each can be written if each number involves two odd and three even digits and no digit 0?

*Solution.   1.   Analysis.*   In writing any number of the required type we may:

(*a*)   *choose a subset of two odd digits from* $\{1, 3, 5, 7, 9\}$*; and then*

(*b*)   *choose a subset of three even digits from* $\{2, 4, 6, 8\}$*; and then*

(*c*)   *form a number by writing a permutation of the five digits chosen in* (*a*) *and* (*b*).

*2.* We can perform (*a*) in $_5C_2$ or 10 ways; (*b*) in $_4C_3$ or 4 ways; (*c*) in $_5P_5$ or 5! or 120 ways. Hence, by the multiplication principle, we can perform (*a*), (*b*), and (*c*) in $10 \times 4 \times 120$ or 4800 ways.

EXAMPLE 3.    A set of fourteen men consists of eight Democrats and six Republicans. In how many ways can committees of five each be selected from the group, if the committee is to contain at least three Democrats?

*Solution.    1.    Analysis.*    The committee (or subset) will contain at least three Democrats if it contains

(*a*)    EXACTLY 3 Democrats and 2 Republicans; or,

(*b*)    EXACTLY 4 Democrats and 1 Republican; or,

(*c*)    EXACTLY 5 Democrats.

*2.* The subsets of types (*a*), (*b*), and (*c*) are mutually exclusive sets. Hence, we shall find the number of ways for occurrence of (*a*), (*b*), and (*c*), respectively, and add the results, because of the addition principle.

*3.* We can choose subsets of 3 Democrats in $_8C_3$ ways; subsets of 2 Republicans in $_6C_2$ ways. Hence, by the multiplication principle, (*a*) can be done in $(_8C_3)(_6C_2)$ ways. Similar results are obtained for (*b*) and (*c*). Hence, the number of ways for forming committees as specified is

$$(_8C_3)(_6C_2) + (_8C_4)(_6C_1) + {}_8C_5, \quad or \quad 1316.$$

We now have at our disposal four methods for calculating the numbers of outcomes of actions: the multiplication principle of page 114, and the addition principle of page 118; methods phrased in the terminology of permutations, and methods described in the language of combinations. It is instructive then to solve problems of a miscellaneous nature where preliminary analysis, as in preceding problems, should indicate which method or methods should be employed.

## Exercise 29

*1.*    Write out (*a*) all combinations of {2, 4, 6, 8} taken three at a time; (*b*) all permutations of {2, 4, 6, 8} taken three at a time.

*2.*    Read each symbol in words and compute it: $_6C_2$; $_6C_4$; $_5C_5$; $_{10}C_6$.

*3.*    From a group of seven people, in how many ways can we form a committee (*a*) of four each; (*b*) of four or five each?

*4.*    A questionnaire for voters during a political campaign lists seven possible issues. A voter is asked (*a*) to select the three issues which he considers most important; (*b*) to arrange the seven issues in what he thinks is their order of importance. In how many ways can he respond to (*a*)? To (*b*)?

5.  In preparing for a program of five disconnected lectures, a visiting professor has ten lecture subjects available. (*a*) In how many ways can he specify a sequence of five lectures? (*b*) In how many ways can he prepare a list of topics for five lectures, with the order of presentation not involved?

6.  If six coins are tossed together, in how many ways can they fall?

7.  From a set of five elements, how many subsets can be formed where each subset consists (*a*) of three elements; (*b*) of four elements or five elements?

8.  In a sociological experiment, the person being interviewed is presented with nine alternatives of which five are consistent with a certain opinion and four are inconsistent with it. In how many ways can he select (*a*) three alternatives which are consistent with the opinion; (*b*) four alternatives, of which at least two are consistent with the opinion?

9.  From a suit of thirteen playing cards, (*a*) how many hands of five cards each can be dealt to a player; (*b*) how many of these hands will include the king; (*c*) how many of the hands specified in (*a*) will include the ace and king?

10. In how many ways can (*a*) six presents be given to four children; (*b*) five presents be given to six children?

11. A bag contains six black, five white, and seven red balls.* In how many ways can we select sets of balls consisting of (*a*) three black or three red balls; (*b*) three black and three red balls; (*c*) three balls all of the same color; (*d*) three balls of each color?

12. If five coins are tossed together (or, in succession), in how many ways can it result that (*a*) all fall tails; (*b*) exactly two fall tails; (*c*) at least two fall tails?

13. In how many relative orders can six people be seated at a round table with a certain three people (*a*) in consecutive chairs; (*b*) not in consecutive chairs?

14. A university is organized into colleges of liberal arts, business administration, education, technology, agriculture, law, dentistry, and medicine. Students who are registered in these colleges are classified as to residence (in-state, out-of-state, foreign); as to college year (freshman, sophomore, junior, senior, graduate); as to housing arrangements (dormitory, off-campus). In a statistical study concerning the students, the statistician will first "*code*" them by assigning numbers $\{1, 2, 3, \cdots\}$ to each of the possible classifications or "*cells*" into which they fall, according to the college in which they are registered and the other information. How many cells are there?

---

* Indistinguishable except as to color. This assumption is implied also in any later problem in the text about bags of balls.

15. From a set of six elements, how many nonempty subsets can be formed?

16. In how many ways can nine different presents be distributed to three children, with each one to receive three presents?

17. From a group of five representatives of labor, four of business, and six of the general public, how many committees of six each can be formed consisting of two people from each group?

18. A shipment of thirty television sets including four defective sets is received by a retailer. He will select four of the sets at random and check them carefully. He will reject the shipment if he finds one or more defective sets in his sample. In how many ways could samples of four sets each be obtained which would cause rejection of the shipment?

19. A manufacturer wishes to learn the relative appeal of four types $\{A, B, C, D\}$ of tooth paste, with each type offered in three common flavors. In retail stores where all of these varieties are being advertised, each customer is encouraged to take three tubes of tooth paste of different types or flavors free, and the choices will be recorded in order to detect preferences. If a customer were to select his three tubes at random from the twelve available varieties, in how many ways could he choose (*a*) all of one type, *A*, *B*, *C*, or *D*; (*b*) all of one flavor; (*c*) just two of one type regardless of flavor?

20. A number of four different digits will be written by use of the digits $\{1, 2, 3, 4, 5, 6\}$. (*a*) How many can be written? (*b*) In how many of these will the digits be in their natural order, from left to right?

21. How many distinguishable combinations can be formed of the digits $\{4, 4, 4, 5, 6, 8\}$ taken three at a time?

## 49.  The binomial theorem

It will be seen that the binomial theorem is an essential element in the discussion of probability and mathematical statistics, even at elementary levels. The theorem will be developed in this section from a viewpoint employing our previous consideration of counting subsets of a given set. First, we shall recall elementary aspects of the expansion of a power such as $(u + v)^n$, where $n$ will be a positive integer throughout this section.

By multiplication, we obtain the following results, which the student should verify.

$$(u + v)^3 = (u + v)(u + v)(u + v) = (u + v)^2(u + v)$$
$$= (u^2 + 2uv + v^2)(u + v)$$
$$= u^3 + 3u^2v + 3uv^3 + v^3,$$

and similarly for $(u + v)^4$. Thus,

$$u + v = u + v;$$
$$(u + v)^2 = u^2 + 2uv + v^2;$$
$$(u + v)^3 = u^3 + 3u^2v + 3uv^2 + v^3;$$
$$(u + v)^4 = u^4 + 4u^3v + 6u^2v^2 + 4uv^3 + v^4.$$

If $n = 1, 2, 3,$ or $4$, the expansion of $(u + v)^n$ is seen to contain $(n + 1)$ terms with the following properties:

(I)  *In any term, the sum of the exponents of u and v is n.*

(II)  *The first term is $u^n$ and, in each succeeding term, the exponent of u is 1 less than in the preceding term.*

(III)  *The second term is $nu^{n-1}$ and, in each succeeding term, the exponent of v is 1 more than in the preceding term.*

(IV)  *If the coefficient of any term is multiplied by the exponent of u in the term and is divided by the number of that term, counting from the left, the result is the coefficient of the next term.*

(V)  *The coefficients of terms equidistant from the ends are equal.*

ILLUSTRATION 1.    In the expansion of $(u + v)^4$, the 3d term is $6u^2v^2$. By (IV), the coefficient of the 4th term is $(6 \times 2) \div 3$ or 4, which checks.

A proof of properties (I)–(V) will occur later.

ILLUSTRATION 2.    By use of (I)–(V),

$$(u + v)^6 = u^6 + 6u^5v + \quad u^4v^2 + \quad u^3v^3 + \quad u^2v^4 + 6uv^5 + v^6,$$

where spaces are left for unknown coefficients. By (IV), the coefficient of the 3d term is $(6 \times 5) \div 2$, or 15. Then the coefficient of the 4th term is $(15 \times 4) \div 3$, or 20. By (V), the coefficient of the 5th term is the same as the coefficient of the 3d term, or 15. Hence,

$$(u + v)^6 = u^6 + 6u^5v + 15u^4v^2 + 20u^3v^3 + 15u^2v^4 + 6uv^5 + v^6.$$

By use of (I)–(V), we obtain the following expansion, which is referred to as the **binomial formula**, or the **binomial theorem**.

$$\left.\begin{aligned} (u + v)^n = u^n + nu^{n-1}v + \frac{n(n-1)}{2!} u^{n-2}v^2 + \cdots \\ + \frac{n(n-1)\cdots(n-r+1)}{r!} u^{n-r}v^r + \cdots + v^n. \end{aligned}\right\} \quad (1)$$

*Proof of* (1).    (*For the case $n = 5$ for convenience.*)    *1.*    By the definition of an exponent,

$$(u + v)^5 = (u + v)(u + v)(u + v)(u + v)(u + v). \quad (2)$$

The expansion of the product on the right in (2) consists of all terms obtained by taking, in all possible ways, one term $u$ or $v$ from each factor and multiplying the resulting five numbers. In this fashion, the following types of terms are obtained:

$$u^5; \quad u^4v; \quad u^3v^2; \quad u^2v^3; \quad uv^4; \quad v^5. \tag{3}$$

*2.* The term $u^5$ in (3) will be obtained by selecting $u$ from each factor on the right in (2), and multiplying these five $u$'s. This can be done in just *one way*. Hence, in the expansion of (2), the coefficient of $u^5$ is 1.

*3.* The term $u^4v$ in (3) will be obtained by selecting a *subset* of one $v$ from the set of five $v$'s in the factors on the right in (2), and then multiplying by $u$ as selected from each of the other factors. The number of ways of doing this is $_5C_1$ or 5, which then is the coefficient of $u^4v$ in the expansion of (2). Or, the term $_5C_1u^4v$ is obtained.

*4.* The term $u^3v^2$ in (3) is obtained by selecting a subset of two $v$'s from the set of five $v$'s in the factors on the right in (2), and multiplying their product by the $u$'s selected from the other three factors. The number of ways of doing this, or of obtaining $u^3v^2$, is $_5C_2$. Hence, the term $_5C_2u^3v^2$ will occur in the expansion of (2).

*5.* For any value of $r \leq 5$, the term $u^{5-r}v^r$ in the expansion of (2) is obtained by selecting a subset of $r$ letters $v$ from the five $v$'s in factors on the right in (2), and multiplying these $r$ numbers $v$ by the $(5 - r)$ numbers $u$ in the other factors. The number of ways of doing this is $_5C_r$, and thus the term $_5C_ru^{5-r}v^r$ will be obtained.

*6.* The expansion of (2) consists of the sum of terms involving all products of the types in (3), with coefficients as just discussed. Hence,

$$(u + v)^5 = u^5 + {}_5C_1u^4v + {}_5C_2u^3v^2 + {}_5C_3u^2v^3 + {}_5C_4uv^4 + v^5.$$

ILLUSTRATION 3. We have $_5C_1 = 5$, $_5C_2 = 10$, etc. Thus, we obtain

$$(u + v)^5 = u^5 + 5u^4v + 10u^3v^2 + 10u^3v^3 + 5uv^4 + v^5.$$

If the method of the preceding proof is applied to $(u + v)^n$, we obtain

$$\left. \begin{aligned} (u + v)^n = u^n + {}_nC_1u^{n-1}v + {}_nC_2u^{n-2}v^2 + \cdots \\ + {}_nC_ru^{n-r}v^r + \cdots + {}_nC_{n-1}uv^{n-1} + v^n. \end{aligned} \right\} \tag{4}$$

By use of (6) on page 127,

$$_nC_r = \frac{_nP_r}{r!} = \frac{n(n - 1)(n - 2) \cdots (n - r + 1)}{r!}.$$

This shows that the coefficients of the general terms involving $u^{n-r}v^r$ in (1) and (4) are identical. We intend to use (4) rather than (1) hereafter.

ILLUSTRATION 4.   By use of (4),

$$(2x - 3y)^6 = (2x)^6 + {}_6C_1(2x)^5(-3y)^1 + {}_6C_2(2x)^4(-3y)^2 + {}_6C_3(2x)^3(-3y)^3$$
$$+ {}_6C_4(2x)^2(-3y)^4 + {}_6C_5(2x)(-3y)^5 + (-3y)^6.$$

We have ${}_6C_1 = 6$, ${}_6C_2 = 15$, ${}_6C_3 = 20$, ${}_6C_4 = 15$, etc. Hence, after computing various products, we obtain

$$(2x - 3y)^6 = 64x^6 - 576x^5y + 2160x^4y^2 - 4320x^3y^3$$
$$+ 4860x^2y^4 - 2916xy^5 + 729y^6.$$

ILLUSTRATION 5.   In (4), suppose that $u = v = 1$. Then ${}_nC_r u^{n-r}v^r = {}_nC_r$. Hence, from (4),

$$(1 + 1)^n = 1 + {}_nC_1 + {}_nC_2 + \cdots + {}_nC_n, \quad or$$
$${}_nC_1 + {}_nC_2 + \cdots + {}_nC_n = 2^n - 1. \tag{5}$$

ILLUSTRATION 6.   The *subsets* which can be formed from a set $E$ of $n$ elements consist of the empty set $\varnothing$, the subsets of *one* element each, of *two* elements each, $\cdots$, of $n$ elements, or $E$ itself. The number of these subsets is, by (5),

$$1 + {}_nC_1 + {}_nC_2 + \cdots + {}_nC_n = 2^n, \tag{6}$$

where the term 1 in (6) corresponds to $\varnothing$. Thus, the number of subsets of a set of six elements is $2^6$ or 64.

The following diagram is called **Pascal's triangle**. The rows show the coefficients in the successive positive integral powers of $(u + v)$. To form any row after the first row, place 1 at the *left*; obtain the 2d number by adding the *first two numbers in the preceding row*; then add its 2d and 3d numbers to find the 3d number in the new row; etc. The triangle was known to Chinese mathematicians early in the 14th century.*

```
                    1
                1       1
            1       2       1
        1       3       3       1
    1       4       6       4       1
1       5      10      10       5       1
            .   .   .   .   .   .
```

* For proof of the facts about Pascal's triangle see page 302 in *College Algebra, Fifth Edition*, by William L. Hart; D. C. Heath and Company, publishers.

If $(u + v)^n$ is desired with a reasonably small value of $n$, it is more convenient to obtain the coefficients in the expansion by quickly constructing part of Pascal's triangle, rather than to use (4).

★ NOTE 1.    Properties (I)–(V) of page 132 can be established by use of (4). Observe that (I) and (II) are simple consequences of the fact that $(u + v)^n$ is the product of $n$ factors $(u + v)$. In (4), the second term is $_nC_1u^{n-1}v = nu^{n-1}v$, which proves (III). Any two successive terms in (4) are of the forms

$$_nC_ru^{n-r}v^r \qquad and \qquad _nC_{r+1}u^{n-r-1}v^{r+1}. \tag{7}$$

From (6) on page 127, with $r$ replaced by $(r + 1)$,

$$_nC_{r+1} = \frac{n(n-1)(n-2)\cdots[n-(r-1)](n-r)}{(r!)(r+1)} = \frac{n-r}{r+1}\,_nC_r,$$

which proves (IV) on page 132. Any two terms in (4) equidistant from the ends are of the forms $_nC_ru^{n-r}v^r$ and $_nC_{(n-r)}u^rv^{n-r}$. From (4) on page 126, we recall that $_nC_r = {_nC_{(n-r)}}$. This proves (V) on page 132. Hence, all of (I)–(V) are consequences of (4).

In our later discussion of probability, sometimes we shall desire only one term or perhaps a few terms from a binomial expansion. Hence it is useful to focus on the following fact, where we agree to **define** $_nC_0 = 1$.

*The term of* $(u + v)^n$ *involving* $v^r$ *is* $_nC_ru^{n-r}v^r$. $\qquad\qquad$ (8)

ILLUSTRATION 7.    By use of (8) with $n = 6$ and $r = 4$, the term of the expansion of $(p + q)^6$ with the factor $q^4$ is $_6C_4p^2q^4 = {_6C_2}p^2q^4 = 15p^2q^4$.

NOTE 2.    The use of the symbol $_nC_r$ in connection with the binomial expansion is so important that, frequently, $_nC_r$ is referred to as the $r$th *binomial coefficient* in the expansion of $(u + v)^n$.

In a problem in the next chapter, it will be proved that, if $n \geq 2$, the *largest coefficient* of the terms in (4) occurs at the *middle term if n is even*, and at each of the *two middle terms if n is odd*. These results can be expected on account of the manner in which Pascal's triangle is formed.

## Exercise 30

*Write out the expansion of the power by use of combination symbols and then compute the coefficients. Check by use of Pascal's triangle.*

1. $(a + b)^4$.    2. $(u - v)^6$.    3. $(x + y)^7$.    4. $(x^2 - y)^3$.
5. $(2u^2 + v^3)^5$.    6. $(x^{1/2} - y)^4$.    7. $(3u + v)^6$.    8. $(a - 3b)^4$.

*Obtain only the specified term in the expansion of the power of the binomial.*

9. $(u + v)^7$; term involving $v^5$.    10. $(p + q)^{10}$; term involving $p^5$.
11. $(x - 2y)^6$; term involving $y^3$.    12. $(1 + .03)^5$; term involving $(.03)^3$.

13. The fifth term of $(2u - v)^8$ in ascending powers of $v$.

14. The middle term of $(u - v)^8$.

15. Calculate the largest coefficient in the expansion of $(a + b)^{10}$.

16. Calculate the largest absolute value possessed by the coefficients in the expansion of $(a - b)^9$.

17. How many subsets can be formed from a set of seven elements?

18. How many different sums of money consisting of one or more coins each can be formed by use of a cent, a nickel, a dime, a quarter, a half dollar, and a dollar bill?

19. A politician has been emphasizing five main issues in his campaign. In preparing for a particular speech, he can choose to discuss all issues or only some of them. How many options does he have as to subject matter?

★20. By use of the symbol $_nC_4$ and the method used to prove (1) on page 132, obtain the expansion of $(x + y + z)^4$; $(x + y + z)^n$.

# 7 | PROBABILITY FOR A FINITE SAMPLE SPACE

## 50. Introduction to probability

The language of probability is in use colloquially as a means for expressing varying degrees of confidence in the possibility that an uncertain event will occur. In common usage, if it is said that an event is *likely to occur*, or that it *probably will occur*, this is taken to mean that its "*probability of occurrence*" is relatively large, even though no particular value of the probability may be implied. However, the familiar language of "*odds*," as employed in games of chance, or in betting at horse races, provides a numerical setting for colloquial references to probabilities. In the mathematical basis of the next section, the probability of an event will be defined as a number $p$ with $0 \leq p \leq 1$, where the event is *certain* to occur when $p = 1$. Intuitional reactions to probability will remain valuable when the mathematical foundation is employed. This is true because the basis adopts some of the colloquial language about probability, and employs definitions of the terminology which are consistent with intuitional meanings.

Although colloquial use of probability occurs largely in connection with games of chance, such use of probability is only of minor importance as compared to other applications in many branches of both pure and applied mathematics. In particular, substantial segments of the theory of statistics are best considered as parts of the field of probability. For instance, the present chapter may be thought of as a first stage in the development of that part of statistical theory dealing with probability.

It is customary to speak of mathematical *models* for defining probability. In any model, the basis involves some set, $T$, of undefined elements, where $T$ is called the *sample space*. In this chapter, we shall consider the model where the sample space is *finite*. Other models exist where the sample space consists of infinitely many outcomes. One model of this variety will be presented in the last chapter of the text.

NOTE 1.   The earliest developments in the mathematical field of probability were induced by interest in games of chance. Some results in the field were first obtained in the 16th century by the Italian mathematician GERONIMO CARDANO (1501–1576), who is famous mainly for his achievements in the solution of equations of degrees three and four in algebra. The Swiss mathematician JAKOB BERNOULLI (1654–1705) may be regarded as the founder of probability as a branch of mathematics. In a posthumous book entitled *Ars conjectandi*, published in 1713, he aimed at a fusion of so-called "*a priori*" probability (to be discussed in this chapter) and early statistical theory based on observation of past trials of an experiment (*a posteriori* methods, to be met on page 152).

## 51.   Definition of probability for a finite sample space

Let $W$ be a finite set of $n$ elements, and let $u$ be a variable whose domain is $W$. Thus $W = \{u\}$, which is read " *W is the set of elements u.*" As an aid to intuition, $W$ will be thought of as the set of possible outcomes of a *random experiment* which, at each performance, produces an outcome $u$ of $W$. When this terminology is used, it is implied that a concept of *probability* will be defined for subsets of $W$. Also, $W$ will be called the **sample space** associated with this concept. Let $E$ be any subset of $W$. Then $E$ is referred to as an **event** which is made possible by the performance of the random experiment. When a particular outcome $\hat{u}$ of the sample space $W$ is examined, it is said that $E$ *occurs* if $\hat{u}$ is in $E$, and then $\hat{u}$ is called a *success* relative to $E$. If $\hat{u}$ is *not* in $E$, that is, if $\hat{u}$ is in the complement* $E'$ of $E$, then $\hat{u}$ is called a *failure* relative to $E$. Thus, $W$ consists of $s$ outcomes in $E$ which are successes, and $f$ outcomes in $E'$ which are failures relative to $E$. In particular, the empty set, $\varnothing$, is an event in $W$, and $W$ itself is an event consisting of *all* outcomes of the random experiment.

DEFINITION I.   *Corresponding to each outcome u of the finite sample space W, let there be assigned a positive number $p_u$, to be called the* **probability** *of u, where the sum of all numbers $p_u$ is 1. Then, the probability of any event E (a subset of W) is defined as the sum of the probabilities of those outcomes of W which are in E.*

Let $P$ be a function whose domain is all subsets of $W$. Then, for any subset $E$ of $W$, we let $P(E)$ represent *the probability of E*, and refer to $P$ as the

* See page 30 for the definition of $E'$.

**probability function** for the sample space $W$. We read "$P(E)$" simply as "$P$ of $E$," as is customary with functional notation, or more fully as "*the probability of E*." Since $W$ is a subset of itself, and consists of *all* of the outcomes, we have $P(W) = 1$, because of Definition I. Also, $P(\varnothing) = 0$ because $\varnothing$ has *no elements*. Observe that probability in $W$ has been defined as a *function of sets of outcomes*. For any sample space $W$, the set of values of $P(E)$, or the range of $P$, consists of a set of nonnegative numbers not greater than 1, including 0 and 1.

ILLUSTRATION 1.    Let the random experiment be the tossing of a common die with faces numbered $1, 2, \cdots, 6$, respectively. If the die is tossed, it will fall with a numbered face up, and we shall speak, for instance, of "*tossing the number 5*," to mean that the face numbered 5 is up. First, suppose that the experimenter assigns the probability $\frac{1}{6}$ to each of the six possible outcomes. Let $E$ be the event of tossing more than 3. Then $E$ consists of the tosses of 4, 5, and 6, and $P(E) = \frac{1}{6} + \frac{1}{6} + \frac{1}{6} = \frac{1}{2}$. As a new basis for probability, suppose that the die is biased or loaded, and that the experimenter assigns the probabilities $\{\frac{1}{3}, \frac{1}{12}, \frac{1}{6}, \frac{1}{12}, \frac{1}{6}, \frac{1}{6}\}$ to the tosses of $\{1, 2, 3, 4, 5, 6\}$, respectively. Let $E$ be the event of tossing at most 4. Then $E$ consists of the tosses of 1, 2, 3, and 4; $P(E) = \frac{1}{3} + \frac{1}{12} + \frac{1}{6} + \frac{1}{12} = \frac{2}{3}$.

In Definition I, each element $u$ is a *subset* of $W$ consisting of just *one* element. Hence, with $u$ representing not only a particular element but also the *subset* consisting of $u$ alone, we have $P(u) = p_u$.

For any event $E$ of a sample space $W$, the complementary event "*not E*," or $E'$ consists of those elements of $W$ which are *failures* relative to $E$. Thus, the union of $E$ and $E'$ consists of all elements in $W$, or $E \cup E' = W$. Hence, $[P(E) + P(E')]$ is the sum of the probabilities of all elements of $W$, so that

$$P(E) + P(E') = 1. \tag{1}$$

Or, the probability of *success* for $E$ plus the probability of *failure* for $E$ is 1.

It will be said that $E$ is *certain to occur* at any trial of the random experiment if $P(E) = 1$. This is equivalent to stating that $E = W$, and $E' = \varnothing$, so that the probability of failure of $E$ is 0, or $P(E') = 0$. To say that $E$ is *certain to fail* at any trial of the random experiment means that $P(E) = 0$. In this case, by (1), we have $P(E') = 1$ or $E' = W$, and thus $E$ is the empty set.

To state that the outcomes in a sample space $W$ are **equally likely** will mean that they have been assigned *equal probabilities*. Thus, if $W$ has $n$ equally likely outcomes, each of them has the probability $1/n$, which is the total probability of $W$ divided by $n$.

THEOREM I.    *Assume that the n outcomes of the sample space W are* **equally likely**. *If an event E consists of s outcomes (successes), and E' consists* *of f outcomes (failures), so that n = s + f, then the probability of success for E is*

$$P(E) = \frac{s}{n} = p, \tag{2}$$

*and the probability of E failing to occur is*

$$P(E') = \frac{f}{n} = q. \tag{3}$$

*Moreover,* $\qquad\qquad\qquad p + q = 1. \tag{4}$

*Proof.* The probability of each outcome is $1/n$. Therefore $P(E) = (1/n)s = s/n$. Similarly, since $E'$ consists of $f$ outcomes, $P(E') = (1/n)f = f/n$. From (2) and (3), we obtain

$$p + q = \frac{s}{n} + \frac{f}{n} = \frac{s+f}{n} = \frac{n}{n}, \quad or \quad p + q = 1,$$

as in (4). If $E$ is *certain to occur* at a trial of the random experiment, then $s = n$ and $p = 1$, with $q = 0$. If $E$ is *certain to fail* at any trial, then $s = 0$, with $p = 0$ and $q = 1$.

Hereafter in this chapter, unless otherwise stated in a problem, assume that the outcomes for any experiment are *equally likely.* However, a reasonable number of problems will be met where the outcomes are *not* equally likely. This case is absolutely essential for the development of statistics. Sometimes, to give special emphasis to the fact that the outcomes of an experiment are to be taken as equally likely, it may be stated that the experiment is performed *at random.*

ILLUSTRATION 2.   Suppose that a box contains five white balls and ten red balls. Then, by (2), if a ball is drawn at random, the probability that it is white is $\frac{5}{15}$ or $\frac{1}{3}$.

In the application of Definition I to a particular situation, first a decision should be made as to the *random experiment* which is involved, and the outcomes should be assigned probabilities. If $P(E)$ is to be obtained in a case where Theorem I applies, it is necessary to compute, separately, the number $s$ of *successful outcomes* in $E$, and $n$, the *total number of outcomes* for the experiment.

EXAMPLE 1.   A bag contains six balls and four cubes. If we draw four objects at random from the bag together (or, in succession *without replacement* after each draw), find the probability that (*a*) two are balls and two are cubes; (*b*) all are balls or all are cubes; (*c*) at most two are balls.

*Solution.   1.* The *random experiment* is that four objects are drawn. The number of outcomes in the sample space is $_{10}C_4 = 210$. The outcomes are considered equally likely, so that (2) applies.

*2.* Let $E_1$ be event (*a*). *Successful outcomes:* the number of ways of drawing two balls and two cubes is $(_6C_2)(_4C_2) = 90$. Hence $P(E_1) = \frac{90}{210} = \frac{3}{7}$.

*3.* Let $E_2$ be event (*b*). *Successful outcomes:* the number of ways of drawing four balls is $_6C_4 = _6C_2 = 15$; of drawing four cubes is $_4C_4$ or 1. Hence, by the addition principle of page 118, the number of successful outcomes is (15 + 1) or 16. Then $P(E_2) = \frac{16}{210} = \frac{8}{105}$.

*4.* Let $E_3$ be event (*c*). *Successful outcomes:* at most two are balls if (*i*) all are cubes, or (*ii*) one is a ball and three are cubes, or (*iii*) exactly two are balls and two are cubes:

the number of outcomes for (*i*) is $_4C_4 = 1$;
the number of outcomes for (*ii*) is $(_6C_1)(_4C_3) = 24$;
the number of outcomes for (*iii*) is $(_6C_2)(_4C_2) = 90$.

By the addition principle of page 118, the number of outcomes in $E_3$ is (1 + 24 + 90) = 115. Hence, $P(E_3) = \frac{115}{210} = \frac{23}{42}$.

EXAMPLE 2.    If a number of four different digits is written at random by use of the digits {2, 3, 4, 5}, find the probability that an *even number* will be obtained.

*Solution.    1.*    The *random experiment* is that a number symbol is written at random by use of four digits. The total number of outcomes in the sample space is $_4P_4$, or 4!, or 24. The outcomes are considered equally likely.

*2.*    Let $E$ be the *event* of obtaining an *even number. Successful outcomes:* by use of the multiplication principle of page 114, the number of outcomes in $E$ is $s = 3 \cdot 2 \cdot 1 \cdot 2 = 12$, as seen in the following diagram. Hence, $P(E) = \frac{12}{24} = \frac{1}{2}$.

Probability based on the model in Definition I is referred to as "*a priori*" probability. This name is appropriate because, in any application, we assume that, before any trial of the random experiment, the number and nature of the possible outcomes is known. In Definition I, the "*probability of an outcome*" is an *undefined term*, subject only to the condition that it is positive and that the sum of the probabilities of all of the outcomes is 1. However, in any application, the person performing the experiment is at liberty to consider the probability which he assigns to any outcome as a measure of his confidence in the possibility of its appearance at any trial of the experiment.

EXAMPLE 3.    At a music shop, the available stock of diamond needles for record players consists of ten perfect needles and five defective needles. Two of the needles are chosen at random for sale to a customer. Find the probability that (*a*) one of those sold is perfect and one is defective; (*b*) at least one is defective.

*Solution.* 1.   The *random experiment* is that two needles are chosen (either together or in succession without replacing the first drawn) from fifteen needles. The number of outcomes in the sample space is $_{15}C_2 = 105$.

2.   Let $E_1$ be the event in (*a*). The number of outcomes in $E_1$ is $10 \times 5$ or 50; $P(E_1) = \frac{50}{105} = \frac{10}{21}$.

3.   Let $E_2$ be the event in (*b*). The complementary event "*not* $E_2$," or $E_2'$, is the event that "*both are perfect.*" It is easier here to find $P(E_2')$ rather than $P(E_2)$, and then use (1) to obtain $P(E_2)$. The number of ways of obtaining two perfect needles from ten needles is $_{10}C_2 = 45$. Hence, $P(E_2') = \frac{45}{105} = \frac{3}{7}$. Then, from (1), $P(E_2) = \frac{4}{7}$.

★ EXAMPLE 4.   In a random group of five people, find the probability that at least two have the same birthday.

*Solution.* 1.   Let $E$ be the event described in the problem. Let $E'$ be the complementary event "*not* $E$," or the event that *all birthdays of the five people are different*. First we shall find $P(E')$.

2.   Suppose that the year consists of 365 days. As the *random experiment*, we think of assigning birthdays for five people. By the multiplication principle of page 114, the number of outcomes in the sample space is

$$(365)(365)(365)(365)(365), \quad or \quad (365)^5,$$

because 365 possible birthdays are available for each person.

3.   The number of outcomes in $E'$ is the number of ways in which five *different* birthdays can be "*placed on five people*"; this number is $_{365}P_5$ or $365 \cdot 364 \cdot 363 \cdot 362 \cdot 361$. Hence, by (3),

$$P(E') = \frac{365 \cdot 364 \cdot 363 \cdot 362 \cdot 361}{365 \cdot 365 \cdot 365 \cdot 365 \cdot 365}.$$

Since $364/365 = (365 - 1)/365$, etc.,

$$P(E') = \left(1 - \frac{1}{365}\right)\left(1 - \frac{2}{365}\right)\left(1 - \frac{3}{365}\right)\left(1 - \frac{4}{365}\right), \quad or \tag{5}$$

$$P(E') \doteq 1 - \frac{1 + 2 + 3 + 4}{365} = 1 - \frac{10}{365} = .973, \tag{6}$$

where "$\doteq$" means "*approximately equals.*" Hence, by (1), we obtain

$$P(E) = 1 - P(E') \doteq 1 - .973 = .027.$$

The approximate result in (6) was obtained by expanding in (5) and omitting all terms on the right involving products of two or more fractions. A more exact computation in (5) by use of logarithms or a computing machine also yields $P(E') = .973$.

COMMENT. Suppose that there are $n$ people in a group, with $n \leq 365$, and that the same probability is asked as in Example 4. The approximate method used in (6) would be very inaccurate if $n$ exceeds 7; hence logarithms or a computing machine would be needed to calculate $P(E')$. If anyone is asked to guess how large $n$ must be so that $P(E)$, as in Example 4, would be *greater than* .5, it is likely that the guess would be very much too large. By the method of Example 4, it is found that $P(E) > .5$ if $n = 23$. This illustrates the fact that mere intuition may lead to very wrong estimates of a probability.

## Exercise 31

1. A bag contains three red, five black, and four white cubes. (*a*) If one cube is drawn at random, find the probability that it is (*i*) black; (*ii*) black or white. (*b*) If two cubes are drawn together at random, find the probability that (*i*) both are red; (*ii*) both are red or black; (*iii*) one is red and one is black; (*iv*) both are of the same color; (*v*) at least one is white.

2. From four juniors and three seniors, a committee of three is chosen at random. Find the probability that the committee will involve (*a*) all juniors; (*b*) all seniors; (*c*) one senior and two juniors; (*d*) at most one senior.

3. If two true dice are tossed together, find the probability (*a*) of tossing each of the possible totals; (*b*) of tossing 2 or 7.

4. From a deck of fifty-two cards, five cards will be dealt to a player in a game of poker. Find the probability that (*a*) all will be clubs; (*b*) all will be of one suit; (*c*) two will be jacks and three will be aces.

5. There are four theatres available for choice. If each of three people chooses a theatre to attend, find the probability that (*a*) all people go to the same theatre; (*b*) two go to one theatre and one to another theatre.

6. An experimenter will toss a loaded die. He assigns the probabilities $\{\frac{1}{24}, \frac{1}{12}, \frac{1}{2}, \frac{1}{6}, \frac{1}{6}, \frac{1}{24}\}$ to the throws of $\{1, 2, 3, 4, 5, 6\}$, respectively. If the die is thrown once, find the probability of tossing (*a*) more than 3; (*b*) less than 3 or more than 4. In each case, also describe the complementary event and find its probability.

7. Two boys and three girls take seats at random in a row of five seats. Find the probability that boys and girls will alternate in the row.

8. A merchant, in buying a consignment of twenty loudspeakers, will test the lot by checking two of the speakers selected at random. He

will reject the shipment if either one or both of those selected is defective. Find the probability that he will reject the shipment if five of the speakers have defects.

9.  A true coin has been tossed ninety-nine times. It has fallen heads forty-nine times, and tails fifty times. How will the coin fall on the hundredth toss?

10. In a multiple choice examination with six questions, three alternatives are provided for the answer to each question, with just one alternative correct. A student decides to make a random choice of the response for each question. (*a*) How many sets of answers can he turn in? (*b*) Find his probability of (*i*) answering all questions wrong; (*ii*) answering all correctly; (*iii*) answering the first four correctly and the last two incorrectly.

11. A wholesaler's stock of forty toasters includes five defectives. Six toasters will be selected at random for shipment to a customer, who will reject the consignment if one or more are found to be defective on arrival. Find the probability that the customer will reject the shipment.

12. A random experiment consists of tossing a warped coin and a loaded die together. For the coin, the probability of falling heads is $\frac{2}{3}$, and tails is $\frac{1}{3}$. For the die, the probabilities of tossing $\{1, 2, 3, 4, 5, 6\}$ are $\{\frac{1}{6}, \frac{1}{24}, \frac{1}{24}, \frac{1}{12}, \frac{1}{3}, \frac{1}{3}\}$, respectively. Define the probability of any outcome of the experiment as the product of the probability for the face tossed with the coin and the number tossed with the die. Make up a table of two rows (for the coin) and six columns (for tosses of the die). List the probabilities of all outcomes of the experiment. (*a*) Verify that the sum of all probabilities is 1, so that the given definition is a legitimate case of Definition I. (*b*) Find the probability of tossing a head and more than 4 on the die.

13. Near the end of summer, a hardware store has only twelve lawnmowers left for sale, of which six are in perfect condition, four have major defects, and two have minor defects. If three lawnmowers are selected at random for a year-end sale, find the probability that (*a*) exactly one is free of defects; (*b*) one is perfect, one has a minor defect, and one has a major defect; (*c*) at most two are defective.

14. By use of the digits $\{1, 2, 3, 4, 5\}$, a number symbol of five different digits will be written at random. Find the probability that (*a*) a symbol for an odd number will be obtained; (*b*) the symbol will represent a number with 2 or 5 as a factor.

15. Four objects will be distributed in turn at random among six boxes. Find the probability that (*a*) all objects are placed in the same box; (*b*) no box will receive two objects; (*c*) each of two boxes will receive two objects.

16. In a matching question on an examination, six events in history are to

be matched with six specified dates, where each item is to be used just once. A student is sure of two dates and chooses to match the others at random. Find his probability of matching correctly (*a*) all items; (*b*) at least four dates.

17. Five coins are tossed together. Find the probability that they will fall with (*a*) all heads; (*b*) two heads and three tails.

18. If four boys and four girls form a ring facing the center, at random, find the probability that boys and girls will alternate.

19. Without consultation, each of three organizations announces a one-day convention to be held at the same hotel in the same month of June. Find the probability that at least two organizations specify the same day for their conventions.

20. Three men receive checks for their hats at the checkroom for a night club, but the attendant fails to place the duplicate checks on the hats. If she hands back one hat to each man at random, find the probability that no man receives his own hat. (Recall Problem 17 on page 125.)

★21. Solve Problem 20 if five men are involved.

★22. In Problem 4, find the probability that the hand will consist of two pairs and an odd card (for instance, two tens, two jacks, and a queen).

## 52.   Random variables

It has been seen that the elements of a sample space often are not numbers. However, in a mathematical investigation of any variety, as a rule the procedures are simplified if the primary elements are numbers. Hence, very frequently, in considering probabilities it proves convenient to associate a *number* with *each element* of the sample space. After this is done, the discussion of probability may be phrased in terms of the numbers which were introduced.

Suppose that the sample space is $W = \{u_1, u_2, \cdots, u_n\}$. Corresponding to each outcome $u_i$, let a number $x_i$ be specified, to produce $n$ ordered pairs:

$$(u_1, x_1), \quad (u_2, x_2), \cdots, \quad (u_n, x_n). \tag{1}$$

In (1), there may be repetitions among the $x$'s; the first components in (1) are the distinct elements of $W$. Let $X$ be the function consisting of the ordered pairs in (1). The domain of $X$ is $W$ and the range of $X$, or its values, is the set of distinct numbers among $\{x_1, x_2, \cdots, x_n\}$. For any $u$ in $W$, let $x = X(u)$, with the particular values

$$x_1 = X(u_1), \quad x_2 = X(u_2), \quad \cdots, \quad x_n = X(u_n). \tag{2}$$

A special name is given to such a function as $X$.

DEFINITION II.   *A **random variable** $X$ on a sample space $W$ is a real-valued function whose domain is $W$. That is, to each outcome $u$ in $W$ there corresponds a number $x = X(u)$.*

ILLUSTRATION 1.   A bag contains three white balls and six red balls. As a basis for a game, a player will draw a ball at random from the bag. He will win a prize of \$8 if he draws a white ball, and \$5 if he draws a red ball. The sample space, $W$, consists of nine elements (balls). Define a random variable, $X$, for $W$ by specifying that $X(u) = 8$ if $u$ is a white ball, and $X(u) = 5$ is $u$ is a red ball. Then, the domain of $X$ consists of nine elements (balls); the range of $X$, or its set of values, consists of just two numbers, 5 and 8. With $X$ at our disposal, certain sets of outcomes in $W$ can be specified by stating corresponding facts about the values of $X$. Thus, the event that the player will win \$8 consists of the white outcomes, and can be described as

$$\text{"the event* that } X = 8,\text{"} \tag{3}$$

whose probability is $\frac{3}{9}$ or $\frac{1}{3}$. The event that he will win \$5 is

$$\text{"the event that } X = 5,\text{"}$$

whose probability is $\frac{6}{9}$ or $\frac{2}{3}$. For this illustration, the set of numbers $\{x_1, x_2, \cdots, x_n\}$ in (2) consists of three 8's and six 5's.

ILLUSTRATION 2.   Let the random experiment be the tossing of a true die. The sample space $W$ consists of six elements $\{u_1, u_2, u_3, u_4, u_5, u_6\}$ corresponding to the tosses of $\{1, 2, 3, 4, 5, 6\}$, respectively. For each outcome $u$ in $W$, let $X(u)$ be defined as the number of dots on the face which has been tossed. Thus, we have

$$X(u_1) = 1; \quad X(u_2) = 2; \quad X(u_3) = 3; \quad \cdots; \quad X(u_6) = 6. \tag{4}$$

Let an event $T$ be described by

$$T = \{X \leq 4\}, \tag{5}$$

which we read "$T$ is the event $X \leq 4$;" $T$ consists of the tosses $\{1, 2, 3, 4\}$. We read "$P(X \leq 4)$" as "*the probability of $X \leq 4$,*" and

$$P(x \leq 4) = \tfrac{1}{6} + \tfrac{1}{6} + \tfrac{1}{6} + \tfrac{1}{6} = \tfrac{2}{3}.$$

Let $X$ be a random variable on the sample space $W = \{u\}$, with $x = X(u)$. Let $V$ be the range for $X$. Thus, $V = \{x\}$, which is read "*V is the set of numbers x.*" Sometimes it is useful to refer to $V$ as the **value space** for $X$. If $x$ is any number in $V$, there is a corresponding set of outcomes $u$ in $W$ for which $x = X(u)$. Then, the probability of any subset of the numbers in $V$ is under-

---

\* The usual rules about functional notation would lead us to write "$X(u) = 8$." However, in such a situation in statistics, it is customary to omit $u$ and to write simply "$X = 8$" as in (3).

stood to be the probability of the corresponding subset of outcomes of the random experiment. The sum of the probabilities thus defined for all numbers in $V$ is 1, because each outcome of $W$ is included among the outcomes corresponding to all values of $x$ in $V$. Thus, we may think of $V$ as a *new sample space*, where the probabilities of the values of $x$ are defined by the probabilities specified for the outcomes in the original sample space $W$. Then, in the usual application of a random variable, we cease mentioning the random experiment and its sample space. Instead, we concentrate all remarks on probability facts about the values for $X$.

NOTE 1.    Although the outcomes of a random experiment may be equally likely, the numbers in the value space $V$ of an associated random variable may not be equally likely. Thus, in Illustration 1, $P(X = 5) = \frac{2}{3}$ and $P(X = 8) = \frac{1}{3}$. This emphasizes the fact mentioned earlier in the chapter that, for the purposes of statistics, it is essential that the definition of probability should *not* require the outcomes of a sample space to be *equally likely*.

Let $X$ be a random variable on some sample space, which no longer need be mentioned. Let $V = \{x\}$ be the value space for $X$, with $P(X = x)$ well defined. Let

$$f(x) = P(X = x). \tag{6}$$

Then, $f$ is called the **probability function** for $X$. It is said that $f$ defines a *probability distribution* over the value space of $X$.

ILLUSTRATION 3.    Suppose that a doctor has six hypodermic needles in a box where three are perfect but three are defective. If a needle is taken at random, the probability that it is perfect is $\frac{1}{2}$, and that it is imperfect also is $\frac{1}{2}$. On the corresponding sample space $W$, with outcomes $u$, define $X(u) = 1$ if $u$ is a perfect needle, and $X(u) = 0$ if $u$ is defective. Then, the value space for $X$ is $\{0, 1\}$ where $f(0) = \frac{1}{2}$ and $f(1) = \frac{1}{2}$.

ILLUSTRATION 4.    Let the random experiment be the tossing of a true coin. The sample space is *{heads, tails}*, where each outcome has probability $\frac{1}{2}$. Define $X(heads) = 1$ and $X(tails) = 0$. The value space for $X$ is $V = \{0, 1\}$ with $f(0) = \frac{1}{2}$ and $f(1) = \frac{1}{2}$.

Notice that the sample spaces in Illustrations 3 and 4 were of different types. However, the random variables which were introduced have the same value space, with the same probabilities for its numbers. This illustrates the fact that, by studying a single probability distribution for a random variable $X$, simultaneously we may be able to obtain probability results concerning different sample spaces for various random experiments.

ILLUSTRATION 5.    A first bag contains five balls numbered $\{1, 2, 3, 4, 5\}$. A second bag contains six cubes numbered $\{1, 2, 3, 4, 5, 6\}$. A random experiment consists of drawing an object from each bag. Thus, the sample space has

30 outcomes. For each outcome $u$, define $X(u) = h + k$, where $h$ is the number of the ball and $k$ is the number of the cube in the outcome. The following table indicates the pairs $(h, k)$ corresponding to the 30 outcomes. The value

| BALL \ CUBE | 1 | 2 | 3 | 4 | 5 | 6 |
|---|---|---|---|---|---|---|
| 1 | (1, 1) | (1, 2) | (1, 3) | (1, 4) | (1, 5) | (1, 6) |
| 2 | (2, 1) | (2, 2) | (2, 3) | (2, 4) | (2, 5) | (2, 6) |
| 3 | (3, 1) | (3, 2) | (3, 3) | (3, 4) | (3, 5) | (3, 6) |
| 4 | (4, 1) | (4, 2) | (4, 3) | (4, 4) | (4, 5) | (4, 6) |
| 5 | (5, 1) | (5, 2) | (5, 3) | (5, 4) | (5, 5) | (5, 6) |

space $V = \{x\}$ for $X$ consists of all integers from 2 to 11 inclusive. Let $f(x) = P(X = x)$. For any particular value of $x$, the value of $f(x)$ is the number of outcomes shown in the table with $h + k = x$, divided by 30 because each outcome has probability $\frac{1}{30}$. Thus, $f(7) = \frac{5}{30}$. The student should verify the following table. A graph of the probability function $f(x)$, that is, a graph

| $x =$ | 2 | 3 | 4 | 5 | 6 | 7 | 8 | 9 | 10 | 11 |
|---|---|---|---|---|---|---|---|---|---|---|
| $30f(x) =$ | 1 | 2 | 3 | 4 | 5 | 5 | 4 | 3 | 2 | 1 |

of $y = f(x)$, is shown in Figure 57. The broken lines in the figure merely emphasize the location of the points on the graph. It is referred to as the graph of a probability distribution over the range of $X$.

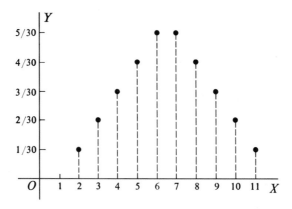

Fig. 57

## Exercise 32

(a) *Specify the set of numbers forming the value space V for the random variable X which is described.* (b) *Obtain* $f(x) = P(X = x)$ *for each number x in V.* (c) *Draw a graph of* $y = f(x)$.

1.  To encourage business on a bargain day, a supermarket permits each customer to draw a ball from a bag containing two white balls, three red balls, and one green ball. His normal number of trading stamps then will be multiplied by 4 if he draws the green ball, by 2 for a red ball, and by 3 for a white ball. For each outcome $u$, define $X(u)$ as the number which multiplies the normal number of stamps.
2.  For each outcome $u$ of the sample space in Illustration 5 on page 147, let $X(u) = 2h + k$, where $h$ is the number on the ball and $k$ is the number on the cube in $u$.
3.  A bag contains two white balls, three red balls and one black ball. A game consists of drawing two balls together from the bag. A prize of $5 will be given for getting the black ball, $3 for a white ball, and $2 for a red ball. For each outcome $u$ of the random experiment, define $X(u)$ as the numbers of dollars received as the prize because of the two balls in $u$.

## 53.   Expected value of a random variable

A substantial portion of the theory and applications of statistics relates to random variables. An elementary feature of such content is introduced as follows.

DEFINITION III.   *Let X be a random variable with the range* $V = \{x_1, x_2, \cdots, x_n\}$, *where* $P(X = x_i) = p_i$. *Then, the* **expected value** *of X is the sum of the products of the values of X multiplied, respectively, by their probabilities.*

If $E(X)$ represents the expected value of $X$, then*

$$E(X) = p_1 x_1 + p_2 x_2 + \cdots + p_n x_n = \sum_{i=1}^{n} p_i x_i. \tag{1}$$

If the $x$'s in $V$ are *equally likely*, we have $p_i = 1/n$ for every value of $i$, and

$$E(X) = \frac{x_1 + x_2 + \cdots + x_n}{n} = \frac{\sum_{i=1}^{n} x_i}{n}. \tag{2}$$

In this case, $E(X)$ is simply the average of the $x$'s. In any case, as seen in (1), $E(X)$ can be referred to as a *weighted average*† of the $x$'s with each $x_i$ weighted by its probability, where the sum of these weights is 1.

* See page 277 for summation notation (not essential here).
† See page 281.

ILLUSTRATION 1.   Let a random experiment consist of drawing a ball from a bag containing four white and eight black balls. Consider a game where the player making the draw will be paid $5 if he draws a white ball and $2 if he draws a black ball. For each outcome $u$, define $X(u)$ as the number of dollars in the prize for drawing $u$. Then $X$ has the values $\{2, 5\}$; $P(X = 2) = \frac{2}{3}$ and $P(X = 5) = \frac{1}{3}$. Hence, by (1),

$$E(X) = \tfrac{2}{3}(2) + \tfrac{1}{3}(5) = \tfrac{9}{3} = 3.$$

Consider a player, $H$, in a game thought of as a random experiment with associated probabilities. Assume that, whenever the game is played, there will occur one or other of a set of mutually exclusive events (three for illustration) $\{T_1, T_2, T_3\}$ whose probabilities of occurrence are $\{p_1, p_2, p_3\}$, respectively. Suppose that $H$ will receive a prize $\$x_1$ if $T_1$ occurs, $\$x_2$ if $T_2$ occurs, and $\$x_3$ if $T_3$ occurs, where one or more of $\{x_1, x_2, x_3\}$ may be zero or negative. Now, define a random variable $X$ on the sample space $W = \{u\}$ of the game as follows, for $i = 1, 2,$ and 3:

$$X(u) = x_i \quad if \quad u \text{ is in } T_i; \quad P(X = x_i) = p_i. \tag{3}$$

We shall call $X$ the *payoff function* for the game. Then, the following terminology proves useful.

DEFINITION IV.   *If a player participates in a game where the payoff function is $X$, then $E(X)$ is called his* **mathematical expectation** (*in money units*).

Thus, if the possible prizes in a game are $\{x_1, x_2, x_3\}$, with the probabilities $\{p_1, p_2, p_3\}$ that the prizes will be won, the mathematical expectation of the player is $E(X) = p_1 x_1 + p_2 x_2 + p_3 x_3$. If only one prize $x_1$ is involved, we have the following result.

> *If $p$ is the probability of a player in a game receiving a* $\Big\}$     (4)
> *prize of $\$x$, his mathematical expectation is $\$px$.*

ILLUSTRATION 2.   In a game, the prize is $100 and the probability that Roberts will win it is $\frac{3}{5}$. Hence, his mathematical expectation is $\frac{3}{5}(\$100)$ or $60.

In order to find the expected value of a random variable $X$ which has been defined on a sample space $W = \{u\}$, first obtain all of the different values for $x = X(u)$. Then, for each $x$ in the range $V = \{x\}$ of $X$, compute $P(X = x)$, and finally use (1).

EXAMPLE 1.   A bag contains four white balls, ten red balls, and six green balls. As a basis for a game, a player will draw a ball at random from the bag. He will win $5 for drawing a white ball, $2 for a red ball, and $3 for a green ball. For any outcome $u$ of the experiment, define $X(u)$ as the number of dollars in the prize for obtaining $u$. Find $E(X)$, the mathematical expectation of the player in dollars.

*Solution.*    The range for $X$ is {2, 3, 5}.

$$P(X = 2) = P(draw\ red\ ball) \quad = \frac{10}{20} = \frac{1}{2}.$$

$$P(X = 3) = P(draw\ green\ ball) = \frac{6}{20} = \frac{3}{10}.$$

$$P(X = 5) = P(draw\ white\ ball) = \frac{4}{20} = \frac{1}{5}.$$

Hence, $E(X) = (2 \times \frac{1}{2}) + (3 \times \frac{3}{10}) + (5 \times \frac{1}{5}) = 2.9$. Or, the mathematical expectation of the player is $2.90.

## 54.  A Bernoulli random variable

Let $T$ be an event in a sample space $W = \{u\}$, with $P(T) = p$ and $P(T') = q$, where $T' = (not\ T)$, the complement of $T$. Let us define a random variable $X$ on $W$ as follows:

$$X(u) = 1\ if\ u\ is\ in\ T;\ X(u) = 0\ if\ u\ is\ in\ T'. \tag{1}$$

The value space for $X$ is $V = \{0, 1\}$ with $P(X = 0) = q$ and $P(X = 1) = p$. If $f$ is the probability function for $X$, then

$$f(0) = q \quad and \quad f(1) = p. \tag{2}$$

A random variable $X$ is called a **Bernoulli random variable** if its value space is $V = \{0, 1\}$ and (2) is true. Thus, in (1) we introduced a Bernoulli variable. Sometimes the set $V$ is called a **Bernoulli sample space.**

ILLUSTRATION 1.    Suppose that a stock of fifty automobile tires consists of forty-eight perfect tires and two defective tires. A tire is selected at random. Let $T$ be the event that the tire is perfect. Define $X(u) = 1$ if a tire $u$ is in $T$ and $X = 0$ if $u$ is in $T'$. Then, $X$ is a Bernoulli random variable, with $f(0) = P(X = 0) = .04$ and $f(1) = P(X = 1) = .96$.

Suppose that we are asked to accept, or that we make, a dogmatic statement that "*the probability of occurrence of some event T is p*" when a certain action is performed, but that no information about the corresponding sample space $W$ is available. In fact, no sample space may be thought of. Then, we agree to act as if $T$ were the event of selecting a number 0 or 1, from the Bernoulli space {0, 1} for a random variable $X$ where $P(X = 1) = p$. Essentially, we have agreed to "*legalize*" any dogmatic statement or assumption of a probability for an event $T$ within the framework of the fundamental Definition I.

ILLUSTRATION 2.    Suppose that the prize for winning a game is $100 and that the probability of a player winning is $\frac{3}{5}$. Then, his mathematical expectation is $(\frac{3}{5})(\$100)$ or $60. In this case, we waived consideration of whatever sample space might be associated with the game.

Consider a random experiment whose outcomes are known to form a sample space $W$, where there is no basis for knowledge of the number or nature of the outcomes in $W$. Suppose, also, that $n$ trials of the experiment are made and that an event $T$ is observed to happen in exactly $s$ of these trials. Then, we agree to use the observed *relative frequency* of successes for $T$ as its probability. That is, we accept* $p = s/n$ as the probability of $T$ at any future trial of the random experiment. We refer to this value of $p$ as an **empirical probability**. Sometimes it is called an "*a posteriori*" probability because it is determined from past experience. We agree to treat any empirical probability $p$ for an event $T$ by introduction of an associated Bernoulli space, as described at the beginning of this section for a probability which is stated dogmatically.

ILLUSTRATION 3.    A coin has fallen heads 49 times out of 100 tosses. Hence, for this coin, we might take $p = .49$ as the probability that the coin will fall heads at any toss in the future.

Empirical probabilities are of fundamental importance in applications of statistics. In particular, such probabilities are essential elements in the conduct of all branches of the insurance industry. The basic principle on which an insurance company operates is that natural risks of uncertain disasters are to be shared by a large group of people. The fact that the risks are unavoidable, instead of being assumed voluntarily as in a game of chance, does not alter the nature of the problem. Statistical evidence in past experience is used to determine empirical probabilities about occurrence of the events against which insurance is offered. For any client being insured, the insurance company computes his present mathematical expectation from the benefits which he is promised if the disaster occurs (death, fire, auto accident, etc.) against which he is being insured. Then, his premiums are specified so that their present value is equal to the client's mathematical expectation, plus increments to provide for company costs and profit.

In the field of life insurance, the desired probabilities for operation are obtained from mortality tables, illustrated in this text by Table III, abbreviated CSO Table. It summarizes the results of extensive observations of the ages at death of men who have carried life insurance. The entries may be considered as a record of the year in which death occurred for each of 1,023,102 people

---

* A background for this acceptance will be met later in the chapter.

who were born on the same day. A mortality table can be used to obtain empirical probabilities about living and dying for people of specified ages.

EXAMPLE 1.    If a man is alive at age 25, find the probability that he will live at least fifteen years.

*Solution.*    In Table III, observe 939,197 men alive at age 25. Of these, 883,342 remain alive at age 40. Hence, the probability that a man of age 25 will live at least 15 years is 883,342/939,197 = .941.

EXAMPLE 2.    An insurance policy for a man aged 20 promises him an endowment of $1000 at age 40 if he is alive then. Find his mathematical expectation.

*Solution.*    Let $p$ be the probability that a man aged 20 will reach age 40, to receive the endowment. Then, from the CSO Table, $p = 883,342/951,483$. Hence, the man's mathematical expectation, in dollars due at age 40, is

$$1000p = 1000(883,342)/951,483 = \$929 \ (by \ logarithms).$$

## 55.  The language of odds

Let $T$ be an event in the sample space $W$ for some experiment. Suppose that $h > 0$, $k > 0$, and that the following assertion is made.

*The **odds** are **$h:k$** (read h to k) that $T$ will occur.*    (1)

We agree that (1) has the following meaning:

*The probability, $p$, of success for $T$ and the probability, $q$, of failure for $T$ at any trial of the random experiment are given by*

$$p = \frac{h}{h + k} \quad and \quad q = \frac{k}{h + k}.$$    (2)

We accept (1) and (2) as implying that $T$ can be treated as if it were an event consisting of $h$ elements in a sample space of $(h + k)$ equally likely elements. If the odds are $h:k$ that event $T$ will occur, then it is said that the odds are $h:k$ *in favor of $T$ occurring if $h > k$*, and $k:h$ *against $T$ occurring if $k > h$.*

ILLUSTRATION 1.    If the odds are $3:2$ in favor of John winning a game, his probability of winning is $\frac{3}{5}$.

ILLUSTRATION 2.    If the odds are $4:3$ against Bob winning $49 in a game, his probability of winning is $p = \frac{3}{7}$ and his mathematical expectation is $\frac{3}{7}(\$49) = \$21$.

## Exercise 33

*In any problem, X is a random variable with a range $V = \{x\}$, and f is the probability function on V.*

1. The value space for a random variable $X$ is $V = \{3, 5, 7, 12\}$, and the numbers of $V$ are equally likely. Find $E(X)$.

2. In Problem 1, find $E(X)$ if $f(3) = .1, f(5) = .4, f(7) = .2$, and $f(12) = .3$.

3. A merchant has twelve transistor radios in a box. Five of the radios are defective and seven are perfect. A random experiment consists of selecting a radio at random. For any outcome, $u$, let $X(u) = 1$ if the radio is perfect and $X(u) = 0$ if it is defective. Find $E(X)$.

4. Let the random experiment be the tossing of a true die. For any outcome $u$, let $X(u)$ be the number of dots on the face of the die which is tossed up. Compute the expected value of the number of dots, that is, the expected "*toss*" of the die.

5. Suppose that the die in Problem 4 is loaded so that the probabilities of the faces $\{1, 2, 3, 4, 5, 6\}$ are $\{\frac{1}{3}, \frac{1}{12}, \frac{1}{3}, \frac{1}{12}, \frac{1}{12}, \frac{1}{12}\}$, respectively. Find $E(X)$, where $X$ is defined as in Problem 4.

6. Find the mathematical expectation of a player in a game where the prize is $80 and his probability of winning it is .4.

7. A gambler will pay a professional for the privilege of drawing a cube at random from a bag containing five white cubes, nine red cubes, and six black cubes. He will receive $6 for drawing a white cube, $5 for a black cube, and $4 for a red cube. Define a random variable $X$ as the payoff function, and find the gambler's mathematical expectation.

8. A game consists of drawing two balls together at random from a bag containing five white and ten black balls. The player will receive $4 for each white ball drawn and $2 for each black ball drawn. Define a payoff random variable $X$ and find the player's mathematical expectation.

9. The odds are $5:3$ in favor of Johnson winning $20. Find his probability of winning and his mathematical expectation.

10. The odds are $7:3$ against Robinson winning a bet of $50. Find his probability of winning the bet and his mathematical expectation.

11. Suppose that a gambler $A$ bets $$S$ against a gambling house or banker $G$ that a certain event $T$ will occur with the odds $h:k$ that $T$ will occur. If $T$ fails to occur, then $A$ pays $$S$ to $G$. If $T$ occurs, then $G$ pays a certain sum $$R$ to $A$. We agree that the bet will be fair if $A$ and $G$ have *equal mathematical expectations*. Prove that $S/R = h/k$. If the bet is $15 at odds of $2:3$ to win, how much will $A$ get if he wins?

12. The posted odds on the pari-mutuel board on any horse at a racetrack are the odds *against* a bettor winning, or are the odds that the horse will *lose*. If the posted odds are $9:2$ on the horse Sheila's Pet, how much will a bettor receiver if he bets $5 and the horse wins?

*Find the probability by use of the mortality table.*

*13.*  That a boy aged 12 will be alive at age 42.

*14.*  That a man who marries at age 23 will be alive at age 50.

*15.*  That a man aged 70 will die within a year.

*16.*  An insurance policy, written for a man now aged 35, promises him an endowment of $1000 at age 55 if he is alive then. Find his mathematical expectation to the nearest dollar in terms of dollars due when he is of age 55.

*17.*  (If logarithmic or slide rule computation can be made.) A man is of age 24 and his wife is of age 20 when they are married. They are promised a gift of $10,000 at the end of ten years if both of them are alive then. Find their mathematical expectation.

*18.*  A consignment of ten portable radios contains four defective and six perfect radios. Three radios will be drawn together at random. For any outcome $u$, define $X(u) = x$ where $x$ is the number of defectives in $u$. Find $E(X)$, that is, *the expected value of the number of defectives* in the sample of three radios.

*19.*  A bag contains four black cubes, six red cubes, and ten white cubes. The experiment is that two cubes are drawn from the bag at random. In a game, the player who performs the experiment will be paid $10 for any black cube, $6 for any red cube, and $4 for any white cube drawn. For any outcome $u$, define $X(u)$ as the number of dollars in the resulting payment. Find the player's mathematical expectation.

## 56.  Probability of the union of mutually exclusive events

Let $S$ and $T$ be two events in the same sample space. Then, the union of $S$ and $T$, or "$S \cup T$," may be referred to as the event "$S$ or $T$." This event consists of all outcomes in $S$ alone, in $T$ alone, or in both $S$ and $T$ when they have common outcomes. We recall that $S$ and $T$ are called *mutually exclusive* when they have no common outcomes, that is, when the intersection $S \cap T = \emptyset$, the empty set.

ILLUSTRATION 1.  A bag contains six white balls, five black balls, and four green balls. A ball is drawn at random. Let the event that the ball drawn is white be $S$, and that the ball drawn is black be $T$. In Figure 58 which follows, the set $S$ is represented by the region with vertical rulings and $T$ by the region with horizontal rulings. $S$ and $T$ are mutually exclusive, or $S \cap T = \emptyset$. $S$ consists of six white balls; $T$ consists of five black balls; $S \cup T$ consists of the eleven balls which are white or black, where there are no duplications.

Hence, the probability of $S \cup T$ is the sum of the probabilities of the outcomes in $S$ and of the outcomes in $T$. We verify that

$$P(S) = \tfrac{6}{15}; \quad P(T) = \tfrac{5}{15}; \quad P(S \cup T) = \tfrac{11}{15} = P(S) + P(T).$$

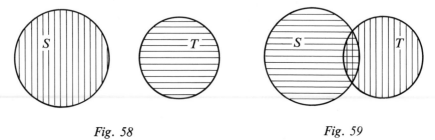

Fig. 58          Fig. 59

The same simple type of argument as in Illustration 1 yields the following result, where the outcomes in the sample space may not be equally likely.

**THEOREM II.** *If S and T are mutually exclusive events in the same sample space W, then*

$$P(S \cup T) = P(S) + P(T). \tag{1}$$

We accept the fact that (1) extends to the case of any number of mutually exclusive events. Thus, for three mutually exclusive events $\{S, T, K\}$,

$$P(S \cup T \cup K) = P(S) + P(T) + P(K). \tag{2}$$

By simply counting outcomes for mutually exclusive events, we have essentially employed (1) in various examples solved before in this chapter. Hereafter, it will prove convenient to use (1) explicitly. On many occasions, (1) will apply when no sample space is described.

ILLUSTRATION 2. In a poll of the voters in a certain city where four political parties will be represented on the ballot, the probability that a voter is a Republican is .45, and that he is a Democrat is .39. Hence, by (1), the probability that he is a "*Democrat or a Republican*" is (.45 + .39) or .84.

Assume that $S$ and $T$ are events in the same sample space, and that $S \cap T \neq \varnothing$, as illustrated by the Venn diagram in Figure 59, where $S$ is represented by the region with horizontal rulings, and $T$ by the region with vertical rulings. Thus, $S \cap T$ is represented by the region with double rulings. Then $P(S \cup T)$ is the sum of the probabilities of the outcomes in $S$, and the outcomes in $T$, *minus* the sum of the outcomes in both $S$ and $T$, or in $S \cap T$, because the probabilities of these outcomes have been added twice. That is,

$$P(S \cup T) = P(S) + P(T) - P(S \cap T). \tag{3}$$

We shall not have much occasion to use (3).

ILLUSTRATION 3.   A bag contains twenty white balls, of which ten have a black spot, and ten red balls, of which five have a black spot. The random experiment consists of drawing a ball at random from the bag. Let $S$ be the event of drawing a white ball. Let $T$ be the event of drawing a ball with a black spot. Then, $T$ consists of fifteen balls, ten white and five red. $S \cap T$ consists of ten white balls with a black spot. $S \cup T$ consists of the white balls and the five red balls with a black spot. Hence,

$$P(S) = \tfrac{20}{30}; \quad P(T) = \tfrac{15}{30}; \quad P(S \cap T) = \tfrac{10}{30};$$
$$P(S \cup T) = \tfrac{25}{30} = P(S) + P(T) - P(S \cap T).$$

NOTE 1.   For the case of a finite sample space $W$, as used in Definition I on page 138, we have given reasoning to justify (1) and (2). With a more general basis for probability, (1) and (2) may be taken as postulates concerning the probability function $P$.

## 57.   Probability with independent experiments

Let $Z_1$ and $Z_2$ be random experiments with sample spaces $W_1 = \{u_1\}$ and $W_2 = \{u_2\}$, and probability functions $P_1$ and $P_2$, respectively. Suppose that $Z_1$ and $Z_2$ may be performed simultaneously or in succession. Also, assume that, at any trial of both experiments, the outcome $u_1$ of $Z_1$ does not depend on the outcome $u_2$ of $Z_2$, and $u_2$ does not depend on $u_1$. That is, the sample space $W$ for the compound experiment $Z = (Z_1, Z_2)$ consists of all pairs $(u_1, u_2)$, where $u_1$ is any outcome in $W_1$ and $u_2$ is any outcome in $W_2$. Then, we shall call $Z_1$ and $Z_2$ *independent experiments.* Suppose that an event $T_1$ may occur at a trial of $Z_1$, and event $T_2$ at a trial of $Z_2$, where

$$p_1 = P_1(T_1) \quad and \quad p_2 = P_2(T_2). \tag{1}$$

Then, any trial of $Z = (Z_1, Z_2)$ may produce the compound event $T = (T_1, T_2)$, where $T_1$ occurs at the trial of $Z_1$ and $T_2$ at the trial of $Z_2$. Let $P$ be the probability function for $Z$. We accept the following definition.

DEFINITION V.   *Suppose that events $T_1$ and $T_2$ may occur, with probabilities $p_1$ and $p_2$, at trials of the independent experiments $Z_1$ and $Z_2$, respectively. Then, the probability that $T_1$ and $T_2$ will occur at a trial of $(Z_1, Z_2)$ is defined by* *

$$P(T_1, T_2) = p_1 p_2. \tag{2}$$

* To make this definition fit in the framework of Definition I on page 138, we should show that (2) is a consequence of definitions of probability for *all* outcomes of $Z$, and that the sum of all of these probabilities is 1. The appropriate definition is that $P(u_1, u_2) = P_1(u_1)P_2(u_2)$. See Problem 12 on page 144 for a special case and Problem 17 on page 161 for the general case.

ILLUSTRATION 1.    A container (I) holds five white and ten black balls, and container (II) holds three red and six yellow balls. Let the drawing of a ball from (I) be experiment $Z_1$, and from (II) be experiment $Z_2$. Let the event of obtaining a white ball from (I) be $T_1$, and of obtaining a yellow ball from (II) be $T_2$. Then $p_1 = P_1(T_1) = \frac{5}{15}$ and $p_2 = P_2(T_2) = \frac{6}{9}$. We accept $Z_1$ and $Z_2$ as independent experiments. Then, by (2),

$$P[white\ from\ (I),\ yellow\ from\ (II)] = \tfrac{5}{15}\cdot\tfrac{6}{9} = \tfrac{2}{9}.$$

The definition in (2) extends to the case of three or more independent experiments, and corresponding events. Thus, with notation similar to that in (2),

$$P(T_1,\ T_2,\ T_3) = p_1 p_2 p_3. \tag{3}$$

EXAMPLE 1.    A clothing manufacturer has one hundred suits in stock in room ($H$) and two hundred in room ($K$), with five per cent of the stock in ($H$) defective, and four per cent defective in ($K$). A suit is selected from each room at random for display at a show. Find the probability of the display consisting of ($a$) one defective and one perfect suit; ($b$) a defective suit from ($H$) and any suit from ($K$).

*Solution.    1.*   Let the act of selection from ($H$) be $Z_1$, and from ($K$) be $Z_2$, with other notation as in the details leading to (2).

*For $Z_1$:*      $P_1(perfect\ suit) = \dfrac{19}{20} = p_1$;   $P_1(defective\ suit) = \dfrac{1}{20} = q_1$.

*For $Z_2$:*      $P_2(perfect\ suit) = \dfrac{24}{25} = p_2$;   $P_2(defective\ suit) = \dfrac{1}{25} = q_2$.

*2.*   One suit is defective and one is perfect if:

(*i*)   *a defective comes from ($H$) and a perfect from ($K$); or*

(*ii*)   *a perfect comes from ($H$) and a defective from ($K$).*

By use of (2),      $P[(i)] = q_1 p_2 = \dfrac{24}{20(25)} = \dfrac{24}{500}$;

$$P[(ii)] = p_1 q_2 = \dfrac{19}{20(25)} = \dfrac{19}{500}.$$

By Theorem II on page 156, since (*i*) and (*ii*) are mutually exclusive,

$$P(one\ defective\ and\ one\ perfect) = P[(i)] + P[(ii)] = \frac{43}{500} = .086.$$

*3.*   The probability of obtaining *any* suit from ($K$) is $P_1$(*whole sample space*) = 1. Hence, by (2),

$$P[defective\ from\ H,\ and\ any\ from\ (K)] = \tfrac{1}{20}\cdot 1 = \tfrac{1}{20} = .05.$$

Let $G$ be any random experiment. Assume that, in successive trials of $G$, the outcome of $G$ at any trial is not affected by the outcomes at previous or future trials. Then, we agree that such successive trials are independent experiments to which (3) and its extensions will apply.

EXAMPLE 2.   The probability that Harris will win a certain game whenever he plays is $\frac{1}{4}$. (*a*) If he plays twice, find the probability that he will win just once. (*b*) If he plays three times, find the probability that he will win just twice.

*Solution.*   *1.*   Let $p$ be the probability of a win, $W$, and $q$ be the probability of a loss, $L$, whenever the game $Z$ is played; we have $p = \frac{1}{4}$ and $q = \frac{3}{4}$.

*2.*   *For* (*a*): Harris wins *just once* if his results in two successive trials, $(Z, Z)$, are $(W, L)$ or $(L, W)$, which are *mutually exclusive events*, each of whose probabilities is obtained from (2). Hence, by use of Theorem II,

$$P(win\ just\ once) = P(W, L) + P(L, W) = pq + qp = \tfrac{3}{16} + \tfrac{3}{16} = \tfrac{3}{8}.$$

*3.*   *For* (*b*): In three trials, Harris wins *just twice* if his results are one or other of the following *mutually exclusive events*, for the sequence of three games:

$$(W, W, L); \quad (W, L, W); \quad (L, W, W). \tag{4}$$

By (3), the probability of each of (4) is $p \cdot p \cdot q = p^2q = \tfrac{3}{64}$. Hence, by Theorem II,

$$P(win\ twice\ and\ lose\ once) = \tfrac{3}{64} + \tfrac{3}{64} + \tfrac{3}{64} = \tfrac{9}{64}. \tag{5}$$

In (4), notice that the number of mutually exclusive events is $_3C_2$, or the number of ways of specifying a set of two games to be won out of three played. Thus, the result in (5) is $_3C_2p^2q$.

## Exercise 34

*The results of Sections 56 and 57 should be used wherever possible.*

1.   In a game where only one player can win, Robinson's probability of winning is $\frac{1}{2}$ and Smith's probability of winning is $\frac{1}{4}$. Find the probability that one of them will win.
2.   The probability that $A$ will win a certain game is $\frac{1}{3}$ and that $B$ will win a different game is $\frac{1}{2}$. Find the probability that (*a*) both will win; (*b*) just one will win; (*c*) at least one will win.
3.   The probability that a certain man will live fifteen years is $\frac{1}{4}$ and his wife will live fifteen years is $\frac{3}{8}$. Find the probability that, at the end of fifteen years, (*a*) both will be dead; (*b*) both will be alive; (*c*) one will be alive and one will be dead; (*d*) at least one will be alive. Notice the relation between the results for (*a*) and (*d*).
4.   Find the probability of throwing four heads in four tosses of a coin.

5. Find the probability of throwing three 7's in three tosses of a pair of dice.

6. The probability of Carlson winning a certain game whenever he plays it is $\frac{1}{3}$. If he plays twice, find the probability that he will win (a) both games; (b) just once; (c) at most once; (d) at least once.

7. From a deck of fifty-two cards, three cards are drawn in succession, with each replaced before the next draw. Find the probability of drawing (a) all hearts; (b) all of one suit; (c) all kings or queens.

8. A sales manager estimates that the probability of a salesman obtaining a purchase order from any prospective customer is .3. A certain salesman fails to get an order from four successive customers. Find the sales manager's estimate of the probability of such an event occurring.

*Container* (I) *holds four oranges and six lemons. Container* (II) *holds three oranges and twelve grapefruit. In Problems 9–11, find the probability of the specified event. All outcomes of any stage of an experiment are taken as equally likely.*

9. If we draw a piece of fruit from each container, we shall obtain (a) two oranges; (b) two different varieties of fruit.

10. If we draw two pieces of fruit together from each container, (a) all will be oranges; (b) just one orange will be obtained from each container.

11. If we draw two pieces of fruit in succession from (I), with replacement of the first piece before the second is drawn, then (a) both will be oranges; (b) just one will be a lemon; (c) at least one will be a lemon.

12. The probabilities of A, B, and C living for fifteen years are $\frac{1}{5}$, $\frac{1}{3}$, and $\frac{2}{5}$, respectively. Find the probability that (a) all will live for fifteen years; (b) all will be dead at the end of fifteen years; (c) just two will be alive at the end of fifteen years.

13. The probability that John will win a certain game whenever he plays is .2. Find the probability that: (a) if he plays twice, he will win just once; if he plays three times, he will win (b) just once; (c) just twice; (d) at least twice.

14. In the manufacture of television tubes in a certain factory, it is found that the probabilities of a tube having defects A and B are .02 and .03, respectively, but that no tube will have both defects. Two tubes will be drawn in succession at random from the production, which is so large that probabilities are essentially unchanged at the second drawing. Find the probability that (a) the tubes drawn will have different defects; (b) the tubes will have the same defect; (c) each tube will be defective.

15. In Problem 14, suppose that three defects A, B, and C are possible, with probabilities .02, .03, and .05, respectively, where no tube will

have more than one defect. If three tubes are drawn in succession, find the probabilities of $(a)$, $(b)$, and $(c)$ of Problem 14; $(d)$ find the probability of just one tube being defective.

*16.* For any individual among white Americans, the probability of having blood of type O is .45, of type A is .41, of type B is .10, and of type AB is .04. If two white Americans are tested, find the probability that: $(a)$ both are of type A; $(b)$ one is of type A and one of type B. $(c)$ If three are tested, find the probability that there will be one of each of the types A, B, and AB. $(d)$ If four are tested, find the probability that there will be one of each of the four types.

★*17.* Let $Z_1$ and $Z_2$ be independent random experiments with probability functions $P_1$ and $P_2$, and sample spaces $W_1 = \{u_1, u_2, \cdots, u_m\}$ and $W_2 = \{v_1, v_2, \cdots, v_n\}$, respectively, with $P_1(u_i) = h_i$ and $P_2(v_i) = k_i$. For the compound experiment $Z = (Z_1, Z_2)$ as in Section 57, let $r = (u, v)$ represent any outcome of $Z$, with $P$ as the probability function for $Z$. Define $P(r) = P_1(u)P_2(v)$. Then prove that $P(W) = 1$, where $W$ is the sample space for $Z$.

## 58.   Probability of $k$ successes in $n$ trials

Let $T$ be an event in the sample space of a random experiment $Z$ with probability function $P_1$, where $P_1(T) = p$ and $P_1(not\ T) = q$. We may think of $Z$ as the act of selecting a number from a Bernoulli space $V = \{0, 1\}$ where $P_1(0) = q$, $P_1(1) = p$, and $T$ is the event of obtaining 1. Successive trials of $Z$ qualify as independent experiments. Special cases of the following result were met in Example 2 on page 159, and in problems of Exercise 34.

THEOREM III.   *Suppose that the probabilities of success of the events T and "not T," or T', at any trial of a random experiment Z are p and q, respectively, Then, the probability of exactly k successes for T in n trials of Z is*

$$_nC_k p^k q^{n-k}. \tag{1}$$

*Proof (for the case n = 5 and k = 3).   1.* We shall act as if $Z$ is the playing of a game, with $W$ and $L$ meaning "*win*" and "*lose*" respectively; $P_1(W) = p$ and $P_1(L) = q$ at any trial of $Z$. If the game is played five times, two illustrations of the event of three wins and two losses are as follows, where subscripts indicate the number of the game won or lost:

$$(W_1, W_2, W_3, L_4, L_5) \quad and \quad (L_1, W_2, L_3, W_4, W_5). \tag{2}$$

By extension of (3) on page 158 to the case of five events, the probabilities of the two sequences in (2) are $p \cdot p \cdot p \cdot q \cdot q$ and $q \cdot p \cdot q \cdot p \cdot p$, or $p^3 q^2$ in each case.

Similarly, the probability of winning *any* three and losing the other two in a succession of five games played is

$$P(win\ a\ particular\ three\ games\ and\ lose\ two) = p^3 q^2,$$

where $P$ is the probability function for the random experiment consisting of five successive trials of $Z$.

2.  The number of mutually exclusive ways, or events, in which three games are won and two are lost, out of five played, is *the number of subsets of three games to be won* which can be selected from five played, which is $_5C_3$ (or 10). The probability of each of these events is $p^3 q^2$. Hence, by Theorem II on page 156, the probability that one or other of the events will occur is the sum of their ten equal probabilities, or

$$P(just\ three\ wins\ when\ five\ games\ are\ played) = {}_5C_3 p^3 q^2.$$

COROLLARY 1.   *The probability that the event $T$ of Theorem* III *will occur at least $k$ times in $n$ trials is*

$$_nC_k p^k q^{n-k} + {}_nC_{k+1} p^{k+1} q^{n-k-1} + \cdots + {}_nC_{n-1} p^{n-1} q + p^n. \tag{3}$$

*Proof.*   By (1), the terms in (3), read from the left, are the probabilities of the mutually exclusive events of just $k$ successes, just $(k + 1)$ successes, $\cdots$, just $n$ successes. By Theorem II on page 156, the sum of the terms is the probability that one or other of the preceding mutually exclusive events will occur, or is the probability of *at least $k$* successes.

From (8) on page 135, notice that $_nC_k p^k q^{n-k}$ in (1) is the term where the power of $p$ is $p^k$ in the expansion of $(p + q)^n$. Similarly, in (3) we observe the *last* $(n - k + 1)$ terms of the expansion of $(q + p)^n$ in descending powers of $q$, or the *first* $(n - k + 1)$ terms of the expansion of $(p + q)^n$ in descending powers of $p$.

EXAMPLE 1.   A bag contains four yellow and eight red balls. If we draw six balls in succession from the bag, with each ball replaced before the next draw, find the probability that (*a*) just four of those drawn will be yellow; (*b*) at least three will be red.

*Solution.*   *1.*   The random experiment $Z$ is that a ball is drawn. Since the ball is replaced before the next draw, the experiment is *unchanged*. Hence, six independent trials of $Z$ occur. Let the probability function for $Z$ be $P_1$, and for the succession of trials $(Z, Z, Z, Z, Z, Z)$ be $P$. Then $P_1(yellow) = p = \frac{1}{3}$, and $P_1(not\ yellow) = q = \frac{2}{3}$. From (1),

$$P[(a)] = {}_6C_4 \left(\frac{1}{3}\right)^4 \left(\frac{2}{3}\right)^2 = {}_6C_2 \cdot \frac{4}{3^6} = \frac{60}{3^6} = \frac{20}{243}.$$

2.  $P_1(red) = p = \frac{2}{3}$; $P_1(not\ red) = q = \frac{1}{3}$. The probability of (b), *at least three red draws*, is the sum of the probabilities of the mutually exclusive events of *exactly* three red, four red, five red, and six red, or

$$P[(b)] = {}_6C_6p^6 + {}_6C_5p^5q + {}_6C_4p^4q^2 + {}_6C_3p^3q^3. \tag{4}$$

The result in (4) is 656/729. We could compute (4) as the first four terms in the following binomial expansion, where the coefficients were obtained by use of Pascal's triangle on page 134, with $p = \frac{2}{3}$ and $q = \frac{1}{3}$:

$$(p + q)^6 = p^6 + 6p^5q + 15p^4q^2 + 20p^3q^3 + \cdots;$$

$$P[(b)] = \frac{1}{3^6}(64 + 192 + 240 + 160) = \frac{656}{729}.$$

The proof* of the following theorem is outlined for the interested student in a problem of the next exercise.

THEOREM IV.   *Under the hypotheses of Theorem* III *with n fixed, n > 2, and 0 < p < 1, let $\eta(k)$ be the probability of k successes in n trials. Then, $\eta(k)$ has its largest value for each integer k satisfying*

$$np - q \leqq k \leqq np + p. \tag{5}$$

We shall recall (5) by the following statement:

*The most probable number of successes for an event T in n independent trials of an experiment Z is approximately np, where p is the probability of success for T at any trial, and is np if np is an integer.*  (6)

ILLUSTRATION 1.   In (6), if $p = \frac{1}{3}$ then $q = \frac{2}{3}$. From (5), the most probable number, $k$, of successes for $T$ in 50 trials satisfies

$$\frac{50}{3} - \frac{2}{3} \leqq k \leqq \frac{50}{3} + \frac{1}{3}, \quad or \quad 16 \leqq k \leqq 17.$$

Hence, 16 and 17 successes have the largest probability of success. If 60 trials occur, then $60 \times (\frac{1}{3})$ or 20 successes is the most probable number of successes.

## Exercise 35

1.  The probability of Paul winning whenever he plays a certain game is $\frac{1}{4}$. If he plays three times, find the probability that he will win (a) exactly twice; (b) at least twice; (c) at most twice.

---

* For the complete proof, see page 332 in *College Algebra, Fifth Edition,* by William L. Hart; D. C. Heath and Company, publishers.

2. The probability of Art winning whenever he plays a certain game is .1. If he plays five times, find the probability that he will win (a) exactly three times; (b) no game; (c) at least four times.

3. If Bruce tosses six coins (or, one coin six times), find the probability that he will toss (a) just two heads; (b) at least three heads; (c) at most two tails.

4. If Bob tosses three dice, find his probability of throwing (a) just two sevens; (b) at least two aces.

5. If Mike tosses two dice three times, find his probability of throwing (a) just two 11's; (b) at least one 11.

*In the remaining problems, use the table of values of $f(x) = {}_nC_x p^x q^{n-x}$ on page* 167 *whenever convenient in final computation.**

6. A bag contains three white and twelve black balls. If we draw ten balls in succession and replace each one before the next is drawn, find the probability that (a) at least four white balls will be obtained; (b) at most three white balls will be drawn.

7. An examination of multiple-choice type has fifteen questions, where each question has five responses, of which just one is correct. A student is sure of his answers on the first five questions, but will choose his response at random on each of the remaining questions. Find the probability that he will receive a grade of (a) 80% on the test; (b) more than 60%.

8. For a given type of biological cell, the probability that the cell will survive for a given time is .4. Find the probability that, out of ten of the cells, at least five will survive.

9. In a certain factory, it is estimated that 2% of the products on any day are defective. If ten articles are selected at random from the production on a certain day and are examined, find the probability that (a) just two are defective; (b) at most three are defective.†

10. Repeat Problem 9 with .05 as the probability of defectives.

*At any trial of a random experiment Z, the probability of success for a specified event T is p. If n trials of Z are made, find the value or values of k for which the probability of k successes in n trials has its largest possible value.*

11. $p = \frac{1}{3}; n = 75.$         12. $p = \frac{1}{4}; n = 83.$

13. $p = \frac{2}{3}; n = 95.$         14. $p = \frac{1}{5}; n = 232.$

15. Let n be a positive integer. By use of Theorem IV on page 163 with $p = \frac{1}{2}$, prove that the largest coefficient in the expansion of $(p + q)^n$ is met at the middle term if n is even, and at the two middle terms if n is odd.

---

\* In the table, $q = 1 - p$. For instance, ${}_{10}C_3(.3^3)(.7^7) = .267.$

† In such a problem, assume that the production is so large that probabilities are not affected by selection of small samples.

★*16.* Suppose that players *A*, *B*, and *C* have the probabilities $\frac{1}{2}$, $\frac{1}{6}$, and $\frac{1}{3}$, respectively, of winning whenever they play together in a game where just one player will win. If they play the game five times, find the probability that *A* will win twice, *B* twice, and *C* just once.

★*17.* Prove Theorem IV on page 163.

HINT.  Write out $\eta(k - 1)$, $\eta(k)$, and $\eta(k + 1)$ in expanded forms by use of formula (6) of page 127 for $_nC_r$. Then, the number *k* specified in Theorem IV must satisfy

$$\eta(k) \geq \eta(k - 1) \qquad and \qquad \eta(k + 1) \leq \eta(k).$$

Each of these inequalities produces an inequality concerning *k*.

## 59.  The binomial distribution

Let *Z* be the random experiment of selecting a number from the Bernoulli space $B = \{0, 1\}$ with $P_1(0) = q$ and $P_1(1) = p$, where $P_1$ is the probability function for *B*. Let *H* represent the random experiment consisting of *n* repetitions of *Z*. Each outcome, *u*, of *H* is a set of *n* numbers where each is 0 or 1, such as $u = \{0, 0, 1, 0, 1, \cdots, 1\}$. Let *K* be the sample space for *H*, or $K = \{u\}$, and let *P* be the probability function for *K*. On *K*, introduce a random variable *X* as follows:

$$\left.\begin{array}{l} \textit{For any outcome } u = \{0, 0, 1, 0, \cdots\}, \textit{ define } X(u) = x, \\ \textit{where x is the number of times 1 appears in u.} \end{array}\right\} \tag{1}$$

Then, the value space, *V*, for *X* is $V = \{0, 1, 2, 3, \cdots, n\}$. Also, $P(X = x)$ is *the probability of x successes in n trials* of the experiment of selecting a number from $\{0, 1\}$; success at any trial means that 1 is obtained. Hence, by (1) on page 161, with $k = x$,

$$P(X = x) = {}_nC_x p^x q^{n-x}. \tag{2}$$

Let $$f(x) = {}_nC_x p^x q^{n-x}. \tag{3}$$

We refer to *f* as a **binomial probability function**, specifying a binomial probability distribution over the range $\{0, 1, 2, 3, 4, \cdots, n\}$ of the random variable *X* defined above.

ILLUSTRATION 1.  With $n = 6$, $p = \frac{1}{3}$, and $q = \frac{2}{3}$ in (3),

$$f(x) = {}_6C_x(\tfrac{1}{3})^x(\tfrac{2}{3})^{6-x}, \tag{4}$$

with the domain for *x* as $\{0, 1, 2, 3, 4, 5, 6\}$. The values of *f* are the seven terms of the following binomial expansion, and are summarized in a table below. A graph of $y = f(x)$ is shown in Figure 60 on page 166.

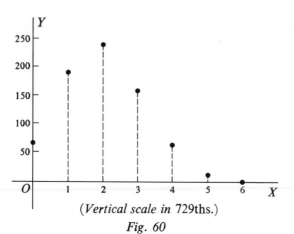

(*Vertical scale in* 729ths.)

Fig. 60

$$\left(\frac{1}{3} + \frac{2}{3}\right)^6 = \left(\frac{1}{3}\right)^6 + 6\left(\frac{1}{3}\right)^5\left(\frac{2}{3}\right) + 15\left(\frac{1}{3}\right)^4\left(\frac{2}{3}\right)^2$$

$$+ 20\left(\frac{1}{3}\right)^3\left(\frac{2}{3}\right)^3 + 15\left(\frac{1}{3}\right)^2\left(\frac{2}{3}\right)^4 + 6\left(\frac{1}{3}\right)\left(\frac{2}{3}\right)^5 + \left(\frac{2}{3}\right)^6$$

$$= \frac{1}{729} + \frac{12}{729} + \frac{60}{729} + \frac{160}{729} + \frac{240}{729} + \frac{192}{729} + \frac{64}{729}.$$

| $x =$ | 0 | 1 | 2 | 3 | 4 | 5 | 6 |
|---|---|---|---|---|---|---|---|
| $729f(x) =$ | 64 | 192 | 240 | 160 | 60 | 12 | 1 |

EXAMPLE 1.    Find $E(X)$ for the binomial distribution in Illustration 1.

*Solution.*    We use (1) on page 149:

$$E(X) = \frac{1\cdot192 + 2\cdot240 + 3\cdot160 + 4\cdot60 + 5\cdot12 + 6\cdot1}{729} = 2. \quad (5)$$

Because of the definition of $X$ in (1), $E(X)$ in (5) can be called "*the expected value of the number of successes in n trials.*" In (5), we have $n = 6$ and $p = \frac{1}{3}$. Hence $2 = np$. This is a special case of the following theorem, whose proof is beyond the scope of this text. However, the result can be verified simply by the student for any particular binomial distribution, as was done in (5).

THEOREM V.    *If p is the probability of success for an event T at any trial of a random experiment Z, and if n trials of Z are made, the* **expected value of the number of successes** *for T in the n trials is np.*

In (5) on page 163, it was seen that the *largest* value for $f(x)$ in (3) occurs when $x = np$, approximately. In Theorem V, $np$ is announced as the *expected value* of *X*, where $P(X = x) = f(x)$. These facts give a theoretical background for the common intuitional impression that, if the probability of success for an event *T* is *p* at any trial, then we may "*expect*" (in the colloquial sense) approximately $x = np$ successes in *n* trials. This implies that the relative frequency $x/n$ is near *p*. Thus, with $p = \frac{1}{3}$ and $n = 60$, there is a theoretical basis for "*expecting*" $\frac{1}{3}(60)$ or 20 successes in 60 trials. Although, in this case, $f(x)$ would have its largest value when $x = 20$, the graph in Figure 60 emphasizes the fact that other values of *x* would have substantial probabilities when $n = 60$.

In many applications of statistics, valuable results are obtained when the data are analyzed on the basis of an assumption that the number of *successes* for the event in question has a binomial probability distribution. The following table will be useful in later problems involving such distributions.

| $f(x) = {}_nC_xp^xq^{n-x};\quad n = 10$ | | | | | | | | | | |
|---|---|---|---|---|---|---|---|---|---|---|
| $x$ / $p$ | 0 | 1 | 2 | 3 | 4 | 5 | 6 | 7 | 8 | 9 | 10 |
| .02 | .817 | .167 | .015 | .000 | .000 | .000 | .000 | .000 | .000 | .000 | .000 |
| .05 | .599 | .315 | .075 | .010 | .001 | .000 | .000 | .000 | .000 | .000 | .000 |
| .1 | .349 | .387 | .194 | .057 | .011 | .001 | .000 | .000 | .000 | .000 | .000 |
| .2 | .107 | .268 | .302 | .201 | .088 | .026 | .006 | .001 | .000 | .000 | .000 |
| .3 | .028 | .121 | .234 | .267 | .200 | .103 | .037 | .009 | .001 | .000 | .000 |
| .4 | .006 | .040 | .121 | .215 | .251 | .201 | .111 | .042 | .011 | .002 | .000 |
| .5 | .001 | .010 | .044 | .117 | .205 | .246 | .205 | .117 | .044 | .010 | .001 |

EXAMPLE 2.    When the manufacturing process for electric batteries in a certain factory is "*in control*," approximately 2% of the output involves defects. For quality control by the management, a random sample of ten batteries from the output will be examined each day. If at most one of these batteries is defective, the process will be considered in control. Otherwise, it will be called "*out of control*" and will be investigated. (*a*) If the process is *in control*, find the probability that the test will declare, (*i*) *correctly*, that the process is in control; (*ii*) *incorrectly*, that the process is out of control. (*b*) On

a day when 10% of the output actually is defective, find the probability that the test will declare, *incorrectly*, that the process is in control.

*Solution.* *1.* (*a*) The test uses ten trials of an experiment where the probability of success for the event $T = $ (*the battery is defective*) is $p = .02$ at any trial. The probability of $x$ defectives in ten trials is

$$f(x) = {}_{10}C_x(.02)^x(.98)^{10-x}, \tag{6}$$

whose values are in the preceding table. For (*i*), let $y$ be the probability that the test will declare the process "*in control.*" Then $y$ is the sum of the probabilities for *no defective* and for *one defective*; from the table,

$$y = f(0) + f(1) = .817 + .167 = .984.$$

For (*ii*), let $z$ be the probability that the test will declare the process to be "*out of control.*" Then, $z$ is the sum of the probabilities of $2, 3, 4, \cdots, 10$ defectives; from the table,

$$z = f(2) + f(3) + \cdots + f(10) = .015 + .000 + \cdots = .015. \tag{7}$$

More simply, we note that "*out of control*" is the complementary event for "*in control,*" and hence the sum of the probabilities of these two events is 1. Thus, without preceding details, by use of the result for (*i*) we find $z = 1 - .984 = .016$, where the difference as compared to (7) is due to rounding off table entries.

*2.* When 10% are defective, $f(x) = {}_{10}C_x(.1)^x(.9)^{10-x}$. From the table, the probability, $y$, of declaring, *incorrectly*, that "*the process is in control*" is

$$y = f(0) + f(1) = .349 + .387 = .736,$$

which is undesirably large. We reach the conclusion that the "0 or 1" test is not defensible unless a much larger sample of batteries is to be tested. Limitations of our brief table prevent use of more realistic data. Much more extensive tables for the binomial distribution are available for computation in statistics.

## Exercise 36

*Use the table of values of the binomial probability function whenever possible.*

*Find all values of the probability function* $f(x) = {}_nC_x p^x q^{n-x}$ *for the random variable X corresponding to the data. Then compute* $E(X)$ *and verify that* $E(X) = np$. *Use Pascal's triangle in calculating terms of* $(p + q)^n$ *when the table for* $f(x)$ *does not apply.*

*1.* $n = 4$ and $p = \frac{1}{4}$.    *2.* $n = 6$ and $p = \frac{1}{2}$.
*3.* $n = 10$ and $p = .3$.    *4.* $n = 10$ and $p = .4$.

5.  In a toss of ten coins, find the probability of obtaining (*a*) five heads; (*b*) at least six heads; (*c*) at most three heads.
6.  If a golfer has a probability of .3 of making a putt of nine feet, and if he will try ten putts from this distance, find the probability that he will sink (*a*) just four putts; (*b*) at least six putts.

*In quality control in a factory producing television sets, ten sets will be selected at random from the production each day and will be tested for defects. The production process will be stated to be "in control" if at most a certain number of the sets (as given in the problem) are found to be defective. Otherwise, the process will be called "out of control," and will be subject to investigation. Solve the stated problem.*

7.  When the process is in control, approximately 5% of the output has defects. The test used is that the process will be declared in control if at most one of the ten sets examined is found defective. If the process is in control, find the probability that the test will (*a*) reach this conclusion; (*b*) *incorrectly* declare the test out of control. (*c*) Find the probability of the test *incorrectly* reaching a wrong conclusion on a day when actually 20% of the output is defective.
8.  When the process is in control, approximately 2% of the output is defective. The test is that the process will be declared in control if none of the ten sets examined has defects. If the process is in control, find the probability that the test will (*a*) reach the *correct* conclusion; (*b*) *incorrectly* declare the test out of control. (*c*) Find the probability of the test *incorrectly* reaching a wrong conclusion on a day when actually 10% of the output is defective.
9.  Solve Problem 7 if the test for "*in control*" is that at most two of the ten sets examined have defects.
10.  Solve Problem 8 if the test for "*in control*" is that at most one of the ten sets has defects.
11.  Solve Problem 7 if the test for "*in control*" is that at most three of the sets examined have defects.
12.  Solve Problem 8 if the test for "*in control*" is that at most two of the sets have defects.
13.  A basketball player *H* has a season average of 40% in making free throws. In a certain game, he makes only three out of ten free throws. (*a*) Find the probability of such an occurrence under the assumption that his ability is unaltered. (*b*) With the same assumption, find the probability that, in the next game, he will sink exactly seven of ten free throws.
14.  In a normal group of people in a certain country, it is assumed that 10% of the men over a given age *k* years have the eye disease *glaucoma*. A random sample of ten men over this age in a certain city is selected. The

city's population will be declared in normal condition with respect to the disease if at most one of the men in the sample exhibits it. (*a*) Find the probability that the test will declare the population of the city to be in normal condition when this actually is the case. (*b*) Find the probability that the test, incorrectly, will declare the population to be in normal condition when, actually, 30% of the men over *k* years of age have the disease.

## 60.   Conditional probability

ILLUSTRATION 1.   A precinct coordinator for the Republican party is making a last minute canvass of his precinct before an election. He is asked to estimate the probability that a registered voter will vote, *given* that he is a Republican. To determine this probability, it is obvious that the coordinator would check intentions only of registered Republicans. In the phraseology of the present section, he desires the *conditional probability* that a registered voter will vote, *given* that he is a Republican. This concept of a conditional probability limits the basis for probability to a *subset* of the original sample space.

Let $T_1$ and $T_2$ be events in the sample space $W$ for a random experiment $Z$ whose probability function is $P$. Also, suppose that $P(T_1) \neq 0$. Let $H = T_1 \cap T_2$, as illustrated in Figure 61, where the whole sample space $W$ is represented by the points inside of the largest circle. $H$ is the event that $T_1$ *and* $T_2$ will occur if $Z$ is performed. When desired, we may write $H = (T_1 \text{ and } T_2)$, in place of $H = T_1 \cap T_2$. If we think of probability spread like butter over the large circle, with total probability 1, then $P(T_1)$ is the ratio of the probability spread over $T_1$ to the probability spread over *all of W*. Now, we ask

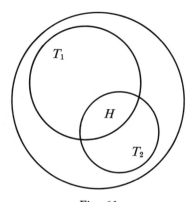

*Fig. 61*

for the ratio of the probability spread over $H$ to the probability spread over *the reduced sample space $T_1$.* The result is given a name as follows.

DEFINITION VI.   *If* $P(T_1) \neq 0$, *the* **conditional probability** *of $T_2$, given that $T_1$ occurs, is represented by $P_c(T_2, given\ T_1)$, and is defined by*

$$P_c(T_2, given\ T_1) = \frac{P(T_1 \cap T_2)}{P(T_1)}. \tag{1}$$

ILLUSTRATION 2.   A group of people consists of four men and eight women, with six boys and eleven girls. A person is selected from the group by lot. Let $T_1$ be the event "*select an adult,*" and $T_2$ be "*select a male.*" Then $P(T_1) = \frac{12}{29}$ and $P(T_2) = \frac{10}{29}$. Also,

$$T_1 \cap T_2 = (4\ men) \quad and \quad P(T_1 \cap T_2) = \tfrac{4}{29}.$$

Then, $P_c(T_2, given\ T_1)$ represents

the conditional probability of selecting a male, given that\
he is an adult. } (2)

From (1),     $P_c(T_2, given\ T_1) = [\tfrac{4}{29} \div \tfrac{12}{29}] = \tfrac{1}{3}.$

If both $P(T_1)$ and $P_c(T_2, given\ T_1)$ are known, we use (1) to obtain $P(T_1 \cap T_2)$. Thus,

$$P(T_1 \cap T_2) = P(T_1)P_c(T_2, given\ T_1). \tag{3}$$

ILLUSTRATION 3.   Suppose that the probability of Robert going to Chicago next week is .6. If he goes, his probability of meeting Hansen is .3. Let $Z$ be the random experiment of Robert's actions next week, with "*going to Chicago*" as event $T_1$ and "*meeting Hansen*" as event $T_2$. The language of the problem permits the inference that

$$P(T_1) = .6 \quad and \quad P_c(T_2, given\ T_1) = .3.$$

Hence, from (3),

*P(of going to Chicago and meeting Hansen)* $= (.6)(.3) = .18.$

DEFINITION VII.   *Events $T_1$ and $T_2$ in a sample space $W$ are said to be* **independent** *(in the probability sense) in case* $P(T_1 \cap T_2) = P(T_1)P(T_2).$

THEOREM VI.   *Let $T_1$ and $T_2$ be events in a sample space $W$ with the probability function $P$. Then, to state that $T_1$ and $T_2$ are independent is equivalent to each of the following statements:*

$$P_c(T_2, given\ T_1) = P(T_2); \tag{4}$$
$$P_c(T_1, given\ T_2) = P(T_1). \tag{5}$$

*Proof.*   If (4) is true, from (1) we obtain

$$P(T_2) = \frac{P(T_1 \cap T_2)}{P(T_1)}, \quad \text{or} \quad P(T_1 \cap T_2) = P(T_1)P(T_2),$$

and hence $T_1$ and $T_2$ are independent. Also, *if* they are independent, then $P(T_1 \cap T_2) = P(T_1)P(T_2)$ and (1) gives

$$P_c(T_2, \text{given } T_1) = \frac{P(T_1)P(T_2)}{P(T_1)} = P(T_2).$$

Hence, (4) is equivalent to the statement that $T_1$ and $T_2$ are independent. The equivalence of (5) is proved similarly.

If two events $T_1$ and $T_2$ in the same sample space are *not* independent, we shall call $T_1$ and $T_2$ **dependent events**. Then, in (1), $P_c(T_2, \text{given } T_1) \neq P(T_2)$.

ILLUSTRATION 4.   A bag contains four black and six white balls, and eight black and twelve white cubes. Let $Z$ be the act of drawing an object from the bag at random. Let the event of obtaining a ball be $T_1$ and of obtaining a white object be $T_2$. With all outcomes of $Z$ equally likely,

$$P(T_1) = \frac{10}{30} = \frac{1}{3}; \quad P(T_2) = \frac{18}{30} = \frac{3}{5}.$$

The event $(T_1 \text{ and } T_2)$, or $T_1 \cap T_2$, is the event that a ball will be drawn which is white. We find that

$$P(T_1 \text{ and } T_2) = \frac{6}{30} = \frac{1}{5},$$

and it is seen that

$$P(T_1 \text{ and } T_2) = P(T_1)P(T_2) = \frac{1}{3} \cdot \frac{3}{5} = \frac{3}{15} = \frac{1}{5}.$$

Hence, $T_1$ and $T_2$ are *independent events.*

Consider a random experiment $Z$ with probability function $P$. Suppose that $Z$ consists of a first experiment $Z_1$, and then an experiment $Z_2$. Let $T_1$ and $T_2$ be events in the sample space for $Z$, where $T_1$ can be caused by an event for $Z_1$ with probability $p_1$ and, if $T_1$ occurs, then $T_2$ can be caused by an event for $Z_2$ with probability $p_2$. Let $T$ be the event $(T_1 \text{ and } T_2)$, or $T = T_1 \cap T_2$. Then, in the sample space for $Z$, we accept

$$P(T_1) = p_1; \quad P_c(T_2, \text{given } T_1) = p_2. \tag{6}$$

On account of (3), agreement (6) is equivalent to defining

$$P(T_1 \cap T_2) = p_1 p_2. \tag{7}$$

Compare (7) with (2) on page 157, where "$(T_1, T_2)$" now is written "$T_1 \cap T_2$." Thus, we notice that (7) includes as a special case Definition V on page 157 for *independent experiments*. Hence, everything accomplished on the basis of Definition V is unaffected by the new agreement (6). However, for independent experiments, the *order* of performance of $Z_1$ and $Z_2$ is immaterial. Then, in (6), the roles of $T_1$ and $T_2$ can be interchanged. This gives $p_2 = P(T_2)$, so that $P_c(T_2, given \ T_1) = P(T_2)$, which implies that $T_1$ and $T_2$ are independent events. In any particular case where (7) is used, the context of the problem should show whether $p_2$ is an *ordinary* or a *conditional* probability. It is emphasized that the multiplication feature in "$p_1 p_2$" occurs in (7), and in (2) on page 157, for *any successive experiments*, or *any simultaneous independent experiments*, $Z_1$ and $Z_2$.

EXAMPLE 1.    There are four white and eight black balls in a bag (I); fifteen white and five black balls in a bag (II). The random experiment, $Z$, consists of selecting a bag at random and *then* drawing a ball. (*a*) Find the probability of obtaining a white ball. (*b*) *Given* that a white ball is obtained, find the probability that it came from (II).

*Solution.*    (*a*) Let $Z_1$ be the experiment of selecting a bag, where $Z_1$ has two equally likely outcomes, so that $P_1[bag \ (I)] = P_1[bag \ (II)] = \frac{1}{2}$. This is equivalent to assigning one-half of the total probability for the experiment $Z$ to the balls (*outcomes*) from each bag. Let $Z_2$ be the experiment of drawing a ball from the selected bag. Thus, $Z$ is the experiment "$Z_1$ and then $Z_2$." A white ball is obtained if either of the following mutually exclusive events $W_1$ and $W_2$ occurs when $Z$ is performed. First, we describe $W_1$ and $W_2$ (and later events) elaborately, and thereafter abbreviate.

$$W_1 = \{(I) \ is \ selected \ and \ white \ is \ drawn\} = \{white \ and \ (I)\}. \qquad (8)$$
$$W_2 = \{(II) \ is \ selected \ and \ white \ is \ drawn\} = \{white \ and \ (II)\}. \qquad (9)$$

2.    For use in (3), think of $T_1$ in (3) as "*obtain* (I)" when a bag is chosen, with $P[(I)] = \frac{1}{2}$. Think of $T_2$ as "*obtain white.*" The probability of drawing a white after (I) is chosen then is the conditional probability

$$P_c[T_2, given \ T_1] = P_c[white, given \ (I)] = \tfrac{4}{12} = \tfrac{1}{3}, \ and$$
$$P[T_1 \ and \ T_2] = P[white \ and \ (I)].$$

Hence, by use of (3), first for $W_1$ and then similarly for $W_2$,

$$P(W_1) = P[white \ and \ (I)] = P[(I)]P_c[white, given \ (I)] = \tfrac{1}{2} \cdot \tfrac{1}{3} = \tfrac{1}{6};$$
$$P(W_2) = P[white \ and \ (II)] = P[(II)]P_c[white, given \ (II)] = \tfrac{1}{2} \cdot \tfrac{3}{4} = \tfrac{3}{8}.$$

Since $W_1$ and $W_2$ are mutually exclusive, and the event "*white drawn*" is $(W_1 \ or \ W_2) = W_1 \cup W_2$, we have

$$P(white) = P(W_1) + P(W_2) = \tfrac{1}{6} + \tfrac{3}{8} = \tfrac{13}{24}.$$

(b) We desire $P_c[(\text{II})$, *given white is drawn*] by use of (1). The event "[*white and* (II)]" is $W_2$. Hence, from (1),

$$P_c[(\text{II}), \textit{given white}] = \frac{P[\textit{white and } (\text{II})]}{P(\textit{white})} = \frac{\frac{3}{8}}{\frac{13}{24}} = \frac{9}{13}.$$

*Comment.* When $\frac{1}{2}$ was assigned as the total probability for all balls in each bag, this implied assigning $\frac{1}{2} \cdot \frac{1}{12}$ or $\frac{1}{24}$ as the probability for each ball in (I), and $\frac{1}{2} \cdot \frac{1}{20}$ or $\frac{1}{40}$ for each ball in (II). Thus, the outcomes of the experiment $Z$ in Example 1 were not equally likely.

The concept of conditional probability extends to the case of any specified number of events in the same sample space, $W$. Thus, if $\{T_1, T_2, T_3\}$ are events in $W$ and $P(T_1 \cap T_2) \neq 0$, we define

$$P_c(T_3, \textit{given } T_1 \cap T_2) = \frac{P(T_1 \cap T_2 \cap T_3)}{P(T_1 \cap T_2)}. \tag{10}$$

From (3) and (10),

$$P(T_1 \cap T_2 \cap T_3) = P(T_1)P_c(T_2, \textit{given } T_1)P_c(T_3, \textit{given } T_1 \cap T_2). \tag{11}$$

The events $\{T_1, T_2, T_3\}$ are said to be *independent* if any two are independent and also*

$$P(T_1 \cap T_2 \cap T_3) = P(T_1)P(T_2)P(T_3). \tag{12}$$

Similarly, we extend agreements (6) and (7) to the case where the experiment $Z$ consists of any number of successive experiments $Z_1, Z_2, Z_3, \cdots$, with corresponding possible events $T_1, T_2, T_3, \cdots$. Thus, if $p_i$ is the probability of $T_i$ when $Z_i$ is performed, and if three experiments $(Z_1, Z_2, Z_3)$ are involved, we have

$$P(T_1 \cap T_2 \cap T_3) = p_1 p_2 p_3. \tag{13}$$

If $(Z_1, Z_2, Z_3)$ are independent, then (13) becomes

$$P(T_1 \cap T_2 \cap T_3) = P(T_1)P(T_2)P(T_3). \tag{14}$$

EXAMPLE 2. A bag contains six blue and nine red balls. If three balls are drawn in succession without replacement, find the probability that they are (*blue, blue, red*), (a) in that order; (b) in any order.

*Solution.* (a) Dependent events are involved. If the first draw is blue, then five blue out of fourteen remain, etc.

$P(\textit{blue, then blue, then red})$

$= P(\textit{blue} \text{ 1st})P_c(\textit{blue} \text{ 2d, given blue } \text{1st})P_c(\textit{red} \text{ 3d, given blue } \text{1st } \textit{and } \text{2d})$

$= \frac{6}{15} \cdot \frac{5}{14} \cdot \frac{9}{13} = \frac{9}{91}. \tag{15}$

---

* Examples would show that (12) is not a consequence of pairwise independence. See Problem 11, page 340, in *Algebra, Elementary Functions, and Probability* by William L. Hart; D. C. Heath and Company, Publishers.

(*b*) Since we consider (*blue, blue, red*) in any order, the *sequence* in which the balls are drawn is of no interest. Hence, we could ask, instead, for the probability of drawing two blue and one red *together*. This problem can be solved as in Exercise 31 by direct use of Definition I of page 138. The probability is

$$p = \frac{{}_6C_2 \cdot 9}{{}_{15}C_3} = \frac{15 \cdot 9}{5 \cdot 7 \cdot 13} = \frac{27}{91}.$$

## Exercise 37

*1.* A class in a school consists of fifteen boys and twenty-five girls, where just five boys and ten girls are able to swim. The experiment is that a child will be selected from the class at random. Let $T$ be the event that the child can swim. Read and find each specified probability: $P(boy)$; $P(girl)$; $P(T)$; $P(boy \cap T)$; $P(girl \cap T)$; $P_c(T, given girl)$; $P_c(T, given boy)$; $P_c(girl, given T)$; $P_c(boy, given T)$.

*2.* A committee consists of four men and six women. In order to fill the positions of chairman and secretary of the committee, first a chairman will be selected by lot and then a secretary by lot. No person will hold two positions. Find the probability that (*a*) the chairman will be a man and the secretary will be a woman; (*b*) both officers will be men or both will be women; (*c*) the secretary will be a man. (*d*) Obtain the conditional probability that the chairman will be a man, given that the secretary is a man.

*3.* A group consists of five men, ten women, fifteen boys, and thirty girls. A person will be picked at random from the group. Let $T_1$ be the event of picking an adult, and $T_2$ be the event of picking a female. Find $P(T_1)$, $P(T_2)$, and $P(T_1 \cap T_2)$. Are $T_1$ and $T_2$ independent events?

*Bag* (I) *contains four white and six blue balls. Bag* (II) *contains five black and ten white balls. Bag* (III) *contains six white and four blue balls. In Problems 4–7, find the requested probability.*

*4.* If a ball is drawn at random from each bag, find the probability that three white balls will be obtained.

*5.* If a ball is drawn at random from a bag selected at random, find the probability that the ball will be white.

*6.* If a ball is drawn at random from a bag selected at random, and if a blue ball is obtained, find the probability that it came from bag (III).

*7.* If three balls are drawn in succession from bag (I), find the probability that all are white if (*a*) each ball is replaced before the next one is drawn; (*b*) if none is replaced after being drawn.

8.  At a television show where guests participate, there are two boxes of
    gifts. In box (I) there are four packages containing valuable gifts and
    eight containing just a lemon. In box (II) there are ten packages con-
    taining valuable gifts and three containing just a lemon. A guest at
    the show is permitted to choose a box at random and then choose a
    package by lot. (*a*) Find the probability of the guest obtaining a
    lemon. (*b*) If he obtained a lemon, find the probability that it came
    from box (I).

9.  In an agricultural experiment on wheat, plant bed (I) contains ten
    stalks which are rust-resistant, and fifteen which do not have this
    property. Plant bed (II) contains eight which are rust-resistant, and
    four which are not. A worker chooses a plant bed at random and then
    a plant at random. Find the probability that he obtains a resistant
    plant (*a*) from (I); (*b*) from (II); (*c*) from either source. (*d*) If he
    obtained a resistant plant, find the probability that it came from bed
    (II).

10. In repeated throws of a die, find the probability that the first toss of 4
    will occur on the third throw.

11. In repeated throws of a coin, find the probability that the first head
    will appear on the third or fourth throw.

12. In repeated throws of two dice, find the probability that the first total
    of 7 will be tossed on the third throw.

*In Problems* 13–14, *cards will be dealt one at a time without replacement
from a well shuffled deck of fifty-two cards.*

13. Find the probability that the first ace will be dealt as the third card.

14. Find the probability that exactly two of the first three cards dealt will
    be kings.

15. A factory warehouse contains forty machines of a certain type, and
    five of these are defective. Two machines were selected at random and
    sent to a customer. He found that both of them were defective,
    and returned them. By error, these machines were placed back in the
    warehouse without being repaired. Later, two machines again were
    selected at random from the warehouse and were shipped to the
    customer, who found that one machine was perfect and one was
    defective. Find the probability of such a sequence of two shipments
    occurring.

NOTE 1.    Human beings can be classified as of blood types O, A, B,
and AB, where AB means that both of the "*antigens*" A and B are
present. In transfusions, blood of type O may be used for a person of
any type. Type A can be used only for a person of type A or type AB.
Type B can be used only for a person of type B or type AB. If the

blood of one person can be used in transfusion to another person, their blood types are said to be *compatible*.

*16.* In a group (I) of sixty people, there are twenty with blood type O, thirty with type A, and ten with type B. In a second group (II) there are twenty people with type O, and ten with each of the types A, B, and AB. A person is picked at random from group (I) to give blood to a person picked at random from group (II). Find the probability that the blood of the donor from group (I) is compatible with that of the recipient in group (II).

*17.* A person will be picked at random from each of groups (I) and (II) of Problem 16. Find the probability that both will have blood type O.

★*18.* On a multiple-choice examination with eight questions, three alternatives are given for the response to each question with only one response correct. Assume that the student will choose his responses at random. The grade on the examination will be the number of correct answers. For each possible set, $h$, of his answers on the examination, let $X(u) = x$ be the number of correct answers. With $f(x) = P(X = x)$, obtain a graph of $y = f(x)$. Find his probability of obtaining a score of 75% or more.

★*19.* For a certain type of biological cell, the empirical probability that the cell will survive for one day is .7. If the cell survives that long, it will split into two new cells of the same type. If a single cell thus starts creation of a population of cells, find the probability that, at the end of two days, there will be (*a*) exactly four cells; (*b*) exactly two cells; (*c*) no cells. Assume that the survival of any cell is not affected by any other cell.

## 61.  Bayes' theorem

EXAMPLE 1.  In the production for one day in a factory providing air conditioners, 30% of them came from production line (I) and 70% from line (II). Previous experience indicates that, with the production process in control, as assumed, just two conditioners per thousand from (I), and three per thousand from (II) will be defective. Out of production for one day, a conditioner is chosen at random and is found defective. Find the probability that it came from (*a*) line (I); (*b*) line (II).

*Solution.* 1.  The set of conditioners manufactured in one day form the sample space, $W$, with probability function $P$. We use the given relative frequencies as probabilities in $W$. Let the event of a conditioner coming from (I) be $T_1$, a conditioner from (II) be $T_2$, and a conditioner being defective be $D$. Then the data are as follows:

$$P(T_1) = .3; P(T_2) = .7; P_c(D, \text{ given } T_1) = .002; P_c(D, \text{ given } T_2) = .003. \quad (1)$$

The problem requests $P_c(T_1,$ *given* $D)$ and $P_c(T_2,$ *given* $D)$.

2.   From (3) on page 171, the probability of the set of defectives in $T_1$, or of the event $T_1 \cap D$, is

$$P(T_1 \cap D) = P(T_1)P_c(D, \text{ given } T_1) = .3(.002) = .0006; \qquad (2)$$

$$P(T_2 \cap D) = P(T_2)P_c(D, \text{ given } T_2) = .7(.003) = .0021. \qquad (3)$$

3.   To obtain $P_c(D,$ *given* $T_1)$ and $P_c(D,$ *given* $T_2)$ we need $P(D)$. We have $W = T_1 \cup T_2$, where $T_1$ and $T_2$ are mutually exclusive. Hence, $D$ consists of the defectives in $T_1$, or the set $D \cap T_1$, *and* the defectives in $T_2$, or $D \cap T_2$. That is,*

$$D = (D \cap T_1) \cup (D \cap T_2), \qquad (4)$$

where the sets $D \cap T_1$ and $D \cap T_2$ are mutually exclusive. The probability of the union of mutually exclusive sets is the *sum of their probabilities*. Hence, from (4), (2), and (3),

$$P(D) = P(D \cap T_1) + P(D \cap T_2) = .0006 + .0021 = .0027. \qquad (5)$$

4.   By use of (1) on page 171,

$$P_c(T_1, \text{ given } D) = \frac{P(T_1 \cap D)}{P(D)} = \frac{.0006}{.0027} = \frac{2}{9}; \qquad (6)$$

$$P_c(T_2, \text{ given } D) = \frac{P(T_2 \cap D)}{P(D)} = \frac{.0021}{.0027} = \frac{7}{9}. \qquad (7)$$

Or, the probability that the defective conditioner came from (I) is $\frac{2}{9}$, and from (II) is $\frac{7}{9}$.

COMMENT.   If 10,000 conditioners were produced in Example 1, then 3000 would come from (I) and 7000 from (II), with $(.002)(3000)$ or 6 defectives from (I), and $(.03)(7000)$ or 21 defectives from (II). With $(6 + 21)$ or 27 defectives out of 10,000, we obtain $P(D) = 27/10,000 = .0027$ as in (5). However, the method of (5) is desirable in future problems.

Let $W$ be a given set of elements (a sample space in our case). Let $\{T_1, T_2, T_3\}$ be mutually exclusive subsets of $W$ such that

$$W = T_1 \cup T_2 \cup T_3.$$

We call $\{T_1, T_2, T_3\}$ an *exhaustive set of subsets* for $W$. Let $D$ be any subset of $W$. Then

$$D = D \cap W = D \cap (T_1 \cup T_2 \cup T_3), \text{ or} \qquad (8)$$

$$D = (D \cap T_1) \cup (D \cap T_2) \cup (D \cap T_3), \qquad (9)$$

* We may obtain (4) formally as follows because $W = T_1 \cup T_2$:
  $$D = D \cap W = D \cap (T_1 \cup T_2) = (D \cap T_1) \cup (D \cap T_2).$$

because $D$ is the *union* of those elements of $D$ in $T_1$, and those in $T_2$, and those in $T_3$. We shall establish the following theorem, which is stated for the general case of $n$ subsets $\{T_i\}$, and will be proved just when $n = 3$.

THEOREM VII.    (**Bayes' rule.**) *If $\{T_1, \cdots, T_n\}$ is an exhaustive set of mutually exclusive events in a sample space $W$, and if $D$ is any event in $W$, then*

$$P_c(T_i, \text{given } D) = \frac{P(T_i \cap D)}{P(T_1 \cap D) + P(T_2 \cap D) + \cdots + P(T_n \cap D)}. \quad (10)$$

*Proof* (*when $n = 3$*).    From (9), the denominator in (10) is $P(D)$. Hence, the right-hand side of (10) becomes $P(T_i \cap D)/P(D)$. By the definition in (1) on page 171, this is $P_c(T_i, \text{given } D)$.

In (4), we met the special case of (9) for two exhaustive sets $T_1$ and $T_2$, with $W = T_1 \cup T_2$. Thus, from (4), in (6) we could have written

$$P_c(T_1, \text{given } D) = \frac{P(T_1 \cap D)}{P(D \cap T_1) + P(D \cap T_2)},$$

which is the special case of (10) with $n = 2$. The student is advised not to use (10) as a formula. The method of solution of Example 1 is more desirable, to emphasize fundamental principles. In Example 1, two conditional probabilities $P_c(D, \text{given } T_1)$ and $P_c(D, \text{given } T_2)$ are provided by the data. Then, we found $P_c(T_1, \text{given } D)$ and $P_c(T_2, \text{given } D)$ where the positions of the events are *reversed*.

## Exercise 38

*1.*  In a certain city, the adult population consists of 45% males and 55% females. Suppose that 3% of the males and 2% of the females have incipient emphysema due to smoking and air pollution.
(*a*)  Specify the conditional probabilities which the data provide.
(*b*)  Find the probability that, if a person picked at random has emphysema, then this person is a male; a female.

HINT.    Let the set of people having emphysema be $E$, the set of males be $M$, and the set of females be $F$. By use of (3) on page 171 obtain $P(E \cap M)$ and $P(E \cap F)$. Then, as for $D$ in (4) on page 178, $E = (E \cap F) \cup (E \cap M)$. Hence obtain $P(E)$ for use in computing $P_c(F, \text{given } E)$ and $P_c(M, \text{given } E)$.

*2.*  In a factory manufacturing typewriters, 40% come from production line (I) and 60% from production line (II). In a quality control program, it is being assumed that, if the production process is in control, .25% of the products from line (I) are defective, and .15% from line (II). If the process is in control, and if a typewriter picked at random from the production on any day is defective, find the probability that the typewriter was produced (*a*) by line (I); (*b*) by line (II).

3. Among the voters in a city, 30% are Democrats, 70% are Republicans, and the mayor is a Republican. A certain recent decision of the mayor is favored by 90% of the Republicans and 40% of the Democrats. If a voter is picked at random and is found to be in favor of the mayor's decision, find the probability that the voter is (*a*) a Democrat; (*b*) a Republican.

4. In a control group for a medical experiment, 70% of the people are white and 30% are black. The blood type is O for 55% of the white group and 40% of the black group. If a person picked at random from the group has blood type O, find the probability that he is (*a*) white; (*b*) black.

5. In a refrigerator factory, 25% of the output is from production line (I) and 75% from line (II). Assume that .1% of the products from line (I) are defective, and .2% from line (II). A refrigerator will be picked at random from the output on any day. If this refrigerator is found to be defective, find the probability that it came (*a*) from line (I); (*b*) from line (II).

6. In a group of sixty men and forty women, it is being assumed that 10% of the men and 15% of the women are diabetic. From the hundred corresponding chemical specimens for a medical test, one sample is picked at random and is found to show the presence of diabetes. Find the probability that the source of the specimen (*a*) was a man; (*b*) was a woman.

7. In a factory producing bathtubs, 30% of the output comes from production line (I), 20% from line (II), and 50% from line (III). Assume that .1% of the bathtubs from (I) are defective, .25% of those from (II), and .15% of those from (III). Find the probability that, if a single tub from a day's production is selected at random and is found defective, then the tub was produced (*a*) by (I); (*b*) by (II); (*c*) by (III).

# 8 | INTRODUCTION TO DIFFERENTIAL CALCULUS

## 62. Historical background

Calculus is concerned mainly with the development and applications of the concepts of the *derivative* and the *integral* of a function. A few clear but isolated uses of equivalent notions occurred in the achievements of brilliant mathematicians long before calculus was organized as a formal discipline. Thus, the Greek mathematician ARCHIMEDES (287–212 B.C.), perhaps the greatest mathematician of history, used the equivalent of an integral. Also, he is credited with application of a method suggesting that he understood the concept of an instantaneous rate of change, now called a *derivative*. After a lapse of almost eighteen hundred years, during which the work of Archimedes lay undiscovered, various mathematicians, who were also astronomers or physicists, began to introduce devices suggestive of derivatives and integrals.

The final explicit development of calculus was preceded by and assisted by the achievements of the French mathematician and philosopher RENÉ DESCARTES (1596–1650) in his introduction of the methods of analytic geometry. Then, late in the 17th Century, the English mathematician Sir ISAAC NEWTON (1642–1727) and the German mathematician GOTTFRIED WILHELM LEIBNITZ (1646–1716) independently formulated the fundamental concepts of calculus. However, it should be remembered that their achievements consisted of appreciating, organizing, and improving on the incomplete and largely disconnected steps which had been taken previously by other mathematicians. This fact was recognized by Newton, who is reputed to have said: "If I have seen a little farther than others, it is because I have stood on the shoulders of giants."

In this text, the concepts of a derivative and an integral will be developed in simple settings, and appropriate applications of the concepts will be considered.

## 63.  Limits

The notion of a limit is an indispensable element in the development of calculus. Fortunately, the universally accepted terminology about limits is such that correct reactions are encouraged on an intuitional basis by the technical vocabulary. We shall accept this basis in our use of limits.

We shall make frequent use of statements like

$$\text{the limit of } f(x) \text{ is } L \text{ as } x \text{ approaches } c, \tag{1}$$

which is abbreviated by writing

$$\lim_{x \to c} f(x) = L. \tag{2}$$

We read (2) as in (1). Or, instead of (2), we may write, with the same meaning,

$$f(x) \to L \quad as \quad x \to c, \tag{3}$$

which is read "$f(x)$ *approaches L as x approaches c,*" where "$\to$" means "*approaches.*"

ILLUSTRATION 1.   If $f(h) = (3h^2 + 2h + 5)/(6 + 3h)$, then

$$\lim_{h \to 0} f(h) = \lim_{h \to 0} \frac{3h^2 + 2h + 5}{6 + 3h} = \frac{0 + 0 + 5}{6 + 0} = \frac{5}{6}. \tag{4}$$

We interpret (4) to mean that $f(h)$ will be *as near $\frac{5}{6}$ as we please for all values of h which are sufficiently near* 0.

In Illustration 1, we met a special case of the following terminology. In it, $f(x)$ is assumed to be defined on an interval $I$ of numbers, except possibly at $x = c$ on $I$. Thus, $f(c)$ is not involved, and *may not exist.*

DEFINITION I.   *To state that* $\lim_{x \to c} f(x) = L$ *means that, if $x \neq c$, f(x) will be as near L as we please at all values of x which are sufficiently near c.*

ILLUSTRATION 2.   $\lim_{x \to 2} (3x^2 + 5x - 4) = 3(2^2) + 5(2) - 4 = 18$.

ILLUSTRATION 3.   Let $$f(x) = \frac{x^2 + x - 6}{x - 2}. \tag{5}$$

In (5), the domain of $f$ consists of all numbers $x \neq 2$. Thus, $f(2)$ does not exist. If $x \neq 2$, from (5) we obtain

$$f(x) = \frac{(x + 3)(x - 2)}{x - 2} = x + 3. \tag{6}$$

A graph of $y = f(x)$, in Figure 62, consists of the line $y = x + 3$, *with a hole at the point* $(x = 2, y = 5)$; this point is *not on the graph* because $f(2)$ is not defined. We have

$$\lim_{x \to 2} f(x) = \lim_{x \to 2} \frac{(x + 3)(x - 2)}{x - 2} = \lim_{x \to 2} (x + 3) = 5. \tag{7}$$

From Definition I, $x = 2$ is *not involved* in consideration of a limit as $x \to 2$. Hence, in (7), the denominator is never zero, and it was legitimate to divide out the common factor $(x - 2)$ before evaluating the limit of the fraction. The geometrical interpretation of (7) is that the ordinate $y$ on the graph of $y = f(x)$ approaches the ordinate 5 of the point $(2, 5)$ as $x \to 2$.

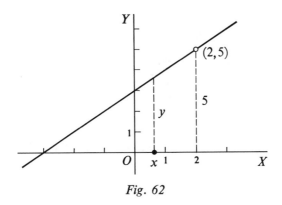

*Fig. 62*

ILLUSTRATION 4. The fraction $(2h^2 + 2h)/(6h^2 + 7h)$ is not defined when $h = 0$. However, $h = 0$ is not involved in a limit as $h \to 0$. Hence, below, we have $h \neq 0$ and may divide out the common factor $h$ from the terms of the fraction, to obtain

$$\lim_{h \to 0} \frac{3h^2 + 2h}{6h^2 + 7h} = \lim_{h \to 0} \frac{3h + 2}{6h + 7} = \frac{0 + 2}{0 + 7} = \frac{2}{7}.$$

We shall accept many facts about limits as being intuitively evident, and usually shall not emphasize the features involved. In a more elaborate introduction to calculus, some of these facts would be stated as theorems, demanding formal proof. In the types of situations met in this text, all of the assumed properties of limits will be true.

## 64.  Continuity

Suppose that a function $f(x)$ is defined at each point $x$ on an interval $I$ of numbers except possibly at $x = c$ on $I$. Then, we present the following terminology.

DEFINITION II.   *A function $f(x)$ is said to be* **continuous** *at $x = c$ in case $f(c)$ exists, $\lim_{x \to c} f(x)$ exists, and*

$$\lim_{x \to c} f(x) = f(c). \tag{1}$$

*If $f$ is not continuous at $x = c$, it is said that $f$ is* **discontinuous** *at $x = c$.*

ILLUSTRATION 1.   In Illustration 3 on page 182,

$$f(x) = \frac{x^2 + x - 6}{x - 2}.$$

We observed that $f(2)$ does not exist; hence $f$ is discontinuous at $x = 2$.

If a function $f(x)$ is continuous at all points $x$ on an interval $I$, it is said that $f$ is *continuous on $I$*. If we state merely that $f$ is *continuous*, this will mean that $f$ is continuous at all values of $x$ in the domain of $f$. The geometrical interpretation of Definition II is that, if $f$ is continuous, the graph of $y = f(x)$ is a "*continuous curve*," that is, *a curve without breaks*. If it is known that the graph of a function $f(x)$ is a continuous curve, in this text we shall permit the immediate inference that $f$ is a continuous function. Then, (1) furnishes a simple means for obtaining $\lim_{x \to c} f(x)$; *we merely substitute $x = c$ in $f(x)$.* This method will apply in the final stage in the computation of any limit which we shall need to evaluate in this text.

ILLUSTRATION 2.   Consider $\lim_{x \to 2} f(x)$, where

$$f(x) = \frac{x^2 + x - 6}{x - 2}. \tag{2}$$

Since $f(2)$ does not exist, $f(x)$ is discontinuous at $x = 2$ and hence (1) does not apply. However, if $x \neq 2$, then

$$f(x) = \frac{(x + 3)(x - 2)}{x - 2} = x + 3.$$

Let $g(x) = x + 3$. Since $x = 2$ is not involved in evaluating a limit as $x \to 2$, we may write

$$\lim_{x \to 2} f(x) = \lim_{x \to 2} g(x) = g(2) = 5. \tag{3}$$

Thus, we first obtained a function $g(x)$, continuous at $x = 2$, with $f(x) = g(x)$ when $x \neq 2$, and then applied (1) to $g(x)$ as in (3). Naturally, the preceding elaborate explanation is needed only to introduce the method. A satisfactory solution is as follows:

$$\lim_{x \to 2} \frac{x^2 + x - 6}{x - 2} = \lim_{x \to 2} \frac{(x + 3)(x - 2)}{x - 2} = \lim_{x \to 2} (x + 3) = 5.$$

This brief solution was given without comment in (7) on page 183. Also, the same method was used in Illustration 4 on page 183.

## Exercise 39

*Evaluate the limit.*

1. $\lim_{x \to 3} (3x^2 - 2x)$.

2. $\lim_{x \to -2} (5x + 7)$.

3. $\lim_{x \to 3} \sqrt[3]{18 + 3x}$.

4. $\lim_{x \to 2} \sqrt{5x^2 + 4x + 8}$.

5. $\lim_{x \to 0} \dfrac{3x^2 + 5x + 3}{2x + 5}$.

6. $\lim_{h \to -1} \dfrac{2h^2 + 3h - 5}{4h^3 + 2}$.

7. $\lim_{w \to 0} \dfrac{5w^3 + 6w}{3w^2 + 5w}$.

8. $\lim_{u \to 0} \dfrac{3u + 4u^3}{5u^2 + 6u}$.

9. $\lim_{x \to 3} \dfrac{x^2 - 4x + 3}{x - 3}$.

10. $\lim_{x \to 1/2} \dfrac{2x^2 + 5x - 3}{4x - 2}$.

11. $\lim_{x \to 3/2} \dfrac{4x - 6}{2x^2 + x - 6}$.

12. $\lim_{h \to -5/2} \dfrac{4h + 10}{2h^2 + h - 10}$.

13. Graph $f(x) = |x|$. Is $f$ continuous at $x = 0$? Find $\lim_{x \to 0} f(x)$.

14. Graph the function $f(x)$ which is defined on the interval from $x = 0$ to $x = 6$ by the equations

$$f(x) = 2x \quad when \quad 0 \leq x \leq 3, \quad and \quad f(x) = 8 - 2x \quad when \quad 3 < x \leq 6.$$

Does $\lim_{x \to 3} f(x)$ exist? If "$\lim_{x \to 3^-}$" means "*limit as $x \to 3$ from the left*," and "$\lim_{x \to 3^+}$" means "*limit as $x \to 3$ from the right*," decide on the values of $\lim_{x \to 3^-} f(x)$ and $\lim_{x \to 3^+} f(x)$. Is $f$ continuous at $x = 3$?

15. Graph $f(x) = [x]$ for $-2 \leq x \leq 4$, where $[x]$ means "*the greatest integer which is less than or equal to x.*" At what values of $x$ is $f$ discontinuous?

## 65.  Corresponding increments of related variables

Let the curve $T$ in Figure 63 on page 186 be the graph of $y = f(x)$. Let $\Delta x$ be any number (usually near zero in our future applications of the notation), and let $x = x_0$ and $x = x_0 + \Delta x$ be neighboring values of $x$, with

$$y_0 = f(x_0) \qquad and \qquad y_0 + \Delta y = f(x_0 + \Delta x); \tag{1}$$
$$\Delta y = f(x_0 + \Delta x) - f(x_0). \tag{2}$$

In (1) and (2), we refer to $\Delta x$ as an *increment* added to $x_0$, and call $\Delta y$ the resulting increment added to $y_0$. On $T$, we have the points $P:(x_0, y_0)$ and $Q:(x_0 + \Delta x, y_0 + \Delta y)$. Thus, $\Delta x$ is the change in $x$ and $\Delta y$ is the change in $y$, in moving from $P$ to $Q$ on $T$.

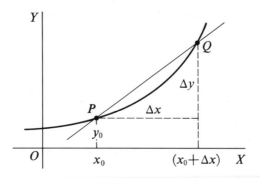

*Fig. 63*

ILLUSTRATION 1.   Let $f(x) = x^2$ in (1) and (2), with $y = f(x)$. If $x_0 = 3$ then $y_0 = f(3) = 9$. If the increment $\Delta x = .2$ is added to 3, we obtain

$$x_0 + \Delta x = 3.2; \qquad y_0 + \Delta y = f(3.2) = 3.2^2 = 10.24;$$
$$\Delta y = 10.24 - 9 = 1.24.$$

In Figure 63, observe secant $PQ$, and let $m(\Delta x)$ be its slope. By the definition of slope for a line on page 54, we find that

$$(\textit{slope of secant } PQ) = m(\Delta x) = \frac{\Delta y}{\Delta x}. \tag{3}$$

## 66.   Average and instantaneous rates of change

In the remainder of this text, the domain of any function $f(x)$ will consist of an interval or intervals of numbers. In any particular discussion about $f(x)$, it will be inferred that $x$ assumes values on only one interval of its domain, unless otherwise specified.

Suppose that $y = f(x)$. With $x_0$ as a fixed number and $\Delta x \neq 0$, let

$$y_0 = f(x_0) \qquad \textit{and} \qquad y_0 + \Delta y = f(x_0 + \Delta x); \textit{ then} \tag{1}$$
$$\Delta y = f(x_0 + \Delta x) - f(x_0). \tag{2}$$

Points $P:(x_0, y_0)$ and $Q:(x_0 + \Delta x, y_0 + \Delta y)$ are shown on the graph, $T$, of $y = f(x)$ in Figure 63. If we move on $T$ from $P$ to $Q$, the change in $x$ is $\Delta x$ which causes the change $\Delta y$ in $y$. Then, it is natural to consider the *rate* at which $y$ changes, with respect to the change in $x$. This leads to the following terminology.

DEFINITION III.   *If* $y = f(x)$, *the* **average rate of change** *of $y$, or $f(x)$, with respect to $x$, from $x = x_0$ to $x = x_0 + \Delta x$ is the ratio of the change in $y$ to the change in $x$, or*

$$\left\{ \begin{matrix} \textbf{av. rate of change } \textit{of } y \\ \textit{with respect to } x \textit{ from} \\ x_0 \textit{ to } (x_0 + \Delta x) \end{matrix} \right\} = \frac{\Delta y}{\Delta x} = \frac{f(x_0 + \Delta x) - f(x_0)}{\Delta x}. \tag{3}$$

EXAMPLE 1.  If $f(x) = x^2 - 4x + 7$, find the average rate of change of $f(x)$ with respect to $x$ from $x = 3$ to $x = 3 + \Delta x$, for values of $\Delta x$ near 0, and investigate the limit of this rate as $\Delta x \to 0$.

*Solution.*  *1.*  Let $y = f(x)$. Then, from $x = 3$ to $x = 3 + \Delta x$, with $x_0 = 3$ in (3),

$$\left\{ \begin{matrix} \text{av. rate of} \\ \text{change of } y \end{matrix} \right\} = \frac{\Delta y}{\Delta x} = \frac{f(3 + \Delta x) - f(3)}{\Delta x}.$$

Since $f(3) = 4$ and $f(3 + \Delta x) = (3 + \Delta x)^2 - 4(3 + \Delta x) + 7$,

$$f(3 + \Delta x) - f(3) = 9 + 6\Delta x + (\Delta x)^2 - 12 - 4\Delta x + 7 - 4, \text{ } or$$

$$\Delta y = (\Delta x)^2 + 2\Delta x; \tag{4}$$

$$\left\{ \begin{matrix} \text{av. rate of change of } y, \\ x = 3 \text{ } to \text{ } x = 3 + \Delta x \end{matrix} \right\} = \frac{\Delta y}{\Delta x} = \frac{(\Delta x)^2 + 2(\Delta x)}{\Delta x} = \Delta x + 2. \tag{5}$$

*2.*  Values of $\Delta y / \Delta x$ are found by substituting for $\Delta x$ in (5):

| $\Delta x =$ | $-.5$ | $-.1$ | $-.01$ | (as $\Delta x \to 0$) | $.01$ | $.1$ | $.5$ |
|---|---|---|---|---|---|---|---|
| $\left\{ \begin{matrix} \text{AV. RATE} \\ \text{OF CHANGE} \end{matrix} \right\} = \dfrac{\Delta y}{\Delta x} =$ | 1.5 | 1.9 | 1.99 | LIMIT *is* 2 | 2.01 | 2.1 | 2.5 |

$$\lim_{\Delta x \to 0} \frac{\Delta y}{\Delta x} = \lim_{\Delta x \to 0} (\Delta x + 2) = 2, \tag{6}$$

which is checked by data in the preceding table.

If the average rate of change of a function $f(x)$ from $x = x_0$ to $x = x_0 + \Delta x$ has a limit as $\Delta x \to 0$, this limit is called the **instantaneous rate of change** of $f(x)$ at $x = x_0$. If $f(x) = x^2 - 4x + 7$, in (6) it was found that the instantaneous rate of change of $f(x)$ at $x = 3$ is 2.

A geometric interpretation can be introduced for the instantaneous rate just described. In Figure 64 on page 188, the parabola, $H$, is the graph of $y = x^2 - 4x + 7$ from Example 1, with $P:(3, 4)$ on $H$. For each value of $\Delta x$, we have $Q:(3 + \Delta x, 4 + \Delta y)$ on $H$, and secant $PQ$ of $H$, as described for Figure 63 on page 186. Figure 64 shows $PQ$ with $\Delta x = -1$. From (3) on page 186 and (5), for any $\Delta x$,

$$m(\Delta x) = (\text{slope of } PQ) = \frac{\Delta y}{\Delta x} = \Delta x + 2. \tag{7}$$

In Figure 64, (*slope of PQ*) $= -1 + 2 = 1$. Each entry in the table for Example 1 thus is the slope of a corresponding secant $PQ$ of the parabola in

Figure 64. If $\Delta x \to 0$, the corresponding point $Q:(3 + \Delta x, 4 + \Delta y)$ moves on $H$ and approaches $P$, while secant $PQ$ revolves about $P$ with

$$\lim_{\Delta x \to 0} (\textit{slope } PQ) = \lim_{\Delta x \to 0} m(\Delta x) = 2. \tag{8}$$

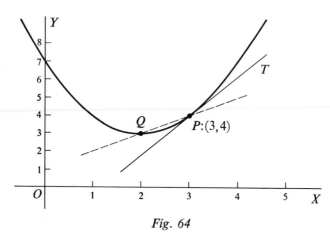

*Fig. 64*

Let $PT$ be the line through $P$ with slope 2. Since the slope of $PQ$ approaches the slope of $PT$, it is sensible to refer to $PT$ as the *limiting position* of $PQ$ as $\Delta x \to 0$. Then, we decide to call $PT$ the **tangent** to $H$ at $P$. Thus, we have interpreted *the instantaneous rate of change of $f(x)$ at $x = 2$ as the slope of a tangent to the graph of $y = f(x)$ at $x = 2$.* To obtain an equation for $PT$ through $P:(3, 4)$, we use the point-slope equation of a line from page 56 with slope 2 and obtain

$$y - 4 = 2(x - 3), \qquad or \qquad y = 2x - 2.$$

The tangent $PT$ is shown in Figure 64.

## 67.  The derivative of a function

In calculus, the instantaneous rate of change of a function $f(x)$ at any value of $x$ is given a name as follows.

DEFINITION IV.   *At any point $x = x_0$ in the domain of a function $f(x)$, if the average rate of change of $f(x)$ from $x = x_0$ to $x = x_0 + \Delta x$ has a limit as $\Delta x \to 0$, this limit is called the* **derivative** *of $f(x)$ at $x = x_0$.*

For each number $x_0$ in the domain of a function $f(x)$ where the derivative of $f(x)$ exists, there is a single corresponding number called the *derivative* of $f$ at $x_0$. This correspondence between values of $x$ and values of the derivative defines a *function*, called the *derivative function* for $f$ and represented by $f'$, read "$f$ *prime.*" Thus, $f'(x)$ is the derivative of $f$ at the point $x$ in the domain of $f$. If $y = f(x)$, then we also let $y' = f'(x)$. From the expression for an *average rate of change* in (3) on page 186 with $x_0$ replaced by the arbitrary number $x$, and from Definition IV, we obtain

$$f'(x) = \lim_{\Delta x \to 0} \frac{f(x + \Delta x) - f(x)}{\Delta x}, \quad or \quad y' = \lim_{\Delta x \to 0} \frac{\Delta y}{\Delta x}, \quad (1)$$

with
$$y + \Delta y = f(x + \Delta x); \quad \Delta y = f(x + \Delta x) - f(x). \quad (2)$$

ILLUSTRATION 1.  Let $f(x) = x^2 - 4x + 7$. From Section 66, with an *instantaneous rate of change* now called a *derivative*, we have $f'(3) = 2$.

If a function $f(x)$ has a derivative at $x = x_0$, then $f$ is said to be *differentiable at $x_0$*. To state merely that "$f$ *is differentiable*," will mean that $f$ has a derivative at each value of $x$ in the domain of $f$. If we refer simply to "*the derivative of $f$,*" we shall mean the derivative function $f'$, or its value $f'(x)$ at an arbitrary point $x$ in the domain of $f$. If $f(x)$ is given, the process of obtaining $f'(x)$ is called **differentiation**. We speak of differentiating $f(x)$ to obtain $f'(x)$. If $y = f(x)$, then $f'(x)$ also may be represented by $y'$, or $D_x y$, or $D_x f(x)$. Thus, we have

$$y' = f'(x); \quad D_x y = f'(x); \quad D_x f(x) = f'(x).$$

"$D_x$" specifies the operation of differentiation. We read "$D_x f(x)$" as "*the derivative (with respect to $x$) of $f(x)$,*" where the phrase in parentheses may be omitted if $x$ is known to be the independent variable. If $y = f(x)$, then $f'(x_0)$ can be represented also by $D_x y|_{x=x_0}$, which is read "*the derivative of $y$ with respect to $x$ at $x = x_0$.*"

Derivatives can be obtained in simple cases by direct use of Definition IV, as summarized in (1). This method will be called the "*increment-method,*" or the "$\Delta$-*process.*" Later, by this method, we shall derive general formulas which will enable us to obtain derivatives without direct use of the $\Delta$-process.

**Summary.**   *The $\Delta$-process for differentiating a function $f(x)$.*

(I)   *Let $y = f(x)$, and consider $x$ as a fixed number.*

(II)   *With $\Delta x \neq 0$, replace $x$ by $(x + \Delta x)$, and $y$ by $(y + \Delta y)$:*

$$y + \Delta y = f(x + \Delta x).$$

(III)   *Subtract:* $\qquad\qquad \Delta y = f(x + \Delta x) - f(x).$

(IV)   *Divide and simplify:* $\qquad \dfrac{\Delta y}{\Delta x} = \dfrac{f(x + \Delta x) - f(x)}{\Delta x}.$

(V)   *Obtain* $\qquad\qquad y' = f'(x) = \lim_{\Delta x \to 0} \dfrac{\Delta y}{\Delta x}.$

EXAMPLE 1.   If $f(x) = x^2 + 3x + 4$, obtain $f'(x)$, and then $f'(4)$.

*Solution.*   Let $\qquad\qquad y = x^2 + 3x + 4.$ $\qquad\qquad$ (3)

Then $\qquad y + \Delta y = (x + \Delta x)^2 + 3(x + \Delta x) + 4$, *or*
$$y + \Delta y = x^2 + 3x + 4 + 2x(\Delta x) + 3\Delta x + (\Delta x)^2. \qquad (4)$$

Subtract, (3) from (4):

$$\Delta y = 2x(\Delta x) + 3\Delta x + (\Delta x)^2; \qquad \frac{\Delta y}{\Delta x} = 2x + 3 + \Delta x.$$

Hence, $\qquad\qquad y' = \lim_{\Delta x \to 0} (2x + 3 + \Delta x) = 2x + 3$, *or*
$$f'(x) = 2x + 3.$$

Then, $f'(4) = 8 + 3 = 11.$

EXAMPLE 2.   If $y = x^3$, obtain $y'$.

*Solution.*   With the routine of the $\Delta$-process, we proceed as follows, where the binomial expansion for $(x + \Delta x)^3$ is used.

$$y = x^3; \qquad\qquad (5)$$
$$y + \Delta y = (x + \Delta x)^3, \ or$$
$$y + \Delta y = x^3 + 3x^2(\Delta x) + 3x(\Delta x)^2 + (\Delta x)^3. \qquad (6)$$

Subtract, (5) from (6):

$$\Delta y = 3x^2(\Delta x) + 3x(\Delta x)^2 + (\Delta x)^3;$$
$$\frac{\Delta y}{\Delta x} = 3x^2 + 3x(\Delta x) + (\Delta x)^2. \qquad (7)$$

Hence, $\qquad y' = \lim_{\Delta x \to 0} \frac{\Delta y}{\Delta x} = 3x^2 + 0 + 0, \quad or \quad y' = 3x^2.$

On the basis of the discussion of a tangent line in Section 66, the following definition is presented. In the $xy$-plane, any line with *slope* is *not vertical.* Hence, the definition introduces the concept of a *nonvertical* tangent. At a later stage, we shall discuss vertical tangents.

DEFINITION V.   *To state that the graph, H, of $y = f(x)$ has a* **nonvertical tangent** *PT at a point $P:(x_0, y_0)$ on H will mean that $f'(x_0)$ exists and that PT is the line through P with slope $f'(x_0)$. That is,*

[**slope of tangent** *at $P:(x_0, y_0)$*] $= f'(x_0) = D_x y|_{x=x_0}.$

ILLUSTRATION 2.   With $f(x) = x^2 + 3x + 4$ in Example 1, we have $f'(x) = 2x + 3$. On the graph, $H$, of $y = f(x)$ in Figure 65, if $x = -2$ then

$y = 2$. At $P:(-2, 2)$ on $H$, the slope of the tangent $PT$ is $f'(-2) = -4 + 3 = -1$. Hence, an equation for $PT$ is

$$y - 2 = -(x + 2), \qquad or \qquad x + y = 0.$$

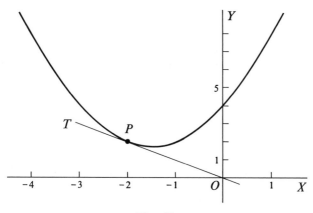

*Fig. 65*

EXAMPLE 3    Graph the function $f(x) = x^2 + 3x + 4$.

*Solution.   1.*   Let $y = x^2 + 3x + 4$. From Example 1, $y' = 2x + 3$.

2.   The graph will have a horizontal tangent when its slope is zero, or when

$$y' = 2x + 3 = 0, \qquad or \qquad x = -\tfrac{3}{2}.$$

Then $y = (\tfrac{3}{2})^2 - 3(\tfrac{3}{2}) + 4 = \tfrac{7}{4}$. Thus, the tangent is horizontal at the point $V:(-1.5, \tfrac{7}{4})$, the vertex of the parabola. Other points on the graph of $y = f(x)$ were obtained as the basis for the parabola in Figure 65.

EXAMPLE 4.   Differentiate: $\qquad\qquad f(x) = \dfrac{3x}{2x + 5}.$   (8)

*Solution.*   Let $y = f(x)$. Then $y + \Delta y = f(x + \Delta x)$;

$$\Delta y = \frac{3(x + \Delta x)}{2(x + \Delta x) + 5} - \frac{3x}{2x + 5}, \quad or$$

$$\Delta y = \frac{(3x + 3\Delta x)(2x + 5) - 3x(2x + 2\Delta x + 5)}{(2x + 2\Delta x + 5)(2x + 5)};$$

$$\frac{\Delta y}{\Delta x} = \frac{15\Delta x}{\Delta x(2x + 2\Delta x + 5)(2x + 5)} = \frac{15}{(2x + 2\Delta x + 5)(2x + 5)}.$$

Hence,    $y' = \lim\limits_{\Delta x \to 0} \dfrac{\Delta y}{\Delta x} = \dfrac{15}{(2x + 0 + 5)(2x + 5)} = \dfrac{15}{(2x + 5)^2}.$

## Exercise 40

*1.* (a) If $f(x) = x^2 + x^c$ and $y = f(x)$, find the average rate of change $\Delta y/\Delta x$ from $x = 2$ to $x = 2 + \Delta x$. (b) Calculate and tabulate $\Delta y/\Delta x$ for $\Delta x$ equal to $\pm.5$, $\pm.1$, and $\pm.01$. (c) Find the limit of the result in (a) as $\Delta x \to 0$, that is, find the instantaneous rate of change of $f(x)$ at $x = 2$, which is $f'(2)$. (d) Obtain an equation for the tangent to the graph of $y = f(x)$ at the point where $x = 2$.

*Use the $\Delta$-process in all remaining problems.*

*2.* Find $f'(x)$ if $f(x) = x$.          *3.* Obtain $f'(x)$ if $f(x) = x^2$.

*4.* If $y = 3x + 5$, calculate $y'$.     *5.* Find $D_x(4x^2 + 3x)$.

*6.* Differentiate the function $(2x^2 + x - 3)$.

*7.* Obtain $D_t(3t + t^2)$.

*8.* Calculate $D_x x^4$.

HINT.   Recall $(a + b)^4 = a^4 + 4a^3b + 6a^2b^2 + 4ab^3 + b^4$.

*Differentiate the function of t, x, or y.*

*9.* $h(x) = 4x + 7$.   *10.* $k(x) = 4x - x^3$.   *11.* $f(x) = x^3$.

*12.* $f(x) = \dfrac{1}{x}$.   *13.* $g(y) = \dfrac{1}{y^2}$.   *14.* $F(t) = \dfrac{t}{2t + 3}$.

*15.* $f(x) = \sqrt{x}$.   *16.* $g(y) = \sqrt{4 + y}$.   *17.* $h(t) = 1/\sqrt{t}$.

HINT for Problem 15.   With $y = \sqrt{x}$,

$$\frac{\Delta y}{\Delta x} = \frac{\sqrt{x + \Delta x} - \sqrt{x}}{\Delta x}.$$

Before attempting to calculate the limit as $\Delta x \to 0$, multiply the numerator and the denominator by $(\sqrt{x + \Delta x} + \sqrt{x})$ to rationalize the numerator.

★ *18.* If a function $f(x)$ has a derivative at $x = x_0$, prove that $\lim_{\Delta x \to 0} f(x_0 + \Delta x) = f(x_0)$, so that $f$ is continuous at $x = x_0$. Thus, a *differentiable* function is a *continuous* function. Also, verify that, if $f(x) = |x|$, then $f$ is continuous at $x = 0$ but $f'(0)$ does not exist. Hence, a function $f(x)$ may be continuous at a point $x = x_0$ but may not have a derivative at $x = x_0$.

## 68.   Differentiation of polynomials

We shall derive certain formulas which will make it possible to differentiate without use of the $\Delta$-process in the types of problems to be met in this text. In particular, we shall be able to differentiate any polynomial function by use of the following formulas. We assume that any function involved in them is differentiable.

*If k is a constant, then*    $D_xk = 0.$    (I)

*If k is a constant, then*    $D_xkf(x) = kf'(x).$    (II)

$$D_x[f(x) + g(x) + h(x)] = f'(x) + g'(x) + h'(x).$$    (III)

**Simple power formula.** *If n is an integer, and* $x \neq 0$ *if* $n \leq 0,$

$$D_xx^n = nx^{n-1}.$$    (IV)

The student may prove (I) in the next exercise. Formulas for differentiation in this chapter will be numbered consecutively in Roman numerals as in (I)–(IV).

*Proof of* (II).   Let $y = kf(x)$. Then

$$y + \Delta y = kf(x + \Delta x); \qquad \Delta y = kf(x + \Delta x) - kf(x);$$

$$\frac{\Delta y}{\Delta x} = k\frac{f(x + \Delta x) - f(x)}{\Delta x}.$$

Hence,    $D_xy = \lim\limits_{\Delta x \to 0} \dfrac{\Delta y}{\Delta x} = k\left[\lim\limits_{\Delta x \to 0} \dfrac{f(x + \Delta x) - f(x)}{\Delta x}\right].$

By the definition of $f'(x)$, we thus obtain $D_xy = kf'(x)$.

*Proof of* (III), *for* $[f(x) + g(x)]$.   Let $y = f(x) + g(x)$. Then

$$y + \Delta y = f(x + \Delta x) + g(x + \Delta x).$$

$$\Delta y = f(x + \Delta x) + g(x + \Delta x) - [f(x) + g(x)];$$

$$\frac{\Delta y}{\Delta x} = \frac{f(x + \Delta x) - f(x)}{\Delta x} + \frac{g(x + \Delta x) - g(x)}{\Delta x}.$$

Hence,    $y' = \lim\limits_{\Delta x \to 0} \dfrac{\Delta y}{\Delta x} =$

$$\lim\limits_{\Delta x \to 0} \frac{f(x + \Delta x) - f(x)}{\Delta x} + \lim\limits_{\Delta x \to 0} \frac{g(x + \Delta x) - g(x)}{\Delta x}, \text{ } or$$

$$y' = f'(x) + g'(x).$$

In previous problems, formula (IV) was proved for the cases $n = 1, 2, 3,$ and 4. Proof of (IV) for any positive integer $n$ is requested of the student in a supplementary problem of the next exercise.

ILLUSTRATION 1.   By use of (IV), $D_xx^4 = 4x^3$. By use of (I)–(IV),

$$D_x(5x^3 - 4x^2 + 7x - 5) = 5D_xx^3 - 4D_xx^2 + 7D_xx - D_x5$$
$$= 5(3x^2) - 4(2x) + 7(1) - 0 = 15x^2 - 8x + 7.$$

The student should aim to omit the intermediate details as given here for illustration, and thus write the result immediately.

In Problems 12 and 13 on page 192, it was proved that $D_x x^{-1} = -x^{-2}$ and $D_x x^{-2} = -2x^{-3}$. These results prove (IV) with $n = -1$ and $n = -2$. Since $x^0 = 1$, we notice that (IV) is true in the trivial case where $n = 0$. In applications, we shall use (IV) only in cases where $n > 0, n = -1$, or $n = -2$. Proof of (IV) for $n < -2$ will be met in a supplementary section. However, in the next exercise, practice will be offered in use of (IV) in cases unproved thus far.

ILLUSTRATION 2.   From (IV) with $n = -4$, and by use of the definition of a power with a negative exponent,

$$D_x\left(\frac{3}{x^4}\right) = D_x(3x^{-4}) = 3(-4)x^{-5} = -\frac{12}{x^5}.$$

## 69.   The chain rule

We shall deal with three related variables, $\{x, u, y\}$, where $y$ is a function of $u$ and $u$ is a function of $x$, so that $y$ also is a function of $x$. That is, there exist functions $f(u)$ and $g(x)$ with

$$y = f(u) \quad and \quad u = g(x), \quad so \ that \quad y = f(g(x)), \tag{1}$$

for all values of $x$ in some set, $H$, of numbers. If we let $F(x) = f(g(x))$, then $F$ is called the **composite function** of $f$ by $g$.

ILLUSTRATION 1.   If $y = 3u + 5u^2$ and $u = 2x + 1$, then

$$y = 3(2x + 1) + 5(2x + 1)^2. \tag{2}$$

If we let $f(u) = 3u + 5u^2$ and $g(x) = 2x + 1$, then the composite of $f$ by $g$ is the function $F$ where $F(x)$ is given on the right in (2).

In connection with (1), it is not always desirable to eliminate the intermediate variable $u$ of the set $\{x, u, y\}$ by substitution. This fact makes the following result important when $D_x y$ is to be calculated.

THEOREM I.   *If $y$ is a differentiable function of $u$, and $u$ is a differentiable function of $x$, then $y$ is a differentiable function of $x$ and*

$$D_x y = (D_u y)(D_x u). \tag{V}$$

*Or, if $y = f(u)$ and $u = g(x)$, then*

$$y' = f'(u)g'(x), \quad where \quad u = g(x). \tag{3}$$

*Proof.* With $(x_0, u_0, y_0)$ and $(x_0 + \Delta x, u_0 + \Delta u, y_0 + \Delta y)$ as two sets of corresponding values of the variables,*

$$\frac{\Delta y}{\Delta x} = \frac{\Delta y}{\Delta u} \cdot \frac{\Delta u}{\Delta x}. \tag{4}$$

As $\Delta x \to 0$, we have $\Delta u \to 0$ because $u$ is a continuous function of $x$. Hence

$$\lim_{\Delta x \to 0} \frac{\Delta y}{\Delta x} = \left( \lim_{\Delta u \to 0} \frac{\Delta y}{\Delta u} \right) \left( \lim_{\Delta x \to 0} \frac{\Delta u}{\Delta x} \right), \text{ or}$$

$$D_x y = (D_u y)(D_x u).$$

ILLUSTRATION 2.   If $y = (3x^2 + 2x)^8$, let $u = 3x^2 + 2x$. Then $y = u^8$ and $u = 3x^2 + 2x$ in (1). From (3), or (V),

$$D_x y = 8u^7 D_x u = 8(3x^2 + 2x)^7(6x + 2).$$

**A general power formula.** *If $u = g(x)$ where $g$ is differentiable, and $n$ is a rational number, then*†

$$D_x u^n = n u^{n-1} D_x u. \tag{VI}$$

*Proof of* (VI) *when $n$ is an integer.*‡   Let $y = u^n$. Then, by use of (IV), $D_u y = n u^{n-1}$. Hence, by use of (V),

$$D_x u^n = D_x y = (D_u y)(D_x u) = n u^{n-1} D_x u.$$

ILLUSTRATION 3.   By use of (VI) with $u = 3x^2 + 2x$,

$$D_x(3x^2 + 2x)^8 = 8(3x^2 + 2x)^7(6x + 2),$$

as obtained less immediately in Illustration 2.

## 70.   The derivative as the slope of a tangent

Let $H$ be the graph of $y = f(x)$, where $f$ is differentiable. On page 190, the tangent (line) to $H$ at any point $P:(x_0, y_0)$ was defined as the line $PT$ through $P$ with slope $f'(x_0)$. Since $PT$ has a slope, it is implied that any tangent as thus defined is *not vertical.*§ The slope $f'(x_0)$ of the tangent at $P$ also may be called the *slope of the graph $H$* at $P$. The tangent at $P$ is *horizontal* when $f'(x_0) = 0$. When this occurs, $P$ is called a **stationary point** of the graph and, also, the function $f(x)$ is said to be *stationary* at $x = x_0$.

EXAMPLE 1.   Graph the function $f(x) = x^2 - 4x + 6$.

*Solution.   1.* Let $y = x^2 - 4x + 6$. Then $y' = 2x - 4$. Hence, the tangent to the graph, $H$, of $f$ will be horizontal when and only when $2x - 4 = 0$,

---

\* To permit a simple, but not complete proof, we assume that $\Delta u \neq 0$ if $\Delta x$ is sufficiently near 0, with $\Delta x \neq 0$. This assumption is unnecessary.

† Except for values of $x$ giving an undefined right-hand side.

‡ The case where $n$ is not an integer will be met in a supplementary section.

§ Consideration of vertical tangents will be met later.

or $x = 2$. In Figure 66, $H$ was drawn by use of the following table of values, where $x = 2$ was used to locate the stationary point $V:(x = 2, y = 2)$.

| $x =$ | 0 | 1 | 2 | 3 | 4 |
|-------|---|---|---|---|---|
| $y =$ | 6 | 3 | 2 | 3 | 6 |

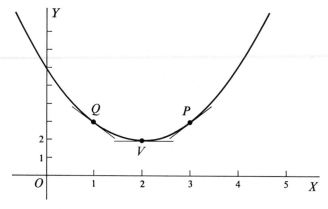

*Fig. 66*

2.   At $x = 3$, we find $y = 3$ and $y' = 6 - 4 = 2$. The tangent to $H$ at $P:(3, 3)$ has the following equation, obtained by using the point-slope form of a line with slope 2:

$$y - 3 = 2(x - 3), \quad or \quad y = 2x - 3.$$

3.   At $x = 1$, we find $y = 3$ and $y' = 2 - 4 = -2$. The tangent at $Q:(1, 3)$ has the equation

$$y - 3 = -2(x - 1), \quad or \quad y = -2x + 5.$$

The tangents at $P$, $Q$, and the stationary point (the vertex) are shown in Figure 66.

DEFINITION VI.   *To state that a function $f(x)$ is* **increasing**, *or* **decreasing**, *when x is on an interval I, has the following meaning, where $x_1$ and $x_2$ are any points on I:*

$f(x)$ *is* **increasing** *in case $f(x_1) < f(x_2)$ when $x_1 < x_2$;*     (1)

$f(x)$ *is* **decreasing** *in case $f(x_1) > f(x_2)$ when $x_1 < x_2$.*     (2)

Observe the graph, $H$, of $y = x^2 - 4x + 6$ in Figure 66. If we move on $H$ from left to right, then $H$ is *falling* in the neighborhood of $Q:(1, 3)$ where $y' = -2 < 0$, or (2) is true; $H$ is *rising* in the neighborhood of $P:(3, 3)$ where $y' = 2 > 0$, or (1) is true. Without added discussion, we take these features as typical of positive or negative slope at a point on the graph of a function $f(x)$ whose derivative $f'$ is continuous. Hence, we accept the following conclusions.

*If x is sufficiently near $x_0$, $f(x)$ is* **increasing** *if*\* $D_x y|_{x=x_0} > 0$, *and is* **decreasing** *if* $D_x y|_{x=x_0} < 0$. $\biggr\}$ (3)

ILLUSTRATION 1.   In Example 1 where $y = f(x)$ and $f'(x) = 2x - 4$, we see that $f(x)$ is *increasing* when $2x - 4 > 0$ or $x > 2$, and is *decreasing* when $2x - 4 < 0$ or $x < 2$. These conclusions are verified by the graph of $f(x)$ in Figure 66. If we move on the graph from left to right, the graph *falls* while $x < 2$, and *rises* when $x > 2$.

## Exercise 41

*Find $f'(x)$ or $y'$ without using the $\Delta$-process.*

1.  $f(x) = 7x^3$.
2.  $f(x) = -3x^5$.
3.  $y = \frac{1}{2}x^2$.
4.  $y = 2x^6$.
5.  $f(x) = 3x^3 + 4x^2 - 5x + 7$.
6.  $y = 3x^4 - 2x^3 + x - 1$.
7.  $y = -2x^4 - 3x^2 + 4x - 3$.
8.  $f(x) = 2x^4 - 3x^2 - x^5 + 7$.

(a) *Find the stationary point of the graph of the function, and then draw its graph, showing the tangent at the stationary point.* (b) *Obtain equations for the tangents at the specified points.* (c) *For what values of x is $f'(x) > 0$ and for what values is $f'(x) < 0$?* (d) *Describe the values of x where $f(x)$ is increasing and where decreasing.*

9.  $f(x) = x^2 - 2x + 2$; tangents where $x = 0$ and $x = 2$.
10. $f(x) = 2x^2 - 6x + 3$; tangents where $x = 2$ and $x = 4$.
11. $f(x) = -x^2 - 4x + 5$; tangents where $x = -3$ and $x = 0$.
12. $f(x) = -x^2 + 2x - 5$; tangents where $x = 0$ and $x = 2$.

13. Obtain $y'$ if $y = \frac{6}{x^3}$; $y = \frac{8}{x^5}$.

*Differentiate the function. Use the chain rule where applicable to avoid expanding.*

14. $3 + 5x - \dfrac{7}{x^4}$.
15. $2x^2 + \dfrac{3}{x^2}$.
16. $2 - x - \dfrac{4}{x}$.
17. $(3x + 5)^6$.
18. $(2x - 3)^4$.
19. $(3s^2 + 4)^5$.
20. $(4x^2 + 3x - 5)^3$.
21. $(2t^3 - 3t + 1)^4$.
22. $(s^2 - 5 + 2s^4)^5$.

★23. Prove differentiation formula (I), and (IV) if $n$ is any positive integer.

HINT.   Let $y = x^n$. By use of the binomial theorem,
$$y + \Delta y = (x + \Delta x)^n = x^n + nx^{n-1}\Delta x$$
$$+ \frac{n(n-1)}{2} x^{n-2}(\Delta x)^2 + \cdots + (\Delta x)^n.$$

\* We read "$D_x y|_{x=x_0}$" as "*the derivative of y with respect to x at $x = x_0$.*"

## 71. Velocity as a derivative

Consider the motion of an object on a straight line, labeled as an $s$-axis, $OS$, in Figure 67, where the object will be called a *particle* and is idealized as a point $P$. Motion of this nature is called **rectilinear motion**. Let any instant of time be designated as $t$ units of time from some fixed instant when $t = 0$, with $t > 0$ after $t = 0$ and $t < 0$ before $t = 0$. Let $s$ be the measure, in some linear unit, of the directed distance of the particle from the origin of the $s$-axis at any time $t$. Assume that $s$ is expressed as some function of the time, $s = f(t)$, where $f$ is differentiable. Then, we shall define the notion of *velocity* for the particle.

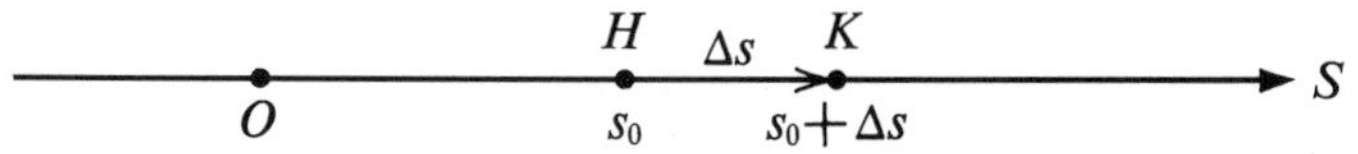

*Fig. 67*

Let $\Delta t$ be a variable increment of time, where $\Delta t \neq 0$. Suppose that $s = s_0$ and $s = s_0 + \Delta s$ when $t = t_0$ and $t = t_0 + \Delta t$, respectively. The corresponding positions $H$ and $K$ of the particle are indicated in Figure 67. Over the time interval from $t_0$ to $(t_0 + \Delta t)$, the *average velocity* of $P$ is defined as follows:

$$\left\{ \begin{array}{c} \textbf{average velocity } \textit{from} \\ t_0 \textit{ to } (t_0 + \Delta t) \end{array} \right\} = \frac{\Delta s}{\Delta t} = \frac{f(t_0 + \Delta t) - f(t_0)}{\Delta t}. \tag{1}$$

Then, the *velocity*, $v$, of $P$ at the instant $t_0$ is defined as the *limit* of the average velocity in (1) as $\Delta t \to 0$, or as the *instantaneous rate of change of $s$* with respect to $t$. Thus, $v$ is defined as $D_t s$:

$$v = \lim_{\Delta t \to 0} \frac{\Delta s}{\Delta t} = D_t s, \quad \textit{or} \quad v = f'(t). \tag{2}$$

Suppose that a projectile, $P$, thought of as a particle, is shot upward from the earth. Let distance from the earth be measured positive upward, and suppose that $v_0$ feet per second is the initial velocity of $P$. Then, if air resistance and other complications are neglected, the projectile's height $s$ in feet above the earth $t$ seconds after the start is given by

$$s = v_0 t - \tfrac{1}{2}gt^2, \tag{3}$$

where $g = 32$ approximately. We shall use (3).

EXAMPLE 1.   A projectile $P$ is shot upward from sea level with an initial velocity of 96 feet per second. (*a*) Find the average velocity from $t = 1$ to $t = 3$. (*b*) Calculate the velocity at any time $t$, and then at $t = 1$.

*Solution.*   *1.*   From (3) with $v_0 = 96$ and $g = 32$,

$$s = 96t - 16t^2. \tag{4}$$

*2.*   $s = 80$ at $t = 1$, and $s = 144$ at $t = 3$. Hence

$$\left\{ \begin{matrix} \textit{average velocity from} \\ t = 1 \textit{ to } t = 3 \end{matrix} \right\} = \frac{144 - 80}{3 - 1} = 32' \text{ per sec.}$$

*3.*   From (2), the velocity $v$ at time $t$ is

$$v = D_t s = 96 - 32t; \qquad v|_{t=1} = 96 - 32 = 64' \textit{ per sec.} \tag{5}$$

*4.*   To study the motion on the $s$-axis in Figure 68, first consider the graph of (4) in Figure 69, where the slope at any point $(t, s)$ is $D_t s = 96 - 32t$. The slope is zero when $96 - 32t = 0$ or $t = 3$, at the stationary point $A:(3,144)$. We have

$$v = 96 - 32t > 0, \textit{ or } s \textit{ is increasing, when } t < 3; \tag{6}$$

$$v = 96 - 32t < 0, \textit{ or } s \textit{ is decreasing, when } t > 3. \tag{7}$$

From (4), $s = 0$ when $96t - 16t^2 = 0$, or when $t = 0$ and $t = 6$. Hence, in Figure 68, $s$ increases or $P$ rises when $0 \leq t < 3$, with $P$ becoming stationary with $v = 0$ at $t = 3$ when $s = 144$. Thereafter, when $t > 3$, $P$ falls and reaches sea level at $t = 6$.

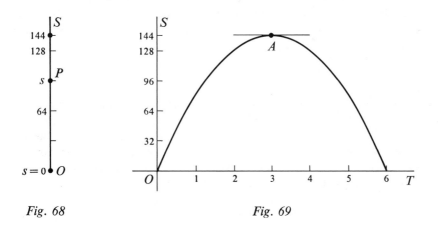

Fig. 68                              Fig. 69

It should be observed that the terminology about average and instantaneous rates of change is particularly natural in connection with rectilinear motion as just considered. This application of the terminology, and then of the derivative in mechanics, was one of the main motivating situations which led to the creation of differential calculus.

## 72.  Derivatives in economic theory

In the development of the subject matter of economics, numerous mathematical functions arise for representation of the fundamental variables. Then, frequently, there is reference to so-called "*marginal values*" of certain variables. In advance of their consideration, it is useful to observe that any *marginal value* is the value of a *derivative* of some function with respect to a specified economic variable. We shall consider a few examples of the concept.

Let $x$ be the *number of units* of a certain commodity which can be sold when the price per unit is $p$ units of money. Let the *total cost* of producing the $x$ units* be $C$. Let the *average cost* of production per unit be $A$ when $x$ units are being produced, and let $R$ be the *revenue* obtained through the sale of the $x$ units. With $p$ and $C$ considered as functions of $x$, we have $p = f(x)$ and $C = g(x)$. Then $R = px$, or

$$R = xf(x); \qquad A = \frac{C}{x}, \qquad or \qquad A = x^{-1}g(x). \tag{1}$$

We call $f$ the **demand function**, $p = f(x)$ the **demand equation**, and $g$ the **cost function**. Assume that $f$ and $g$ are differentiable. Recall that we considered linear demand equations on page 86.

Suppose that $x_0$ units are being sold, with $C_0$ as their production cost, where $C_0 = g(x_0)$. If production is increased by $\Delta x$ units, at an additional cost $\Delta C$, the *average rate of change* of the cost is $\Delta C/\Delta x$, which is the *cost per unit* of the added production of $\Delta x$ units. The limit of $\Delta C/\Delta x$ as $\Delta x \to 0$ is called the **marginal cost**, at the time when $x_0$ units are being produced. Thus, the marginal cost is the *instantaneous rate of change in production cost with respect to change in output*, or

$$(\textbf{marginal cost } at \ x = x_0) = \lim_{\Delta x \to 0} \frac{\Delta C}{\Delta x} = C' = g'(x_0). \tag{2}$$

The preceding discussion shows that the marginal cost can be thought of as an *approximation* to the cost $\Delta C/\Delta x$ per unit of *a small increase in output*.

Similarly, at an instant when $x_0$ units are being produced, the increase in revenue per unit of added production, $\Delta x$, is $\Delta R/\Delta x$. At this instant, the *instantaneous rate of change of revenue* with respect to production change is called the **marginal revenue**, which therefore is a derivative:

$$(\textbf{marginal revenue}) = \lim_{\Delta x \to 0} \frac{\Delta R}{\Delta x} = R'.$$

EXAMPLE 1.   For a firm making steel drums, the demand equation is $p = 300 - 9x - x^2$, where the unit for $p$ is \$1, and for $x$ is a certain trade unit. Find the marginal revenue at a time when four units are being produced.

---

* The unit might be a "trade unit." For instance, it might consist of 1000 of the individual articles being manufactured.

*Solution.*   From (1),

$$R = px, \quad or \quad R = 300x - 9x^2 - x^3.$$

Hence,          *(marginal revenue)* $= R' = 300 - 18x - 3x^2.$

At $x = 4$,          $R' = 300 - 72 - 48 = 180.$

Thus, the marginal revenue is approximately $180 per additional unit produced, if production is increased from a stage where four units are being produced.

In the preceding discussion, without comment, we illustrated a fundamental method which is applied in many fields of application. In (1), the domain of $x$ usually is a set of positive rational numbers. However, we used derivatives with respect to $x$, which implies that $x$ is a *continuous variable*, whose domain is *all positive numbers*. In doing this, clearly we were approximating to the true situation. A procedure of this sort is met frequently in the applications of calculus in any field where the domain of the independent variable is a discrete set of numbers, such as in (1), rather than an *interval* of numbers.

## Exercise 42

*Use* (3) *on page* 198 *in Problems* 1 *and* 2.

1.  A projectile $P$ is shot upward from the earth's surface with an initial velocity $v_0 = 480$ feet per second. (*a*) Find the velocity of $P$ at any time $t$ seconds after the start of the motion. (*b*) Find the velocity when $t = 3$ and $t = 5$. (*c*) Find the average velocity over the time interval from $t = 3$ to $t = 5$. (*d*) When will the projectile reach the highest point in its flight, and what is the corresponding height?

2.  Repeat Problem 1 with $v_0 = 800$.

*The equation specifies the location of a moving particle P on an s-axis at any time t. Find the velocity of P at each value of t.*

3.  $s = t^3 - 3t^2 + 4t + 6$; find $v$ at $t = 2$; $t = -4$.

4.  $s = 2t^3 - 3t + 4t^2 - 5$; find $v$ at $t = -1$; $t = 3$.

5.  $s = -5t^2 + t^3 - 3t + 7$; find $v$ at $t = -2$; $t = 4$.

*Recall the notations and terminology for* (1) *on page* 200. *We assume that, if a manufacturer produces x units of his commodity, then all of the units will be sold. That is, he never will produce more than the consumers will buy, as shown by the demand equation.*

6.  The demand function for a manufacturer's product is $f(x) = 500 - 2x$. (*a*) By graphing $p = f(x)$, find the least upper bound for the price per unit at which the product can be sold, and also the least upper bound for the number of units which can be sold (or given away). (*b*) Graph

$R = xf(x)$; at what value of $x$ does the revenue have its largest value? (*c*) Find the marginal revenue at a time when 10 units are manufactured; when 0 units are produced (this is approximately the revenue *per unit* when only a few units are produced). (*d*) For what values of $x$ is the marginal revenue positive; negative; zero?

7.  The cost equation, with $C$ in dollars, for a manufacturer is $C = 2000 + 30x - .05x^2$, where \$2000 may be thought of as an unavoidable expense even when production is zero. Find the marginal cost at the start of production, when $x = 0$; when $x = 10$; when $x = 50$.

    COMMENT.  Notice that $\Delta C/\Delta x$ is the added cost *per unit* of additional production $\Delta x$. Since $C' = \lim_{\Delta x \to 0} \Delta C/\Delta x$, we may think of the marginal cost at $x = x_0$ as an approximation to the *cost per unit* of added production when production is $x_0$ units. Notice that the marginal cost here decreases as $x$ increases.

8.  In the notation of (1) on page 200, the profit $P from production of $x$ units is $P = R - C$. Suppose that the same manufacturer is involved in Problems 6 and 7. (*a*) Find $P$ as a function of $x$. (*b*) Find the marginal profit at $x = 0$; $x = 10$; $x = 100$. (*c*) At what values of $x$ is the marginal profit positive; negative; zero? (*d*) When should the manufacturer cease increasing his production?

9.  Repeat Problem 6 if the demand function is $f(x) = 900 - 3x$.

10.  Repeat Problem 7 if the cost equation is $C = 1600 + 60x - .1x^2$.

11.  Repeat Problem 8, with the data for Problems 9 and 10 assumed to relate to the same manufacturer.

12.  By use of (1) on page 200, in each of Problems 7 and 10, obtain the average cost, $A$, as a function of the number, $x$, of units produced. Prove that $A$ decreases for all values of $x$.

## 73.  Graph of a polynomial function, and its extremes

To graph a polynomial function $f(x)$, first we obtain the values of $x$ where $f'(x) = 0$, to locate the stationary points of the graph.

EXAMPLE 1.   If $f(x) = -x^3 + 3x^2 + 9x - 3$, graph $f$.

*Solution.*   1.   We wish to graph    $y = -x^3 + 3x^2 + 9x - 3$,    (1)

where    $y' = -3x^2 + 6x + 9 = -3(x^2 - 2x - 3)$.    (2)

2.   To locate the points where $y' = 0$, we solve

$$x^2 - 2x - 3 = 0, \quad or \quad (x - 3)(x + 1) = 0,$$

and obtain $x = 3$ and $x = -1$. In the following table, we use $-1$, 3, and other values of $x$ as a basis for the graph of (1) in Figure 70. Some of the points from the table fall outside the range of the figure.

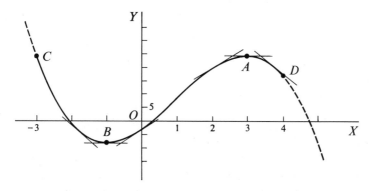

*Fig. 70*

| $x =$ | $-4$ | $-3$ | $-1$ | $0$ | $1$ | $3$ | $4$ | $5$ |
|-------|------|------|------|-----|-----|-----|-----|-----|
| $y =$ | 73 | 24 | $-8$ | $-3$ | 8 | 24 | 17 | $-8$ |

Suppose that a function $f(x)$ has a *largest* value, $M$. Thus, assume that, at some point $x = x_0$, we have $M = f(x_0)$, and also $f(x) \leq M$ *at all values of* $x$. Then $M$ is called the (**absolute**) **maximum** of $f(x)$, or of $f$, where the word *absolute* is redundant but useful. If $f$ has a *smallest* value $m$, this means that there exists some point $x = x_0$ where $f(x_0) = m$, and $m \leq f(x)$ *at all values of* $x$. Then, $m$ is called the (**absolute**) **minimum** of $f(x)$. The determination of absolute maxima or minima is aided by investigation, first, of related function values, referred to as *local maxima or minima*.

ILLUSTRATION 1.   In Figure 70, observe the stationary point $A:(3, 24)$ on the graph $H$ of $y = f(x)$ of (1). At $A$, the ordinate $f(3)$ or 24 is *greater* than the ordinate $f(x)$ at any *neighboring** point of $H$, because $A$ is *higher* than the *neighboring* points of $H$. However, there are infinitely many other points of $H$ where the ordinate $f(x) > f(3)$, for instance, the point $(-4, 73)$ from the preceding table. Hence, we say that $f(x)$ has a **local maximum** 24, attained when $x = 3$. Similarly, $f(x)$ has a **local minimum** $-8 = f(-1)$, attained at $x = -1$, because $B:(-1, -8)$ in Figure 70 is *lower* than the *neighboring* points of $H$. We see that there is no absolute maximum for $f(x)$, or largest ordinate on the graph, because it is known to extend upward beyond all bounds. Similarly, there is no absolute minimum for $f(x)$, because the graph extends downward beyond all bounds.

Either a maximum or a minimum of either variety, as just considered, may be called an **extreme value**. If a function $f(x)$ has a *local extreme* at

* Meaning "*sufficiently close.*"

$x = x_0$, we agree to call the corresponding point $(x_0, y_0)$ on the graph of $y = f(x)$ an **extreme point** of the graph.

In more advanced texts, it is proved that, *if a function $f(x)$ is continuous on a closed interval $I = \{a \leq x \leq b\}$, then $f$ has an absolute maximum and an absolute minimum on $I$.*

Suppose that the domain of a function $f(x)$ is an interval $I$, and that $f$ has an *absolute maximum* $M = f(x_0)$. Then $f(x) \leq f(x_0)$ for all $x$ on $I$. Hence, $f(x_0)$ *also is a local maximum*, because $f(x) \leq f(x_0)$ **for all $x$ sufficiently near $x_0$** if $f(x) \leq f(x_0)$ for **all $x$ on $I$**. Similarly, if $f(x_0)$ is the *absolute minimum* of $f$ on $I$, then $f$ also has $f(x_0)$ as a *local minimum* at $x = x_0$. Therefore, if we are primarily interested in *absolute* extremes for $f(x)$, when such extremes exist, we may first find all of the *local* extremes. Then the largest *local* maximum is the *absolute* maximum; the *smallest* local minimum is the *absolute* minimum.

EXAMPLE 2.   Let $f(x) = -x^3 + 3x^2 + 9x - 3$, as in Example 1, but with the restricted domain $I = \{-3 \leq x \leq 4\}$. Find the local extremes of $f(x)$ and also any absolute extreme which exists.

*Solution.   1.*   The graph of $y = f(x)$ is the continuous part of the curve in Figure 70, from $C:(-3, 24)$ to $D:(4, 17)$.

*2.*   Since $f$ is continuous on $I$, $f$ has *absolute extremes* on $I$, and they are found among the *local extremes*. Hence, we first obtain all of these.

*3.*   From Figure 70, $f$ has a local maximum $24 = f(3)$ and a local minimum $-8 = f(-1)$ at interior points of $I$. By inspection of Figure 70, $f$ also has a local maximum $24 = f(-3)$, attained at the endpoint $-3$ of $I$, and a local minimum $17 = f(4)$, attained at the endpoint $4$ of $I$. We list these extremes:

$$\text{Local minima:} \quad f(-1) = -8; \quad f(4) = 17.$$
$$\text{Local maxima:} \quad f(3) = 24; \quad f(-3) = 24.$$

Hence the absolute minimum is $-8$, attained at $x = -1$; the absolute maximum is 24, attained at $x = 3$ and also at $x = -3$.

In future discussion of extremes, we shall assume that any function $f(x)$ involved is continuous. Also, if $f'$ exists at any point $x = x_0$, we shall suppose that $f'(x)$ exists and $f'$ is continuous at all values of $x$ on some interval including $x_0$ as an *interior point*. Our remarks will be so informal that the force of the preceding hypotheses will not be apparent. Also, in certain places, the preceding hypotheses will be somewhat redundant.

THEOREM II.   *If a function $f(x)$ has a local extreme at a point $x_0$ interior to the domain of $f$, and if $f'(x_0)$ exists, then $f'(x_0) = 0$.*

*Proof.*   (Observe $A$ and $B$ in Figure 70 for illustration.) If we had $f'(x_0) < 0$ or $f'(x_0) > 0$, then $f(x)$ would be decreasing or increasing, respectively, near $x_0$, and hence we could not have an extreme at $x = x_0$. Therefore we must have $f'(x_0) = 0$.

In view of Theorem II, if $f'(x_0) = 0$ then we shall call $x_0$ a **critical value** of $x$ for the investigation of extremes of $f(x)$. From Examples 1 and 2, we see that $f$ *may* have an extreme where $f'(x_0) = 0$. In later examples, it will be observed that $f'(x_0)$ may be zero when $f(x)$ *does not have an extreme at* $x = x_0$. Also, $f(x)$ may have an extreme value at $x = x_0$ where $f'(x_0)$ *does not exist*; we shall give negligible attention to such a situation. With $A$ and $B$ in Figure 70 taken as typical for extreme points, we give the following tests for a local extreme at an *interior point* $x_0$ of the domain of a function $f(x)$.

(I)  $f(x_0)$ *is a* **local maximum** *for f in case*
$$f'(x) > 0 \text{ if } x < x_0 \quad and \quad f'(x) < 0 \text{ if } x > x_0. \Big\} \tag{3}$$

(II)  $f(x_0)$ *is a* **local minimum** *for f in case*
$$f'(x) < 0 \text{ if } x < x_0 \quad and \quad f'(x) > 0 \text{ if } x > x_0. \Big\} \tag{4}$$

When (3) is true, we say that $f'(x)$ *changes sign* from $(+)$ to $(-)$ at $x = x_0$. When (4) is true, we say that $f'(x)$ *changes sign* from $(-)$ to $(+)$ at $x = x_0$.

ILLUSTRATION 2.    To check (3), observe the short tangents at points on the graph sufficiently close to the local maximum point $A:(3, 24)$ in Figure 70. With $x < 3$, the tangent has *positive slope*, and $f(x)$ is *increasing to* $f(3) = 24$. With $x > 3$, the tangent has *negative slope*, and $f(x)$ is *decreasing from* $f(3) = 24$. Similarly, the slopes of the tangents near $B:(-1, -8)$ in Figure 70 illustrate (4).

To obtain all local extremes of a function $f(x)$ at interior points of the domain of $f$, first we solve $f'(x) = 0$ to obtain the critical values for $x$, and then apply tests (3) and (4). Notice that this should be done *before* a graph of $y = f(x)$ is drawn, as an aid in graphing. Also, in later applications, frequently the extremes will be desired without any need for the graph.

EXAMPLE 3.    Find all local extremes of
$$f(x) = -x^3 + 3x^2 + 9x - 3.$$

*Solution.    1.*    The domain for $f$ consists of all real values of $x$. Hence, the only extremes of $f(x)$ occur at interior points of the domain, where Theorem II applies.

2.    *The critical values of x.*    Let $y = f(x)$. Then
$$y' = -3x^2 + 6x + 9 = -3(x^2 - 2x - 3), \text{ or}$$
$$y' = -3(x - 3)(x + 1) = -3(x - 3)[x - (-1)]. \tag{5}$$
Hence, $y' = 0$ at $x = -1$ and at $x = 3$, which are the critical numbers.

*3. Tests.*   Let $x$ be sufficiently near 3, on either side; for instance consider $x = 2.5$ and $x = 3.5$, where it would be satisfactory to use any values greater than $-1$ so as to avoid alterations in the sign of $(x + 1)$.* With $x = 2.5$ in (5), $y' = -3(-.5)(3.5) > 0$. Thus, in (5), as indicated in the following table where only signs of factors are of interest, we find $y' > 0$ if $x < 3$ and $y' < 0$ if $x > 3$ Hence, by (3), $f(x)$ has a local *maximum* $24 = f(3)$, at $x = 3$ At $x = -1$, $f(x)$ has a local *minimum*, $-8 = f(-1)$. The tests are summarized as follows.

| NEAR $x = -1$ IN (5): | NEAR $x = 3$ IN (5): |
|---|---|
| *if* $x < -1$, $y' = (-)(-)(-) = (-)$; | *if* $x < 3$, $y' = (-)(-)(+) = (+)$; |
| *if* $x > -1$, $y' = (-)(-)(+) = +$. | *if* $x > 3$, $y' = (-)(+)(+) = (-)$. |
| *By* (4), *a* **loc. min.** *at* $x = -1$. | *By* (3), *a* **loc. max.** *at* $x = 3$. |

*4.*   Notice that† $f(x) \to -\infty$ if $x \to +\infty$, and $f(x) \to +\infty$ if $x \to -\infty$. Hence $f(x)$ is not "*bounded*," and thus has no absolute maximum or minimum. The preceding results check with Figure 70 on page 203.

### Exercise 43

*Locate and test each local extreme of the function $f(x)$ which is attained at an interior point of the domain of f. Then graph $y = f(x)$, showing the tangent at each stationary point. Also, specify each local extreme and any absolute extreme which exists. The domain of f consists of all values of x except where otherwise specified.*

1. $f(x) = x^2 - 6x + 9$.
2. $f(x) = 2 - 4x - x^2$.
3. $f(x) = 2x^3 - 3x^2 - 36x + 12$. In graphing, use a small $y$-unit.
4. $f(x) = 2x^3 - 3x^2 - 36x + 12$; with $-3 \leq x \leq 4$.
5. $f(x) = -x^3 + 3x^2 + 24x + 7$.
6. $f(x) = -x^3 + 3x^2 + 24x + 7$; with $-3 \leq x \leq 5$.
7. $f(x) = -x^3 - 3x^2 + 9x$.
8. $f(x) = x^3 - 3x^2 + 3x - 4$.
9. $f(x) = x^3 + 6x^2 + 12x - 5$.

* In (5), we wrote $[x - (-1)]$ to give the form "$(x - a)$," which is *negative* if $x < a$, and *positive* if $x > a$.
† This means that "$-f(x)$ *grows large without bound if x grows large without bound.*" "$f(x) \to +\infty$ *if* $x \to -\infty$" means that "$f(x)$ *grows large without bound if* $-x$ *grows large without bound.*" Also, we may read "$\infty$" as "infinity."

## 74.  Applications of maxima and minima

In the typical application of extreme values of a function, an *absolute* extreme will be desired. We recall that any absolute extreme also is a local extreme. Hence, if an absolute extreme is requested, first we should obtain all local extremes, and then test them to find which one satisfies the conditions of the problem. The following procedure frequently is convenient.

(I)  *Introduce natural auxiliary variables, and express the fundamental dependent variable, W, as a function of the auxiliary variables.*

(II)  *If two\* auxiliary variables were used, search for an equation relating them. Then, use this equation to eliminate one variable. Thus, obtain an expression for W as a function of a single independent variable, call it x.*

(III)  *Obtain each value of x for which W attains a local extreme. Test these critical values of x to learn which value yields the solution of the problem.*

EXAMPLE 1.  A rectangular field along a river with a straight bank is to have an area of 800 square yards, and is to be fenced along the sides not on the bank. Find the dimensions to minimize the fencing.

*Solution.  1.* Let $y$ yards be the length of the field along the river bank, and $x$ yards be the other dimension. Let $P$ yards be the length of the fence. Then, as illustrated in Figure 71,

$$xy = 800 \qquad and \qquad P = 2x + y. \tag{1}$$

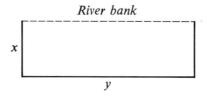

*River bank*

$x$

$y$

*Fig. 71*

We desire the values of $x$ and $y$ which cause $P$ to attain its absolute minimum, subject to the *constraint*, or restrictive condition, $xy = 80$.

*2.* From (1), $y = 800/x$. Hence,

$$P = 2x + \frac{800}{x}. \tag{2}$$

*3.* In (2), the domain for $x$ is the infinite open interval $I = \{0 < x < \infty\}$. Any (absolute) minimum thus will occur at an interior point of $I$, and hence also will be a local minimum, where $P' = 0$.

---

\* If $k$ auxiliary variables were used, search for $(k - 1)$ equations relating them.

4.  From (2),                 $$P' = 2 - \frac{800}{x^2}.$$                 (3)

A *necessary* condition for $P$ to have a minimum is

$$2 - \frac{800}{x^2} = 0, \quad or \quad x^2 = 400; \quad x = \pm 20.$$

The negative root does not apply. Hence, the only critical value for a minimum is $x = 20$.

5.   *Test of* $x = 20$:

*If* $x < 20$, *for instance if* $x = 19$,    $P' = 2 - \dfrac{800}{361} < 0$,

because $800/361 > 2$.

*If* $x > 20$, *for instance if* $x = 21$,    $P' = 2 - \dfrac{800}{441} > 0$,

because $800/441 < 2$.

Hence, by (4) on page 205, $P$ has a local minimum at $x = 20$. Since this is the only local minimum, it also is the desired absolute minimum. When $x = 20$, from $xy = 800$ we find $y = 40$. Thus, for minimum fencing, the dimensions are 40 yards by 20 yards.

EXAMPLE 2.   In an isosceles triangle, the base measures 10′, and the altitude 20′. A rectangle has its base on the base of the triangle, and two vertices on the equal sides, as in Figure 72. Find the dimensions of the rectangle to give it the largest possible area.

*Solution.  1.*   For the rectangle, let the length of the base be $2x$ feet, the altitude be $y$ feet, and the area be $W$ square feet. Then $W = 2xy$.

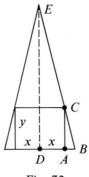

Fig. 72

2. In Figure 72, $\triangle$'s *ABC* and *DBE* are similar, with $\overline{AB} = 5 - x$. Hence, from ratios of lengths of corresponding sides, $\overline{AB}/\overline{AC} = \overline{DB}/\overline{DE}$, or

$$\frac{5-x}{y} = \frac{5}{20}, \quad \text{or} \quad y = 20 - 4x. \tag{4}$$

Thus, $$W = 2x(20 - 4x). \tag{5}$$

3. In (5), the domain for $x$ is the interval $I = \{0 \leq x \leq 5\}$. Let $f(x) = 40x - 8x^2 = W$. Then, $f(0) = 0 = f(5)$. Also, for all values of $x$, $W \geq 0$. Hence, $W$ attains its *absolute minimum* value, which is 0, at the endpoints $x = 0$ and $x = 5$. Any absolute maximum also will be a local maximum attained at an interior point of $I$, where $W' = 0$.

4. From (5), $$W' = 40 - 16x.$$

The critical value for a maximum is the solution of $40 - 16x = 0$, or $x = 2.5$. It is plain that $W > 0$ when $0 < x < 5$, and $W$ is continuous on the closed interval $I$. Hence, $W$ has an absolute maximum, $M$, which must be *positive*. The only possible value of $x$ where $M$ can be attained is $x = 2.5$, which therefore gives $W$ its maximum. We could also test $x = 2.5$ by use of (3) on page 205. From $y = 20 - 4x$, we find $y = 10$ when $x = 2.5$. Hence, the dimensions of the rectangle with maximum area are 10' by 5'.

## Exercise 44

*Solve by first expressing the principal quantity involved as a function of a single variable. Then locate and test the desired extreme of the function by use of a derivative. Any requested extreme is understood to be an absolute extreme.*

1. Divide 80 into two parts whose product is a maximum.
2. Find the dimensions of a rectangular field with maximum area if the perimeter of the field is 1600 yards.
3. A rectangular field is to be surrounded by a fence, and also will have a similar fence parallel to one side dividing the field into two equal parts. Find the dimensions of the field to minimize the cost of fencing, if the area is to be 3750 square yards.
4. A restaurant chain, in planning a new cafeteria, estimates that, with a capacity of 50 to 100 chairs, the monthly profit per chair will be $24. If the capacity grows beyond 100 chairs, the monthly profit per chair for the whole cafeteria decreases by 15¢ on account of each added chair. What seating capcity would yield maximum profit? (Express money in cents.)
5. A manufacturer uses a machine whose original cost is $C. The expense of taxes and interest on $C$ per year is $rC$, where $r$ is a fixed rate (a small decimal). The amount which would be spent on repairs in $x$ years is

$bx^2$ dollars, where $b$ is a constant. If the machine is to be used for just $x$ years, the annual depreciation charge is $\$C/x$. Let the average annual cost of operation be $\$A$. Then

$$A = rC + \frac{C}{x} + \frac{bx^2}{x}, \quad or \quad A = rC + \frac{C}{x} + bx.$$

If $r = .08$, $C = 72,000$, and $b = 500$, find the life, $x$ years, of the machine which will yield the minimum value for $A$.

6.  A rectangular box with an open top will be made by cutting equal squares from the corners of a 10″ by 20″ piece of galvanized iron, and folding up the sides. Find the size of the square involved, if the box is to have maximum capacity.

7.  A farmer buys cattle weighing 500 pounds each, at 50¢ per pound. He estimates that each animal will gain $\frac{3}{4}$ pound per day, at a cost of 18¢ per pound. The selling price, starting at 50¢ per pound, will decrease by .04¢ per day during the next three months. When should he sell the cattle in order to realize maximum profit?

8.  A closed box is to be a rectangular parallelepiped with a square base and a capacity of 1125 cubic feet. The cost per square foot of the material for the base and top of the box is 5¢ and for the sides is 15¢. Find the dimensions of the box to create minimum cost of the material.

*In Problems 9–10, recall (1) on page 200. C is the total cost of x units, and A is the average cost. Find $x_0$ so that A has its minimum at $x = x_0$. Verify that the average cost is a minimum when the average cost is equal to the marginal cost.*

9.  $C = .001x^3 - .02x^2 + 15x.$    10.  $C = .002x^3 - .04x^2 + 25x.$

11.  The demand equation for a manufacturer is $p = 88 - 1.99x$, and his cost equation is $C = 350 + 12x + .01x^2$. (a) Find the price $p$ per trade unit at which the profit will be a maximum (first find $x$). (b) Verify that, at the price in (a), the marginal revenue is equal to the marginal cost. (c) If the government imposes a sales tax of $\alpha$ money units per unit sold, find the increase in the price (including the tax) paid by the consumer at which total profit for the manufacturer is a maximum. [The demand equation remains unaltered, but the manufacturer receives only $(p - \alpha)$ per unit.]

12.  Solve Problem 11 if $p = 128 - 2.98x$ and $C = 300 + 20x + .02x^2$ for part (a), and the tax is $\alpha$ per unit for part (c).

13.  The cost and the demand equations for a manufacturer are $C = x^3 - 15x^2 + 76x + 25$ and $p = 55 - 3x$. If $P$ is the profit when $x$ units are sold, and $P = w(x)$, find $w(x)$. (a) Find the production, $x_0$ units, for which $P$ will reach its maximum. (b) Obtain the marginal cost and the marginal revenue when $x = x_0$.

14.  In Problem 13, prove that, with $C = g(x)$, $g$ is an increasing function for all positive values of $x$ (this is a natural requirement).

HINT.  Obtain $C' = g'(x)$. Graph $y = g'(x)$ and show that $g'(x) > 0$ for all positive values of $x$.

15.  In Problem 13, with $P = w(x)$, obtain a graph of $y = w(x)$. Approximately how much production is necessary for the business to become profitable? Also, check the graph with results in Problem 13.

16–18.  Repeat Problems 13–15, respectively, if $C = x^3 - 21x^2 + 200x + 50$ and $p = 173 - 6x$.

19.  Consider the general data in (1) on page 200. Prove that the profit of the manufacturer is a maximum when the marginal revenue is equal to the marginal cost.

20–22.  Repeat Problems 13–15 if $C = x^3 - 23x^2 + 180x + 45$ and $p = 120 - 5x$.

## 75.  Differentials and the derivative as a fraction

Let $f$ be a differentiable function. Then, at a point $P:(x, y)$ on the graph of $y = f(x)$, there is a tangent $PT$ with slope $f'(x)$. Let $dx$, instead of $\Delta x$ as formerly, represent an increment, not zero, in the value of $x$. If $dx$ is added to a fixed value $x$, let $dy$ or $df(x)$ be the corresponding increment of *the ordinate of the tangent PT*, and let $\Delta y$ be the increment of the function value $y$, or $f(x)$, as shown in Figure 73. Then the point $Q:(x + dx, y + \Delta y)$ is on the graph of $y = f(x)$, and $S:(x + dx, y + dy)$ is on the tangent $PT$. The slope of $PT$, or $PS$ in Figure 73, is $dy/dx$ and also is $f'(x)$. Therefore,

$$\frac{dy}{dx} = f'(x), \quad \text{or} \quad \frac{df(x)}{dx} = f'(x). \tag{1}$$

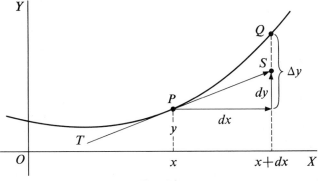

*Fig. 73*

The numbers $dx$, $dy$, and $df(x)$ are called **differentials**. We may read "$dx$" simply as "$d, x$," or as "*differential x*," and also read $dy$ or $df(x)$ similarly. On multiplying both sides of either equation in (1) by $dx$, we obtain

$$dy = f'(x)dx, \quad or \quad df(x) = f'(x)dx. \tag{2}$$

Then $dy$, or $df(x)$, is a function of *two* variables, $x$ and $dx$, where $dx \neq 0$.

ILLUSTRATION 1.   If $f(x) = x^3$, then $f'(x) = 3x^2$ and $df(x) = 3x^2dx$. If $x = 3$ and $dx = .2$, then $df(x) = 27(.2) = 5.4$.

ILLUSTRATION 2.   If $f(x) = x$, then $f'(x) = 1$ and $df(x) = 1 \cdot dx = dx$. That is, $dx$ may be considered either as a variable, not assuming the value 0, or as the differential of the identity function "$x$."

Figure 73 emphasizes the fact that, if $dx$ is relatively small, then $dy$ may be a useful approximation to the increment $\Delta y$ resulting from the change from $x$ to $(x + dx)$ in the independent variable. If it is requested that an increment $\Delta y$ be computed *approximately by use of differentials*, this means that

$$dy \text{ is to be used as an approximation to } \Delta y. \tag{3}$$

EXAMPLE 1.   The interior of a box is a cube with a 10″ edge, and the walls of the box are $\frac{1}{8}$″ thick. (*a*) Find the volume of the material forming the walls, approximately by use of differentials.

*Solution.   1.* Let $x$ inches be the length of an edge of a variable cube with volume $V$ cubic inches. Then $V = x^3$ and $dV = 3x^2dx$.

2.   The volume of the walls is the increment $\Delta V$ due to a change from $x = 10$ to $x = 10\frac{1}{4}$ (two extensions of an edge by $\frac{1}{8}$″ are involved for an outside edge). Hence, we compute $dV$ with $x = 10$ and $dx = \frac{1}{4}$:

$$\Delta V \doteq dV = 3x^2dx = 3(100)(\tfrac{1}{4}) = 75 \text{ cu in.},$$

where "$\doteq$" is read "*approximately equals*."

In (1), we introduced two useful new symbols for $f'(x)$. Thus, if $y = f(x)$, we now have the following symbols for the value of the derivative of $f$ at point $x$ in the domain of $f$:

$$f'(x); \; y'; \; D_xy; \; D_xf(x); \; \frac{dy}{dx}; \; \frac{df(x)}{dx}. \tag{4}$$

In (4), $dy/dx$ can be read "*dy over dx*," and can be considered as an *actual quotient*, where $dx$ is any number not zero such that $(x + dx)$ is in the domain of $f$, and $dy = f'(x)dx$. Or, when we choose, $dy/dx$ can be considered *as a whole*, representing $f'(x)$. The quotient notation for a derivative was introduced by LEIBNITZ, and is very useful and popular.

ILLUSTRATION 3.   If $y = 3x^2 + 5x + 7$, then $\frac{dy}{dx} = 6x + 5$.

EXAMPLE 2.   In a certain manufacturing process, suppose that the cost, $C$, in dollars of an output of $x$ units of the product is

$$C = 4800 + 50x - .04x^2. \tag{5}$$

In (5), 4800 is a consequence of overhead costs which exist even if there is no output; $50x$ shows that the added cost per unit is \$50 when production commences; $-.04x^2$ accounts for savings in cost as production increases (with a reasonable limit on the size of $x$). By use of differentials, find approximately the increase in cost of manufacture due to an increase of $dx$ units from the stage when 100 units are being produced.

*Solution.*   $C' = 50 - .08x$; $dC = (50 - .08x)dx$. Hence, if $x = 100$, then $dC = (50 - 8)dx = 42dx$. Thus, the approximate increase in cost if one added unit is produced is $dC = 42(1)$, or \$42.

## Exercise 45

*Find dy/dx or dz/dx.*
1. $y = 3x + 5$.
2. $y = 5x^3$.
3. $y = 4 - 5x - x^4$.
4. $z = -4x^2 + x^4$.
5. $z = 4 - 5x^3$.
6. $z = 2 - x^3 - x^5$.
7. If $y = 3x + x^2$, obtain $dy$ when $x = 3$ and $dx = .2$.
8. If $y = 5 - 3x - x^3$, obtain $dy$ when $x = -2$ and $dx = .3$.

*Obtain the requested result approximately by use of differentials.*
9. If the radius $x$ inches of a circle is changed from $x = 4$ to $x = 4.3$, find the change in (a) the circumference of the circle; (b) the change in its area.
10. A solid cube, whose edge is 12″ long, is coated with plastic .03″ thick, to form a new cube. Find the volume of plastic which is used.
11. A cylindrical steel rod, 50″ long, has been ground down to reduce its radius from 3″ to 2.8″. Find the volume of steel that was ground off in the process.
12. The edge of a cube is measured as 15″, with a possible error of at most .03″. Find the maximum possible error that may occur in the computed volume.
13. An aluminum spherical shell has an inner radius of 5″ and thickness of .04″. Find the volume of the aluminum in the shell. (Volume of a sphere of radius $r$ is $\frac{4}{3}\pi r^3$.)

*The notation and terminology of (1) on page 200 is used in the following problems. Use differentials.*
14. The demand equation is $p = 24 - 2x - x^2$, where $p$ is the price at which the manufacturer can sell $x$ thousands of his product. At an

instant when $x = 3$, find approximately how large a reduction must be made in the price in order to increase the demand by 300 units of the product.

15. In Problem 11 on page 210, find approximately the increase in total cost if production is increased from 25 units to 25.5 units of the product.

16. In Problem 12 on page 210, find approximately the increase in profit if production increases from 10 to 10.5 units.

17. In Problem 13 on page 210, find approximately the increase in cost of production if output increases from $x = 7$ to $x = 7.5$.

## ★ 76. Differentiation of any algebraic function

The added technique of differentiation in this section will not be employed in applications in this text, but is fundamentally important in more extensive introductions to calculus.

An equation in the variables $x$ and $y$ is called a *polynomial equation* in case it is of the form $h(x, y) = k(x, y)$, where the functions $h$ and $k$ are polynomial functions of $x$ and $y$. A function $f(x)$, with domain $D$, is called an **algebraic function** in case there exists a polynomial equation $h(x, y) = k(x, y)$ which is satisfied when $y = f(x)$, for all $x$ on $D$.

Suppose that $f(x)$ is defined by a formula involving operations of algebra applied to the value of $x$, and let $y = f(x)$. Then, this equation can be simplified to a form $h(x, y) = k(x, y)$ and hence $f$ *is an algebraic function*. In particular, if $f$ is a rational function [that is, if $f(x) = P(x)/Q(x)$ where $P(x)$ and $Q(x)$ are polynomials], then $f$ is an algebraic function.

ILLUSTRATION 1. If $f(x) = 3x/\sqrt[3]{1 + x}$, and if we let $y = 3x/\sqrt[3]{1 + x}$, then $y\sqrt[3]{1 + x} = 3x$. If both sides of this equation are raised to the 3d power, we obtain $y^3(1 + x) = 27x^3$. Thus, if $x \neq -1$ and $y = f(x)$, then $(x, y)$ is a solution of a polynomial equation. Hence, $f$ is an algebraic function.

Algebraic functions of $x$ exist for which it is impossible to obtain algebraic formulas for the function values.

By use of the previous formulas (I)–(VI) for differentiation, and methods to be presented in this section, an expression can be obtained for the derivative of any algebraic function of $x$. We assume that any function appearing in later formulas is differentiable.

*Derivative of a product:*

$$D_x[f(x)g(x)] = g(x)f'(x) + f(x)g'(x). \tag{VII}$$

*Derivative of a fraction:*

$$D_x\left[\frac{f(x)}{g(x)}\right] = \frac{g(x)f'(x) - f(x)g'(x)}{[g(x)]^2}. \tag{VIII}$$

*General power formula.*   *If $u = g(x)$ and $n$ is any rational number, then*

$(u \neq 0 \text{ if } n - 1 \leq 0)$ $\qquad\qquad D_x u^n = n u^{n-1} D_x u.$ $\qquad\qquad$ (VI)

*Proof of* (VII).   *1.*   Let $y = f(x)g(x)$. With $x$ fixed, and $\Delta x > 0$, let $y + \Delta y = f(x + \Delta x)g(x + \Delta x)$. Then

$$\Delta y = f(x + \Delta x)g(x + \Delta x) - f(x)g(x), \text{ or}$$
$$\Delta y = f(x + \Delta x)[g(x + \Delta x) - g(x)] + g(x)[f(x + \Delta x) - f(x)];$$
$$\frac{\Delta y}{\Delta x} = f(x + \Delta x)\frac{g(x + \Delta x) - g(x)}{\Delta x} + g(x)\frac{f(x + \Delta x) - f(x)}{\Delta x}. \qquad (1)$$

*2.*   Since $f$ is differentiable, hence $f$ is continuous, and therefore $f(x + \Delta x) \to f(x)$ if $\Delta x \to 0$. Then, from (1),

$$D_x y = \lim_{\Delta x \to 0} f(x + \Delta x)\left[\lim_{\Delta x \to 0} \frac{g(x + \Delta x) - g(x)}{\Delta x}\right]$$
$$+ g(x)\left[\lim_{\Delta x \to 0} \frac{f(x + \Delta x) - f(x)}{\Delta x}\right], \text{ or}$$

$D_x y = f(x)g'(x) + g(x)f'(x)$, as stated in (VII).

*Proof of* (VIII).   Let $h(x) = f(x)/g(x)$. Then $h(x)g(x) = f(x)$. To obtain a simple (but somewhat incomplete) proof, let us assume that $h$ has a derivative. Then, $D_x[h(x)g(x)] = D_x f(x)$ or, by use of (VII),

$$h'(x)g(x) + h(x)g'(x) = f'(x); \qquad h'(x)g(x) = f'(x) - h(x)g'(x).$$

Since $h(x) = f(x)/g(x)$, we obtain

$$g(x)h'(x) = f'(x) - \frac{f(x)g'(x)}{g(x)}, \qquad or \qquad h'(x) = \frac{g(x)f'(x) - f(x)g'(x)}{[g(x)]^2},$$

which proves (VIII).

ILLUSTRATION 2.   By use of (VII),

$$D_x(x^2 + 5x)(2x - 3) = (2x - 3)D_x(x^2 + 5x) + (x^2 + 5x)D_x(2x - 3)$$
$$= (2x - 3)(2x + 5) + (x^2 + 5x)(2) = 6x^2 + 14x - 15.$$

ILLUSTRATION 3.   By use of (VIII),

$$D_x\left[\frac{5x + 3}{2x^2 - x}\right] = \frac{(2x^2 - x)(5) - (5x + 3)(4x - 1)}{(2x^2 - x)^2} = etc.$$

We have already proved (VI) when $n$ is an integer.*

---

* The proof involved use of (IV) of page 193 with $n$ as a positive or negative integer. No proof of (IV) with $n < 0$ has been given as yet. A proof for this case by use of (VIII) is outlined in a problem of the next exercise.

*Proof of* (VI) *with* $n = p/q$, *where* $p$ *and* $q$ *are integers;* $p/q$ *is in lowest terms with* $q > 0$.   *1.*   Let $y = u^{p/q}$. Then $y^q = u^p$. Hence, differentiate each side of $y^q = u^p$ with respect to $x$.

*2.*   By use of the chain rule on page 194,

$$D_x y^q = D_x u^p \qquad becomes \qquad (D_y y^q)(D_x y) = (D_u u^p)(D_x u).$$

From (IV) on page 193, $\qquad\qquad\qquad qy^{q-1}D_x y = pu^{p-1}D_x u,$ or

$$D_x y = \frac{pu^{p-1}}{qy^{q-1}}\, D_x u = \frac{p}{q} \cdot \frac{yu^{p-1}}{y^q}\, D_x u, \qquad\qquad (2)$$

where both numerator and denominator were multiplied by $y$. In (2) on the right, use $y = u^{p/q}$ in the numerator and $y^q = u^p$ in the denominator. Then

$$D_x y = \frac{p}{q} \cdot \frac{u^{p/q}u^{-1}u^p}{u^p}\, D_x u = \frac{p}{q} u^{(p/q)-1}D_x u,$$

which proves (VI) with $n = p/q$.

To differentiate a radical, first express the root as a power.

ILLUSTRATION 4.   By use of (VI) with $u = 3x^2 + 5x$,

$$D_x \sqrt[3]{3x^2 + 5x} = D_x(3x^2 + 5x)^{1/3}$$
$$= \tfrac{1}{3}(3x^2 + 5x)^{(1/3)-1}(6x + 5) = \tfrac{1}{3}(3x^2 - 5x)^{-2/3}(6x + 5).$$

## ★ Exercise 46

*Find* $dy/dx$, $dy/dt$, $du/dx$, *or the derivative of the given function. Differentiate without expanding any product or power.*

1.   $y = (2x - 5)(3x + 7)$.       2.   $y = (2t^2 - 3t)(4 - t + t^2)$.
3.   $u = (3 + 5x)(x^3 - x^2 + 3)$.   4.   $g(x) = (x + 3x^2)(x^3 - 2x + 3)$.
5.   $f(s) = (s^3 - 3)(s + s^2 - 5)$.   6.   $h(t) = (t^2 - 2t)(t - 1)(2t + 5)$.

HINT for Problem 6.   Apply (VII) with
$$h(t) = [(t^2 - 25t)(t - 1)]\,(2t + 5).$$

7.   $y = (3x - 1)(2x + 5)(2 - 4x)$.

8.   $y = \dfrac{2x + 5}{3x - 2}$.       9.   $y = \dfrac{4 - 3t}{2 + 5t}$.       10.   $y = \dfrac{2 - x^2}{3x + 9}$.

11.   $f(z) = \dfrac{3z - 2z^2}{z^3 + 3}$.   12.   $h(s) = \dfrac{5}{3s - 8}$.   13.   $y = \dfrac{6}{3x + 2}$.

14.   $y = 1/x^5$; differentiate first by use of (VIII), and second by use of a negative exponent and (IV) on page 193.

15.   $\dfrac{3}{x^3}$.       16.   $\dfrac{8}{3x^2}$.       17.   $\dfrac{7}{2x^5}$.       18.   $-\dfrac{2}{x^6}$.

HINT.   Use $x^{-3} = 1/x^3$, $x^{-2} = 1/x^2$, etc.

*19.* $y = x^{5/2}$.  
*20.* $y = 5t^{3/4}$.  
*21.* $y = 3x^{5/3}$.  
*22.* $y = \sqrt{9 - x^2}$.  
*23.* $y = \sqrt{3t^3 + 1}$.  
*24.* $y = \sqrt[3]{x + x^3}$.  
*25.* $f(x) = \dfrac{3}{\sqrt{2x - 5}}$.  
*26.* $g(z) = \dfrac{6}{\sqrt[3]{z}}$.  
*27.* $y = \dfrac{2}{\sqrt{x^2 - 4}}$.  

HINT.  Write $f(x) = 3(2x - 5)^{-1/2}$.

*28.* $y = \sqrt{\dfrac{2x}{x - 3}}$.  
*29.* $y = \sqrt{\dfrac{3t - 2}{t + 1}}$.  
*30.* $u = \sqrt[3]{\dfrac{2x^2}{5x + 2}}$.  

HINT.  In Problem 28, $y = [2x/(x - 3)]^{1/2}$.

*31.*  By use of (VIII), show that, if $k$ is a positive integer then $D_x(1/x^k) = (-k - 1)x^{-k-1}$. Thus, prove that (IV) on page 193 is true when $n$ is a negative integer, $n = -k$.

## ★77.  Differentiation of implicit functions

Consider an equation

$$h(x, y) = 0. \tag{1}$$

Suppose that there exists a function $f(x)$ so that, for every value of $x$ in the domain of $f$, the pair $(x, y)$ with $y = f(x)$ is a solution of (1). Then, on page 68 we called $f$ a *solution function* of (1) for $y$ as a function of $x$. If (1) is sufficiently simple, we may be able to obtain such solution functions by solving (1) for $y$ in terms of $x$. However, it may be impossible or inconvenient to do this. In any case, when one or more solutions of the type $y = f(x)$ are known to exist for (1), even though $f(x)$ is not available, we say that (1) defines $y$ *implicitly* as a function of $x$. In contrast, any equation such as $y = g(x)$ is said to define $y$ *explicitly* as a function of $x$. Similarly, (1) may define $x$ implicitly as a function of $y$.

ILLUSTRATION 1.  If $x^2 + y^2 = 16$, then $y^2 = 16 - x^2$; $y = \sqrt{16 - x^2}$ or $y = -\sqrt{16 - x^2}$, which gives two solution functions for $y$ as a function of $x$. Similarly, we obtain $x = \sqrt{16 - y^2}$ or $x = -\sqrt{16 - y^2}$, which gives two solution functions for $x$ as a function of $y$.

If $h(x, y)$ is a polynomial, then (1) may define either variable implicitly as an *algebraic* function of the other variable. If we ask for $dy/dx$, this denotes $x$ as the *independent variable*. If we request $dx/dy$, this denotes $y$ as the *independent variable*. By means of preceding formulas for differentiation, if $h(x, y)$ is a polynomial, we may obtain an expression involving $x$ and $y$ for either $dy/dx$ or $dx/dy$ from (1) without first solving explicitly for the dependent variable in terms of the independent variable. This method is referred to as the **implicit method of differentiaion**. It assumes that $dy/dx$, or $dx/dy$, exists for some domain of values of the independent variable involved. Either $dy/dx$ or $dx/dy$ may fail to exist for certain values of the variables, even when $h(x, y)$ in (1) is a polynomial.

ILLUSTRATION 2.    Suppose that $y$ is known to be a function of $x$. Then, by (VI) and (VII) on pages 214–15,

$$D_x y^2 = 2y \frac{dy}{dx}; \qquad D_x(xy) = y + x \frac{dy}{dx}.$$

EXAMPLE 1.    If $\qquad\qquad x^2 + y^2 = 25,$ $\qquad\qquad$ (2)

obtain $dy/dx$ and $dx/dy$ by the implicit function method.

*Solution.    1.    To obtain $dy/dx$*:    Consider $x$ as the independent variable. Then (2) defines $y$ as a differentiable function of $x$, and each side of (2) represents the same value of a function of $x$. Thus, the derivative of the left-hand side of (2) is equal to the derivative of the right-hand side. Hence, we differentiate each side with respect to $x$ and equate the results:

$$D_x(x^2 + y^2) = D_x(25), \text{ or}$$

$$2x + 2y \frac{dy}{dx} = 0; \qquad \frac{dy}{dx} = -\frac{x}{y}. \qquad (3)$$

*2.    To obtain $dx/dy$*:    Differentiate the sides of (2) with respect to $y$ and equate the results:

$$D_y(x^2 + y^2) = D_y(25), \text{ or}$$

$$2x \frac{dx}{dy} + 2y = 0; \qquad \frac{dx}{dy} = -\frac{y}{x}. \qquad (4)$$

In (3) and (4), notice that

$$\frac{dy}{dx} = \frac{1}{\left(\dfrac{dx}{dy}\right)}. \qquad (5)$$

Let us permit reckless mathematical action, and act as if $dy/dx$ and $dx/dy$ may be treated as fractions in the context of (5). Then, (5) is a simple consequence of taking the reciprocal of a fraction. This action can be justified by a more elaborate discussion. We accept (5).

In any equation $y = f(x)$, if it defines $x$ implicitly as a function of $y$, say $x = g(y)$, so that

$$y = f(x) \qquad \textit{is equivalent to} \qquad x = g(y), \qquad (6)$$

then $f$ and $g$ are called **inverse functions**. If both $dy/dx$ and $dx/dy$ exist and neither is zero at a solution point $(x_0, y_0)$ of (6), then equation (5) is valid at this point.

Let $T$ be the graph of $h(x, y) = 0$ in (1), and suppose that the point $P:(x_0, y_0)$ of $T$ is on the graph of a solution function $y = f(x)$ of (1). Suppose that $f$ has an inverse $g$, so that $x = g(y)$ is equivalent to $y = f(x)$. By the definition of a tangent line, if $f'(x_0)$ exists then $T$ has a nonvertical tangent at $P$, and

$$\left.\begin{array}{r}\textit{the tangent at P is parallel to the x-axis if*}\\[2mm]\dfrac{dy}{dx}\bigg|_{(x_0,y_0)} = 0.\end{array}\right\} \qquad (7)$$

If $dy/dx$, or $f'(x)$ does not exist at $P$, previously we have *not defined a tangent to T at P*. In such circumstances, suppose that $dx/dy$ exists, which we shall find is possible. Then, we cannot have $dx/dy \neq 0$ at $P$ because, in such a case, (5) would show that $dy/dx$ exists at $P$. Hence, if $dx/dy$ exists at $P$, *we must have $dx/dy = 0$ at P*. Then, we add to our previous definition for tangents the following statement.

$$\left.\begin{array}{l}\textit{If } \dfrac{dx}{dy}\bigg|_{(x_0,y_0)} = \mathbf{0}, \textit{ the } \textbf{vertical line } \textit{through } P:(x_0, y_0) \textit{ is}\\[2mm]\textit{defined as the tangent to the graph, T, of } h(x, y) = 0 \textit{ at P.}\end{array}\right\} \qquad (8)$$

ILLUSTRATION 3.   Let $T$ be the graph of $x = y^3$ in Figure 74. We have

$$\frac{dx}{dy} = 3y^2 \qquad \textit{and hence} \qquad \frac{dy}{dx} = \frac{1}{3y^2}. \qquad (9)$$

At the origin $O:(0, 0)$ on $T$, $dy/dx$ does not exist because $1/3y^2$ is not defined at $y = 0$. However, $dx/dy = 0$ at the origin. Hence, by (8), the tangent to $T$ at $O$ is the vertical line $x = 0$. It cuts the curve at $(0, 0)$.

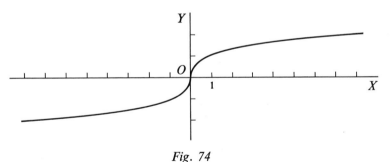

*Fig. 74*

ILLUSTRATION 4.   In Example 1, $dy/dx = -x/y$ and $dx/dy = -y/x$. Hence, the tangent to the graph of $x^2 + y^2 = 25$ is horizontal where $dy/dx = 0$, or where $x = 0$. This occurs at the points $(0, 5)$ and $(0, -5)$ on the circle

* We read $``\dfrac{dy}{dx}\bigg|_{(x_0, y_0)}\,"$ as $``\dfrac{dy}{dx}$ at $(x_0, y_0)."$

$x^2 + y^2 = 25$ in Figure 75. The tangent to the circle is vertical where $dx/dy = 0$, or where $y = 0$; this occurs at the points $(5, 0)$ and $(-5, 0)$ on the circle.

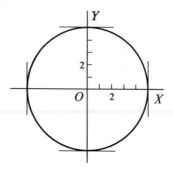

*Fig. 75*

EXAMPLE 2.   Obtain $dy/dx$ and $dx/dy$ in case

$$2x^2 - 3xy + y^2 = 15. \tag{10}$$

*Solution.*   *1.*   To obtain $dy/dx$, differentiate both sides of (10) with respect to $x$, considering $y$ as a differentiable function of $x$:

$$D_x(2x^2 - 3xy + y^2) = D_x(15), \ or$$

$$4x - 3y - 3x\frac{dy}{dx} + 2y\frac{dy}{dx} = 0;$$

$$\frac{dy}{dx}(2y - 3x) = 3y - 4x; \qquad \frac{dy}{dx} = \frac{3y - 4x}{2y - 3x}.$$

*2.*   To obtain $dx/dy$, we could use (5). We prefer to check (5) by proceeding without use of it. Differentiate both sides of (10) with respect to $y$:

$$D_y(2x^2 - 3xy + y^2) = D_y(15), \ or$$

$$4x\frac{dx}{dy} - 3y\frac{dx}{dy} - 3x + 2y = 0;$$

$$\frac{dx}{dy}(4x - 3y) = 3x - 2y; \qquad \frac{dx}{dy} = \frac{3x - 2y}{4x - 3y}. \tag{11}$$

In (11), we see that $dx/dy = 1/(dy/dx)$.

## ★78.   Derivatives of higher orders

Let $y = f(x)$, and suppose that $f'(x)$ exists. Then, $f'$ may have a derivative. In such a case it is represented by $f''$, and is called the *second derivative function for f*. If $f''$ has a derivative, it is called the *third derivative of f*, and is denoted by $f'''$; in this way, derivatives of all orders can be defined. Thus, the *n*th derivative of *f* is the result of differentiating *f* in succession *n* times, and is represented by $f^{(n)}$, when it exists. Also, we may call $f'$ the *first derivative of f*. However, a reference merely to *the derivative of f* means the *first derivative of f*, or $f'$. When $y = f(x)$, the values of the successive derivatives of *f* are represented by

$$y'' = f''(x) = \frac{d^2y}{dx^2}, \quad y''' = f'''(x) = \frac{d^3y}{dx^3}, \quad y^{(IV)} = f^{(IV)}(x) = \frac{d^4y}{dx^4}, \cdots. \quad (1)$$

In (1), we read $y''$ as "*y* second," $f'''$ as "*f* third," $d^2y/dx^2$ as "*the second derivative of y with respect to x*," etc.

ILLUSTRATION 1.   If $f(x) = x^4 + 3x^3 - x + 5$, then

$$f'(x) = 4x^3 + 9x^2 - 1; \quad f''(x) = 12x^2 + 18x; \quad f'''(x) = 24x + 18.$$

ILLUSTRATION 2.   Suppose that the motion of a particle on an *s*-axis, as on page 198, is defined by $s = f(t)$, where *t* represents the time. We have seen that, at any instant *t*, the *velocity* is $v = f'(t)$. Then, the *instantaneous rate of change* of *v* at any instant *t* is called the **acceleration** of the particle. If $\alpha$ represents this acceleration, then

$$\textbf{acceleration} = \alpha = \frac{dv}{dt} = f''(t). \quad (2)$$

ILLUSTRATION 3.   In economics, suppose that the relation between the consumer demand, *x* units, and the price $p at which *x* would be the demand, is $x = h(p)$, which we have called a *demand equation*. Then, at an instant when the price is *p*, the instantaneous rate of change of the demand is $dx/dp$ or $h'(p)$. The instantaneous rate at which this rate of change is changing, or the *acceleration of demand* is

$$\frac{d^2x}{dp^2} = h''(p).$$

Similarly, with the total production cost $C = g(x)$, the marginal cost is $C' = g'(x)$, and the instantaneous rate of change of the marginal cost is $C'' = g''(x)$.

## ★Exercise 47

*If y is known to be a function of x, obtain an expression for the specified derivative in terms of x, y, and dy/dx.*

1.  $D_x(x^2y)$.
2.  $D_x(3y^2)$.
3.  $D_x(x/y)$.
4.  $D_x(x + 2y)^2$.
5.  $D_x(3x - y)^4$.
6.  $D_x\sqrt{2x + 3y}$.

*Find each of dy/dx and dx/dy by use of the implicit function method. Then verify that dy/dx = 1/(dx/dy).*

7.  $3x + 2y^2 = 5.$          8.  $x + xy = 8.$          9.  $xy = 6.$
10. $x^2 + y^3 = 1.$          11. $x^2 - y^2 = 16.$       12. $x^2 + 5y^2 = 12.$

*Find one of dy/dx and dx/dy by the implicit function method, and the other derivative by use of the reciprocal relation (5) on page 218.*

13. $x^2 - 3xy + y^2 = 4.$                14. $x^3 - xy^2 + 7y = 2x - 4.$
15. $x^2y + y^3 = 5.$                      16. $x^3 + y^3 - 6xy = 0.$
17. $2\sqrt{x} + 3\sqrt{y} = 5.$            18. $x - 2\sqrt{xy} = 6.$

*Obtain dy/dx and dx/dy. Locate the points where the graph of the equation will have a horizontal or vertical tangent. Then graph the equation.*

19. $4x^2 + 9y^2 = 36.$         20. $x = y^2.$          21. $y = x^3.$
22. $x^2 + y^2 - 4y = 21.$                    23. $x^2 - 4y^2 = 16.$

*Obtain the 1st, 2d, and 3d derivatives of f.*

24. $f(x) = 4x^4 - 5x^3 + x^2 - 3.$     25. $f(x) = 3x^5 - 4x^3 + 3x.$

26. A particle $P$ is moving on an $s$-axis with $s = 5t^3 + 6t^2 - 3t + 2$ at time $t$. Find the velocity and acceleration of $P$ when $t = 4$.

27. Suppose that the cost equation of a manufacturer is $C = 8300 + 4x - .02x^2$, where $x$ is the number of units of production. When $x = 50$, find the marginal cost and its rate of change with respect to production.

28–32.  In Problems 9–13, respectively, on page 210, find the marginal cost and its rate of change. Also, in Problems 10–13, compute the acceleration of cost when production is ten units.

# 9 | ANTIDERIVATIVES AND INTEGRALS

## 79. Introduction to antiderivatives

If $F$ and $f$ are functions such that $F'(x) = f(x)$, it is said that $F$ is an **antiderivative** of $f$, or that $F(x)$ is an *antiderivative of $f(x)$*. Thus,

$$\left.\begin{array}{l} \text{to state that } F(x) \text{ is an \textbf{antiderivative} of } f(x) \text{ means that} \\ F'(x) = f(x). \end{array}\right\} \tag{1}$$

To verify any particular case of (1), differentiate $F$ to verify that $F'(x) = f(x)$.

ILLUSTRATION 1. If $f(x) = x^2$, then an antiderivative of $f(x)$ is $\frac{1}{3}x^3$ because $D_x(\frac{1}{3}x^3) = \frac{1}{3} \cdot 3x^2 = x^2$. Also, if $F(x) = 5 + \frac{1}{3}x^3$, then $F(x)$ is another antiderivative of $f(x)$, because

$$D_x(\tfrac{1}{3}x^3 + 5) = D_x(\tfrac{1}{3}x^3) + D_x 5 = x^2 + 0.$$

Similarly, if $k$ is any constant then $(\frac{1}{3}x^3 + k)$ is an antiderivative of $x^2$, because $D_x k = 0$.

Suppose that $D_x f(x) = 0$. Then, the graph of $y = f(x)$ has a horizontal tangent at each point. Hence, it is evident intuitively that the graph is a line parallel to the $x$-axis, or that $y = k$ at all values of $x$, or $f(x) \equiv k$ (*is identically equal to $k$*) where $k$ is some constant. This apparently simple result is very important. Actually, its proof is far from trivial, but will not be given in this text. Thus, we shall assume the fact that

$$D_x f(x) \equiv 0 \quad \textit{is equivalent to} \quad f(x) \equiv k. \tag{2}$$

In Illustration 1, we met a special case of the following result.

**THEOREM I.** *If $F(x)$ is a particular antiderivative of $f$, then the set of all antiderivatives of $f$ is the set of all functions $\{F(x) + k\}$, where $k$ is any constant.*

*Proof.* With $F$ known to be a particular antiderivative of $f(x)$, let $G(x)$ be *any* antiderivative of $f(x)$. Then

$$D_x[G(x) - F(x)] = D_xG(x) - D_xF(x) = f(x) - f(x) = 0.$$

Hence, by (2), to state that "*G is an antiderivative of f*" is equivalent to stating that "$G(x) - F(x) = k$," where $k$ is some constant, or $G(x) = F(x) + k$.

If $f$ has antiderivatives, we shall let *any* antiderivative of $f$ be represented by "$\int f(x)dx$," to be read at present "*antiderivative of f*." The reason for using this apparently peculiar symbol will become apparent later. In $\int f(x)dx$, the symbol "$dx$" serves to emphasize the fact that $x$ is the independent variable. By Theorem I, if $F(x)$ is a particular antiderivative of $f(x)$, then

$$\int f(x)dx = F(x) + k.$$

In more extensive treatments of calculus, formulas are developed for the antiderivatives of numerous functions. We shall employ only one of these formulas, as follows.

*If $m$ is any rational number, not $-1$, then*

$$\int x^mdx = \frac{x^{m+1}}{m+1} + k, \tag{3}$$

where $k$ is any constant. We prove (3) by differentiating on the right by use of (VI) on page 215 to obtain $x^m$:

$$D_x\left[\frac{x^{m+1}}{m+1} + k\right] = \frac{(m+1)x^{m+1-1}}{m+1} = x^m.$$

ILLUSTRATION 2.     $\int x^3dx = \dfrac{x^4}{4} + C.$

By the definition of an antiderivative,

$$D_x \int f(x)dx = f(x), \quad or \quad d(\int f(x)dx) = f(x)dx. \tag{4}$$

The operation of finding an antiderivative may be called **antidifferentiation**. Then, because of (4), we see that the operation of differentiation, symbolized by $D_x$, cancels the operation of antidifferentiation. Some of the useful properties of antidifferentiation are as follows.

$$\int [f(x) + g(x)]dx = \int f(x)dx + \int g(x)dx. \tag{5}$$

*If c is a constant,* $\qquad\qquad \int cf(x)dx = c\int f(x)dx.$ (6)

We may prove (5) or (6) by differentiating on the right. Thus,

$$D_x[\int f(x)dx + \int g(x)dx] = D_x\int f(x)dx + D_x\int g(x)dx$$
$$= f(x) + g(x).$$

Hence, the right-hand side of (5) gives the values of a function of $x$ where the derivative is $[f(x) + g(x)]$. Thus, the right-hand side is an antiderivative of $[f(x) + g(x)]$, as stated by (5).

ILLUSTRATION 3. If $c$ is a constant, then $\int cdx = cx + k$, because $D_x(cx + k) = c$. Or, we could think of obtaining the result by use of (3) with $m = 0$, and (6). In particular,

$$\int dx = x + k.$$ (7)

By means of (3), (5), and (6), we may find the antiderivative of any polynomial in $x$.

ILLUSTRATION 4. $\quad \int (3x^2 + 5x^3 - 6x + 4)dx$

$$= 3\int x^2dx + 5\int x^3dx - 6\int xdx + \int 4dx$$
$$= \frac{3x^3}{3} + \frac{5x^4}{4} - \frac{6x^2}{2} + \frac{4x}{1} + k$$
$$= x^3 + \tfrac{5}{4}x^4 - 3x^2 + 4x + k.$$

Let $F(x) = \int f(x)dx$. Then, we have $F'(x) = f(x)$, and the differential $dF(x) = f(x)dx$. This convenient fact justifies the following statement:

*If* $\quad dF(x) = f(x)dx,$ $\quad$ *then* $\quad F(x) = \int f(x)dx.$ (8)

Equation (8) is particularly useful because, in many applications, the differential $dF(x)$ of some unknown function $F$ arises naturally. In case the derivative $F'(x)$ is known, we write $dF(x)$ promptly so that (8) can be used.

EXAMPLE 1. A particle, $P$, is moving on an $s$-axis so that the velocity $v$ at any instant $t$ is $v = 6t + 5$. If $P$ is located at $s = 4$ when $t = 2$, find the location of $P$ at any instant $t$.

*Solution.* 1. From (2) on page 198, $v = ds/dt$. Hence, if $s = f(t)$, then $s$, or $f(t)$, is an antiderivative of $v$. We have

$$\frac{ds}{dt} = 6t + 5, \quad or \quad ds = (6t + 5)dt.$$ (9)

By use of (8), and then (3), (5), and (6),

$$s = \int (6t + 5)dt = \frac{6t^2}{2} + 5t + k, \, or$$
$$s = 3t^2 + 5t + k,$$ (10)

where $k$ is an arbitrary constant.

*2.* The *"initial conditions"* are ($s = 4$ at $t = 2$). With these values inserted in (10),

$$4 = 12 + 10 + k, \qquad or \qquad k = -18.$$

Hence, from (10), we have $s = 3t^2 + 5t - 18$ at any instant $t$.

Example 1 illustrates one of the most important types of application of calculus. In (9), we met a **differential equation**, that is, an equation involving one (or more) derivatives of an unknown function, which is to be determined. The solution of (9) typically brought in an *arbitrary constant*. Then, the *initial conditions* of the problem determined a value for the arbitrary constant. Thus, in Example 1, we solved a differential equation supplemented by initial conditions.

EXAMPLE 2.    On a certain curve which is the graph of an equation $y = f(x)$, the slope of the tangent at any point $P:(x, y)$ is $(2x - 3)$. Also, the curve passes through $P:(2, -3)$. Find the equation of the curve.

*Solution.    1.*    The slope at any point is $y'$. Hence

$$\frac{dy}{dx} = 2x - 3, \qquad or \qquad dy = (2x - 3)dx, \tag{11}$$

with the initial conditions "*if $x = 2$ then $y = -3$.*"

*2.*    From (8) and (11),  $\int dy = \int (2x - 3)dx$, or

$$y = x^2 - 3x + k, \tag{12}$$

where $k$ is an arbitrary constant. In (12), if $x = 2$ and $y = -3$, then $-3 = 4 - 6 + k$, or $k = -1$. Hence, the desired equation is $y = x^2 - 3x - 1$, whose graph is shown as the continuous curve in Figure 76.

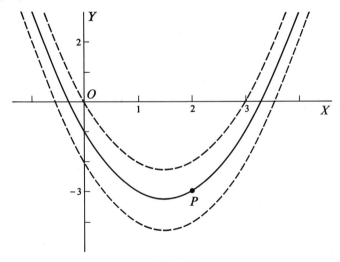

*Fig. 76*

COMMENT. The solution of the differential equation (11), without initial conditions, is given in (12), which represents a *family of parabolas*, corresponding to all values of $k$. A few of these parabolas, in addition to the solution of Example 1, are given as broken curves in Figure 76. The initial conditions served to pick out that parabola of the family passing through $P:(2, -3)$.

EXAMPLE 3.    A new machine being used in a factory will need increasing repair costs as the machine ages. Suppose that the annual repair or upkeep cost after $x$ years of use is $U(x)$, where the function $U$ is differentiable. Then, the *marginal repair cost* after $x$ years of use is defined as the instantaneous rate of change of $U(x)$ with respect to $x$, or $D_x U(x)$. If the marginal repair cost is $cx$, where $c$ is a constant, find $U(x)$ if the cost in the 1st year is nil.

*Solution.*   If $y = U(x)$, then $U'(x) = cx$ with $y = 0$ when $x = 0$. Hence,

$$\frac{dy}{dx} = cx, \qquad or \qquad dy = cxdx; \tag{13}$$

$$y = \int cxdx = \frac{cx^2}{2} + k. \tag{14}$$

With $(x = 0, y = 0)$ in (14), we find $k = 0$. Hence,

$$y = \tfrac{1}{2}cx^2, \qquad or \qquad U(x) = \tfrac{1}{2}cx^2.$$

## Exercise 48

*A particle is moving on an s-axis so that, at any instant t, the velocity s' has the given value. Find the coordinate s of the particle at any instant t corresponding to the specified initial conditions.*

1.  $s' = -4t + 3$; $s = 3$ when $t = 2$.
2.  $s' = 5t - 2$; $s = -2$ when $t = 3$.
3.  $s' = t^2 - 3t + 4$; $s = -2$ when $t = 2$.
4.  $s' = -2t^2 + 4t - 5$; $s = 3$ when $t = -2$.
5.  $s' = -t^2 - 3t$; $s = 0$ when $t = 0$.

*In an xy-plane, on a curve which is the graph of an equation $y = f(x)$, the slope of the tangent at any point $P:(x, y)$ has the specified value. Find an equation for the curve if it passes through the specified point.*

6.  Slope $= 6$; through $(-2, 3)$.
7.  Slope $= 3x - 2$; through $(2, -3)$.
8.  Slope $= -4x + 5$; through $(1, 0)$.
9.  Slope $= x^2 - 2x$; through $(0, 0)$.
10.  Slope $= 3x^2 + x - 2$; through $(-1, 1)$.
11.  Slope $= -2x^2 + 3x - 4$; through $(2, -3)$.

*In the remaining problems, recall the discussion preceding* (1) *on page* 200: *p is the price at which x units of a product can be sold in unit time, R is the resulting revenue, and C is the total cost of production. All derivatives are derivatives with respect to x.*

12.  It is known that, when the demand is $x$ units, the instantaneous rate of change of price is $(-9 - 2x)$. If $\lim_{x \to 0} p = 300$, find the demand equation.

13.  When the demand is $x$ units, the marginal revenue is $(100 - 3x - 2x^2)$. Find the expression for the revenue $R$ as a function of $x$. (What are the automatic initial conditions?)

14.  When the demand is $x$ units, the marginal cost is $(30 - .1x)$. Find an expression for the cost $C$ in terms of $x$ if the fixed cost is \$15,000 even if the factory produces none of the product.

15.  For a certain product, the marginal profit is $(500 - 1.90x)$ at a time when $x$ units are being produced. If the manufacturer's loss is \$5000 per unit time when he is producing none of the product, find the profit, $P$, as a function of the demand.

## 80.   Introduction to definite integrals

An interesting fact about calculus is that its two main concepts, that of a derivative and that of an integral, are independent, although various powerful methods in calculus are consequences of a relation which can be established between the concepts. We shall emphasize the independence just described by presenting the concept of an integral without mention of a derivative.

Let $f$ be a function with domain $I = \{a \le x \le b\}$ where $a < b$. Let $I$ be divided into $n$ subintervals of equal* length (five subintervals in Figure 77), by points $\{a = x_0, x_1, x_2, x_3, \cdots, x_n = b\}$, as in Figure 77. Such a sub-division is called a **partition** of $I$. Let $\Delta_n x$ be the length of each subinterval; then $\Delta_n x$ is *one nth of the length of I*, or $\Delta_n x = (b - a)/n$. With the sub-intervals of $I$ numbered from the *left* to the *right*, on the $i$th subinterval select arbitrarily a point $x = h_i$ and form the product $f(h_i)\Delta_n x$. Then, let $S_n$ be the sum of all of these products. Thus, with $S_5$ given first for illustration,

$$S_5 = f(h_1)\Delta_5 x + f(h_2)\Delta_5 x + f(h_3)\Delta_5 x + f(h_4)\Delta_5 x + f(h_5)\Delta_5 x; \quad (1)$$
$$S_n = f(h_1)\Delta_n x + f(h_2)\Delta_n x + \cdots + f(h_n)\Delta_n x. \quad (2)$$

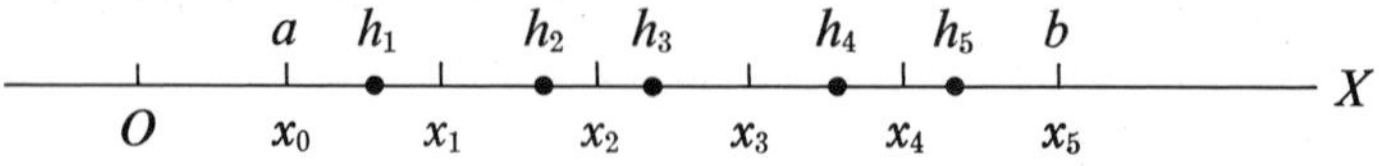

*Fig. 77*

* This restriction, and certain later features, cause our definition of an integral to be less general than, although a special case of, the type of definition met in more advanced texts.

Sometimes, $S_n$ as in (2) is called a **Riemann sum** for $f$, in honor of the great German mathematician GEORG FRIEDRICH BERNHARD RIEMANN (1826–1866).

ILLUSTRATION 1.   Let $f(x) = x^2 + 2$, where the domain of $f$ is $I = \{1 \leq x \leq 4\}$. With $n = 6$ in (2), the endpoints of the subintervals of the partition, as in Figure 78, are $\{1, \frac{3}{2}, 2, \frac{5}{2}, 3, \frac{7}{2}, 4\}$, and $\Delta_6 x = \frac{1}{2}$. Let the arbitrary points $\{h_i\}$ of (2) be taken as the midpoints of the corresponding subintervals. Then, in Figure 78, $h_1 = \frac{5}{4}$, $h_2 = \frac{7}{4}$, etc. With $\Delta_6 x$ taken as a factor, (2) gives

$$S_6 = \frac{1}{2}\left[f\left(\frac{5}{4}\right) + f\left(\frac{7}{4}\right) + f\left(\frac{9}{4}\right) + f\left(\frac{11}{4}\right) + f\left(\frac{13}{4}\right) + f\left(\frac{15}{4}\right)\right]$$

$$= \frac{1}{2}\left[\left(\frac{25}{16} + 2\right) + \left(\frac{49}{16} + 2\right) + \cdots + \left(\frac{225}{16} + 2\right)\right] = 26.94.$$

Fig. 78

DEFINITION I.   *Suppose that $a < b$. Then, "the* **definite integral** *of $f(x)$ from $x = a$ to $x = b$" is represented by $\int_a^b f(x)dx$ and is defined as follows:* *

$$\int_a^b f(x)dx = \lim_{n \to \infty} S_n,$$   (3)

*where*        $S_n = (\Delta_n x)[f(h_1) + f(h_2) + \cdots + f(h_n)].$   (4)

In (3), we read "*the integral† of $f(x)$ from $a$ to $b$ is equal to the limit of $S_n$ as $n$ becomes infinite.*" This means that $S_n$ of (4) will be as near the number $\int_a^b f(x)dx$ as we please for all values of $n$ sufficiently large. For any value of the integer $n$, and any choices of the arbitrary points $\{h_i\}$ on the subintervals of the corresponding partition of the interval $\{a \leq x \leq b\}$, $S_n$ of (4) may be thought of as an approximation to the integral on the left in (3). We anticipate that $S_n$ will improve as an approximation to the integral if $n$ grows large. In (3), we refer to $f(x)$ as the **integrand**, to $x$ as the **variable of integration**, and to $I = \{a \leq x \leq b\}$ as the **interval of integration**.

ILLUSTRATION 2.   From Illustration 1,

$$\int_1^4 (x^2 + 2)dx \doteq 26.94,$$

where "$\doteq$" is read "*approximately equals.*" Later, we shall see that the exact value of the preceding integral is 27.

* Provided that the limit exists.
† *Integral* will mean *definite integral* unless otherwise qualified.

If $a = b$ and if $b < a$, Definition I is supplemented by the following agreements.

$$\int_a^a f(x)dx = 0. \qquad \textit{If } b < a, \quad \int_a^b f(x)dx = -\int_b^a f(x)dx. \qquad (5)$$

It is important to recognize that the letter, $x$, used in $\int_a^b f(x)dx$ is immaterial. Thus, $\int_a^b f(x)dx = \int_a^b f(u)du$, because only the values of $f$, and the *interval of numbers* between $a$ and $b$ are involved in the approximating sum $S_n$ of (4). For this reason, in $\int_a^b f(x)dx$, we call $x$ a *dummy variable*. The computation of a definite integral is called *integration*.

NOTE 1.   It can be proved that the limit in (3) exists if $f$ is a continuous function, which we shall assume to be the case hereafter for any integrand which we consider.

## 81. Area as a definite integral

A set, $T$, of points in a plane is called a *bounded set of points* in case there is some rectangle $R$ such that all points of $T$ are inside $R$. If $C$ is a closed curve* in a plane, then $C$ divides the plane into two sets of points where one set, $T$, is bounded and the other set is *not* bounded (*unbounded*). We agree that the bounded set $T$ includes its boundary $C$. Any point of $T$ *not* on $C$ is called an **interior point** of $T$. Hereafter, if we refer to a bounded set of points, it will be a set $T$ with some closed curve $C$ as the boundary. Also, we may call $T$ a *region*.

ILLUSTRATION 1.   The set of points bounded by a rectangle is a bounded set, which we may call a *rectangular* set of points. A circle bounds a *circular* set, consisting of all points on the circle or interior to it.

The concept of *area* for a bounded set of points in a plane is familiar intuitively, but is not simple to define. We shall define area only for sets of points with certain types of boundaries.

In any reference to the *area of a rectangle*, we shall mean the area of the set bounded by the rectangle. Then, as a basis for our discussion of area, we *define* the area of a rectangle in square units as the product of the dimensions of the rectangle in the corresponding linear unit. Also, the area of any set of points will be a certain number of square units.

Suppose that the function $f(x)$ has the domain $I = \{a \leq x \leq b\}$, with the curve, $H$, in Figure 79 taken as the graph of $y = f(x)$. Assume that $f(x) \geq 0$ for convenience. Let $R$ be the set of points bounded by the $x$-axis, the graph of $y = f(x)$ and the vertical lines $x = a$ and $x = b$. We wish to

---

* Of one of the types considered in this text.

define the area of $R$. For any positive integer $n$, let $I$ be divided into $n$ equal subintervals, as in Figure 79, where $n = 6$ for illustration. The length of each subinterval is $\Delta_n x = (b - a)/n$. On the $i$th subinterval, counting from the left, select arbitrarily a point $h_i$. (In Figure 79, $h_i$ was selected at the center of the $i$th subinterval for illustration.) On each subinterval as a base, construct a rectangle with altitude $f(h_i)$; the area of this rectangle is $f(h_i)\Delta_n x$. Form the sum of the areas of the $n$ rectangles thus described:

$$S_n = f(h_1)\Delta_n x + f(h_2)\Delta_n x + \cdots + f(h_n)\Delta_n x. \tag{1}$$

Then, we *define** the area, $A$, of $R$ as follows:

$$A = \lim_{n \to \infty} S_n. \tag{2}$$

We observe that $S_n$ in (1) is a special case of $S_n$ in (4) on page 229. Hence, the definition in (2) leads immediately to the following result.

**THEOREM II.**  *If $f(x) \geqq 0$ and $a \leqq b$, the area, $A$, of the region $R$ bounded by the x-axis, the ordinates $x = a$ and $x = b$, and the graph of $y = f(x)$ is given by*

$$A = \int_a^b f(x)dx. \tag{3}$$

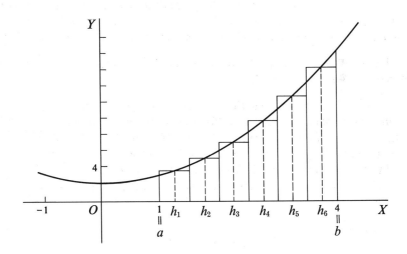

*Fig. 79*

* This definition is a special case of, and is consistent with the  definition  of area as met in more advanced treatments of calculus.

ILLUSTRATION 2.   Let $f(x) = x^2 + 2$. A graph of $y = f(x)$ is shown in Figure 79. By Theorem II, the area, $A$ of the set of points bounded by the graph of $y = x^2 + 2$, the $x$-axis, and the lines $x = 1$ and $x = 4$ is

$$A = \int_1^4 (x^2 + 2)dx. \tag{4}$$

In (4), the interval of integration is $I = \{1 \leq x \leq 4\}$. To compute an approximation to $A$ with $I$ divided into 6 subintervals, we carry out the work of Illustration 1 on page 229 and obtain

$$A = \int_1^4 (x^2 + 2)dx \doteq S_6 = 26.94. \tag{5}$$

Suppose that $f(x) \leq 0$ on $\{a \leq x \leq b\}$, and let $R$ be the set of points described in Theorem II. Then, the area, $A$, of $R$ is defined as follows:

$$(f(x) \leq 0) \qquad A = \int_a^b -f(x)dx. \tag{6}$$

NOTE 1.   The application of a definite integral in defining the area of a bounded plane set of points is closely related to the method of *exhaustion* used by early Greek geometers in studying areas. A related method was exploited by ARCHIMEDES in his work in geometry and mechanics.

We shall apply definite integrals in applications not involving areas in later sections. Also, a method will be presented for calculating integrals exactly, instead of approximately as at present by use of (3) on page 229.

NOTE 2.   The area, $A$, of a bounded set, $T$, of points in a plane may be referred to as a *measure* of $T$.

NOTE 3.   In stating that the area of a rectangle is the product of its dimensions, implicitly we assumed that they were measured in the *same unit*. Hence, this condition is implied in Theorem II. In using (3), frequently it will be desirable to graph $y = f(x)$ in an $xy$-plane where the vertical unit is *not* equal to the horizontal unit. In such a case, the region observed in the figure is thought of merely as a means to visualize the actual region whose area is given by (3).

## Exercise 49

*Wherever an approximating sum, $S_n$, for a definite integral is requested in this exercise, use the midpoint as the "arbitrary point" on each subinterval of the corresponding partition of the interval of integration, except where otherwise directed.*

*For the specified $\int_a^b f(x)dx$, compute the requested approximating sum $S_n$.*
*Also, graph $y = f(x)$, show the region R whose area is the given integral, and*
*exhibit rectangles whose total area is $S_n$, for one of the specified values of n.*

1. $\int_0^3 2x^2 dx$; calculate $S_3$ and $S_6$ (the exact value is 18).

2. $\int_2^6 4x dx$; calculate $S_4$ and $S_8$. Also, by geometry, compute the exact area of the corresponding region $R$.

*Obtain an integral which is equal to the area of the region R in the problem,*
*and show R in a figure. Compute an approximating sum $S_n$ for the area, A, of*
*R by use of the specified number of subintervals, and show corresponding*
*rectangles in the figure.*

3.  $R$ is bounded by the curve $y = 4 - x^2$, the $x$-axis, and the lines $x = -2$ and $x = 2$. Use eight subintervals. (Notice symmetry, to reduce the arithmetic by 50%.)

4.  $R$ is bounded by the parabola $y = x^2 - 4x$ and the $x$-axis, from $x = 0$ to $x = 4$. Use eight subintervals.

5.  $R$ is bounded by the curve $y = 1 + x^2$, the $x$-axis, and the lines $x = 0$ and $x = 3$. Use six subintervals and take each arbitrary number $h_i$ on its subinterval (a) as the midpoint; (b) the left-hand endpoint; (c) the right-hand endpoint.

## 82.  Fundamental theorem of integral calculus

The power of calculus is greatly enhanced by the manner in which the independent concepts of a derivative and an integral can be associated. The discovery and exploitation of this association was one of the major achievements of LEIBNITZ and NEWTON in their development of calculus. The corresponding basic theorems involve settings and proofs which are not appropriate for this text. The major theorem involved will be presented informally.

Suppose that the function $f(x)$ is continuous on the interval $I = \{a \leqq x \leqq b\}$, so that $\int_a^x f(t)dt$ exists for all values of $x$ on $I$. Notice that, for later convenience, we have used $t$ instead of $x$ as the dummy variable in the integrand. With $x$ on $I$, let

$$G(x) = \int_a^x f(t)dt. \tag{1}$$

Then the following theorem can be proved.

THEOREM III.  *For every $x$ on the interval $I = \{a \leqq x \leqq b\}$, the function $G(x)$ has a derivative, and*

$$G'(x) = f(x), \quad \text{or} \quad D_x\left[\int_a^x f(t)dt\right] = f(x). \tag{2}$$

In the following special case, we illustrate the essential features of any proof of (2).

ILLUSTRATION 1.    Suppose that $f(x) = x^2 + 4$, and consider $\int_1^x f(t)dt$, with $x$ on the interval $I = \{1 \leqq x \leqq 5\}$. Let $T$ be the graph of $y = f(x)$ in Figure 80, and define

$$G(x) = \int_1^x f(t)dt. \tag{3}$$

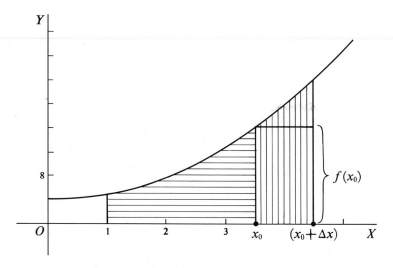

Fig. 80

For any number $x_0$ on $I$, in Figure 80, we may interpret $G(x_0)$ as the *area* of the region $R$ which is ruled horizontally, and is bounded by the $x$-axis, the curve $T$, and the vertical lines $x = 1$ and $x = x_0$. We shall apply the $\Delta$-process to investigate the existence of $G'(x_0)$. Let $\Delta x$ be assigned, with $\Delta x > 0$ for convenience. Then, in Figure 80, $G(x_0 + \Delta x)$ is the area of the region ruled with either vertical or horizontal line segments, between $x = 1$ and $x = x_0 + \Delta x$. Let

$$\Delta G(x_0) = G(x_0 + \Delta x) - G(x_0). \tag{4}$$

In Figure 80, $\Delta G(x_0)$ is the area of the region between $x = x_0$ and $x = x_0 + \Delta x$ which is ruled vertically. Notice that $\Delta G(x_0)$ is approximately equal to the area of the rectangle with altitude $f(x_0)$, which is the ordinate of $T$ at $x = x_0$, and base of length $\Delta x$. Thus

$$\Delta G(x_0) \doteq f(x_0)\Delta x. \tag{5}$$

Hence,

$$\frac{\Delta G(x_0)}{\Delta x} \doteq f(x_0). \tag{6}$$

Because of (6), we then accept the fact that

$$\lim_{\Delta x \to 0} \frac{\Delta G(x_0)}{\Delta x} = f(x_0) = 4 + x_0^2,$$

or $G'(x_0) = f(x_0)$, which is a special case of (2).

We shall proceed by use of Theorem III, with $f(x)$ as described at the beginning of this section.

THEOREM IV.   (**Fundamental theorem of integral calculus.**)   *If $F(x)$ is any antiderivative of $f(x)$, then*

$$\int_a^b f(t)dt = F(b) - F(a). \tag{7}$$

ILLUSTRATION 2.   To calculate $\int_2^5 x^3 dx$, recall that an antiderivative of $x^3$ is $F(x) = \frac{1}{4}x^4$. Hence, by (7),

$$\int_2^5 x^3 dx = F(5) - F(2) = \frac{1}{4}(5^4) - \frac{1}{4}(2^4) = \frac{625}{4} - 4 = \frac{609}{4}.$$

*Proof of Theorem* IV.   *1.*   Let $G(x) = \int_a^x f(t)dt$. By (2), we have $G'(x) = f(x)$, so that $G$ is an antiderivative of $f(x)$. Hence, by Theorem I on page 224, $G(x) = F(x) + k$, where $k$ is some constant, or

$$\int_a^x f(t)dt = F(x) + k. \tag{8}$$

*2.*   In (8), let $x = a$. Then

$$0 = \int_a^a f(t)dt = F(a) + k, \quad or \quad k = -F(a). \tag{9}$$

Hence, by use of (8),   $$\int_a^x f(t)dt = F(x) - F(a). \tag{10}$$

*3.*   When $x = b$ in (10), we obtain $\int_a^b f(t)dt = F(b) - F(a)$, as in (7).

At this stage in calculus, it proves convenient to refer to "$\int f(x)dx$" as "*the* **indefinite integral** *of* $f(x)$." However, it is important to remember that $\int f(x)dx$ is an *antiderivative* of $f(x)$. Then, our method for calculating a definite integral can be described as follows.

**Summary.**   *To calculate $\int_a^b f(x)dx$, find any indefinite integral $F(x) = \int f(x)dx$, and then use $\int_a^b f(x)dx = F(b) - F(a)$.*

In using the Summary, it is convenient to let

$$F(b) - F(a) = F(x)\Big]_a^b. \tag{11}$$

We recall the following formula, which applies when $m$ is any rational number except $m = -1$.

$$\int x^m dx = \frac{x^{m+1}}{m+1} + k. \tag{12}$$

EXAMPLE 1.   Compute          $H = \int_1^3 (2x^2 - 4x + 5)dx. \tag{13}$

*Solution.*   Find a corresponding indefinite integral, $F(x)$:

$$F(x) = \int (2x^2 - 4x + 5)dx = \tfrac{2}{3}x^3 - 2x^2 + 5x. \tag{14}$$

Hence, by (7),     $H = F(3) - F(1) = (\tfrac{2}{3}x^3 - 2x^2 + 5x)\Big]_1^3$

$$= [\tfrac{2}{3}(3^3) - 2(3^2) + 5(3)] - (\tfrac{2}{3} - 2 + 5) = 11\tfrac{1}{3}.$$

COMMENT.   In (14), we could have written

$$F(x) = \tfrac{2}{3}x^3 - 2x^2 + 5x + k, \tag{15}$$

where $k$ is an arbitrary constant. However, *any* indefinite integral, or anti-derivative, is acceptable for use in (7). Hence, in (14) we used $k = 0$. If $k$ were retained in any similar use of (7), then $k$ would cancel out in the subtraction $[F(b) - F(a)]$.

EXAMPLE 2.   Find the total area of the regions bounded by the graph of the equation $y = (x + 2)(x - 1)(x - 3)$ and finite intervals of the x-axis.

*Solution.   1.*   Let $f(x) = (x + 2)(x - 1)(x - 3)$, and let $H$ be the graph of $y = f(x)$. The x-intercepts of $H$ are $x = -2$, $x = 1$, and $x = 3$, where $f(x) = 0$. The corresponding points of $H$, and just a few other points give the graph of $y = f(x)$ in Figure 81.

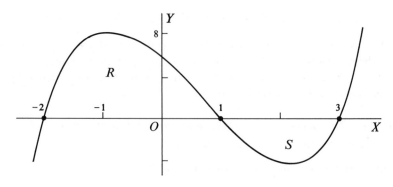

*Fig. 81*

2.  On expanding the product for $f(x)$, we find

$$f(x) = x^3 - 2x^2 - 5x + 6.$$

In Figure 81, $R$ is the region *above* the $x$-axis bounded by $y = f(x)$ and the interval $-2 \le x \le 1$ of the $x$-axis. $S$ is the region *below* the $x$-axis bounded by $y = f(x)$ and the interval $1 \le x \le 3$. The combined area, $A$, of $R$ and $S$ is as follows, where the area of $R$ is the integral at the left and the area of $S$ is the integral at the right, as obtained from (6) on page 232:

$$A = \int_{-2}^{1} (x^3 - 2x^2 - 5x + 6)dx + \int_{1}^{3} -(x^3 - 2x^2 - 5x + 6)dx. \quad (16)$$

3.  We calculate the following indefinite integral:

$$\int (x^3 - 2x^2 - 5x + 6)dx = \int x^3 dx - 2 \int x^2 dx - 5 \int x dx + 6 \int dx$$

$$= \tfrac{1}{4}x^4 - \tfrac{2}{3}x^3 - \tfrac{5}{2}x^2 + 6x = M(x). \quad (17)$$

The indefinite integral for the integral at the right in (16) is $-M(x)$.

4.  From (16) and (17), by use of the fundamental theorem of integral calculus,

$$A = [M(1) - M(-2)] + \{-M(3) - [-M(1)]\};$$

$$M(1) = \tfrac{1}{4} - \tfrac{2}{3} - \tfrac{5}{2} + 6 = \tfrac{37}{12}; \quad M(-2) = -\tfrac{38}{3}; \quad M(3) = -\tfrac{9}{4}.$$

$$A = \tfrac{37}{12} + \tfrac{38}{3} + \tfrac{9}{4} + \tfrac{37}{12} = \tfrac{253}{12}.$$

## Exercise 50

*Calculate the integral.*

1.  $\int_{2}^{4} (2x + 5)dx.$     2.  $\int_{-1}^{3} (x^2 + 3x)dx.$     3.  $\int_{-4}^{-1} (2x^3 - 5)dx.$

4.  $\int_{0}^{3} (4x^2 + 7x^3)dx.$     5.  $\int_{-2}^{0} (2 - x^2)dx.$     6.  $\int_{-3}^{1} (1 - 3x^2)dx.$

*Obtain a graph of $y = f(x)$. Any $x$-intercepts must be obtained accurately. If $f$ is a quadratic function, the graph may be obtained by use of the routine on page 67. Then find the area of the region $R$ bounded by finite intervals of the $x$-axis, the graph, and any ordinates which are mentioned.*

7.  $f(x) = x^2 + 3$; $R$ is bounded also by the lines $x = -2$ and $x = 3$.
8.  $f(x) = 2x - 6$; $R$ is bounded also by the $y$-axis.
9.  $f(x) = 4x - x^2$; $R$ is bounded simply by the graph and the $x$-axis.
10. $f(x) = (x + 2)(x - 3)$; $R$ is bounded simply by the graph and the $x$-axis.
11. $f(x) = (x - 2)(4 - x)$; $R$ is bounded simply by the graph and the $x$-axis.
12. $f(x) = x(x - 2)(x - 4)$; $R$ is bounded simply by the graph and the $x$-axis.

13. $f(x) = x(x + 3)(x - 1)$; $R$ is bounded simply by the graph and the $x$-axis.

★14. Find the area of the region bounded by the line $y = x$ and the parabola $y = x^2 - 3x$.

★15. Find the area of the region bounded by the line $y = x + 2$ and the parabola $y = (x - 1)(6 - x)$.

## ★ 83.  A distribution of mass on a line

The physical concept of the *mass* of an object will be accepted as a basic undefined term. Mass is measured in grams, pounds, and other units.

Let us conceive of mass spread on an $x$-axis from $x = a$ to $x = b$. This distribution of mass can be visualized as the mass of a wire of negligible diameter. Suppose that there is a constant $\delta$ (Greek *delta*) such that the mass $\Delta m$ on any interval of length $\Delta x$ on the $x$-axis is given by $\Delta m = \delta \Delta x$. Then, we shall say that mass is spread on the $x$-axis with *uniform density* $\delta$. If a mass $\Delta m$ is distributed uniformly with density $\delta$ on an interval $\{x_1 \leqq x \leqq x_2\}$ of length $\Delta x = x_2 - x_1$, then

$$\Delta m = \delta \Delta x = (x_2 - x_1)\delta = \int_{x_1}^{x_2} \delta dx, \tag{1}$$

because

$$\int_{x_1}^{x_2} dx = x \Big]_{x_1}^{x_2} = x_2 - x_1.$$

The form of (1) suggests the following terminology.

DEFINITION II.   *Suppose that the function $\delta(x)$ is continuous, has the domain $I = \{a \leqq x \leqq b\}$, and is never negative if $x$ is on $I$. Then, to state that $\delta$ is the* **density function** *for a distribution of mass on $I$ means that the mass on any subinterval $\{x_1 \leqq x \leqq x_2\}$ of $I$ is the integral of $\delta(x)$ from $x_1$ to $x_2$.*

In the setting of Definition II, let $\Delta m$ be the mass on the interval $\{x_1 \leqq x \leqq x_2\}$. Then

$$\Delta m = \int_{x_1}^{x_2} \delta(x)dx. \tag{2}$$

The total mass, $m$, on the interval $I$ is

$$m = \int_a^b \delta(x)dx. \tag{3}$$

When Definition II applies, it is said that there is a *continuous distribution of mass* on $I$ with the density function $\delta(x)$.

ILLUSTRATION 1. Suppose that mass is distributed on the interval $I = \{1 \leq x \leq 3\}$ with the density function $\delta(x) = 3x - x^2$. Then, the total mass on $I$ is

$$m = \int_1^3 (3x - x^2)dx = \left(\tfrac{3}{2}x^2 - \tfrac{1}{3}x^3\right)\Big]_1^3 = \tfrac{10}{3}.$$

In order to introduce certain concepts, let us consider the case of a distribution of mass over the interval $I = \{2 \leq x \leq 5\}$, with density $\delta(x) = 1 + 2x$. A graph of $y = \delta(x)$ is shown in Figure 82. The mass on $I$ is

$$m = \int_2^5 \delta(x)dx = \int_2^5 (1 + 2x)dx$$
$$= (x + x^2)\Big]_2^5 = 24. \tag{4}$$

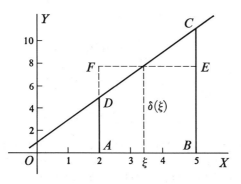

Fig. 82

The mass $m$ thus can be interpreted as the *area* of the region, $R$, in the $xy$-plane bounded by the $x$-axis, the graph of $y = \delta(x)$, and the ordinates at the endpoints of $I$. In Figure 82, $R$ is the region bounded by the trapezoid $ABCD$. It is evident geometrically that, if the horizontal broken line $FE$ in Figure 82 is located at a proper height, the area of the rectangle $ABEF$ will equal the area of $ABCD$. Let $\xi$ be the value of $x$ where the broken line then intersects the graph of $y = \delta(x)$. The altitude of rectangle $ABEF$ is $\delta(\xi)$ and the area is $3\delta(\xi)$, where 3 is the length of $I$. Thus, we conclude that

$$(mass\ on\ I) = \delta(\xi)\cdot(length\ of\ I).$$

On the basis of the preceding illustration, we permit certain general conclusions as follows.

Suppose that mass is distributed on an interval $I = \{a \leq x \leq b\}$ with density $\delta(x)$. Then, the mass on any subinterval $T = \{x_1 \leq x \leq x_2\}$ of $I$ can be interpreted as the *area* of the region of an $xy$-plane bounded by the curve $y = \delta(x)$, the $x$-axis, and the ordinates $x = x_1$ and $x = x_2$. Moreover, there exists* a point $\xi$, where $x_1 \leq \xi \leq x_2$, such that the mass on $T$ is equal to $\delta(\xi)$ times the length of $T$. Or, by use of (2),

$$\Delta m = \int_{x_1}^{x_2} \delta(x)dx = \delta(\xi)(x_2 - x_1). \qquad (5)$$

From (5), a constant density of mass $\delta(\xi)$ on the interval $T = \{x_1 \leq x \leq x_2\}$ creates the same mass, $\delta(\xi)(x_2 - x_1)$, as the variable density $\delta(x)$. Hence, in (5), $\delta(\xi)$ will be called the *average density* of mass on $T$. For any subinterval of $T$, we thus give the following definition:

$$\left\{\begin{array}{c}\textbf{average mass density}\\ \textit{on an interval}\end{array}\right\} = \frac{\textit{mass on the interval}}{\textit{length of the interval}}. \qquad (6)$$

ILLUSTRATION 2.   From (4), the average density of mass on the interval involved is 24/3, or 8.

In (5), with $\Delta x = x_2 - x_1$,

$$\frac{\Delta m}{\Delta x} = \delta(\xi), \qquad (7)$$

where $x_1 \leq \xi \leq x_2$. If $\Delta x \to 0$ with $x_1$ fixed, then $\xi \to x_1$. Hence, from (7),

$$\lim_{\Delta x \to 0} \frac{\Delta m}{\Delta x} = \lim_{\Delta x \to 0} \delta(\xi) = \delta(x_1).$$

Thus, for any value of $x$, $\delta(x)$ is *the limit of the average density, on an interval including $x$, as the length of this interval approaches* 0. For this reason, sometimes $\delta(x)$ is called the density of mass *at the point $x$.*

With the name "*density of mass*" changed to "*probability density*," in a later section we shall find that Definition II is a basic element in the development of mathematical statistics.

Suppose that a mass of magnitude $m$ is considered as concentrated at a point $H:(c)$ on an $x$-axis. Then, we shall refer to $m$ as a *mass particle.* Visualize the $x$-axis as a horizontal lever, supported at the origin as a fulcrum. Then, the *moment* of $m$ about the origin is defined as $mc$. In the terminology of Physics, $mc$ is the moment about the origin of the *force* of $m$ pounds with which the mass $m$ is attracted by the earth's gravitational field of force. In Physics, problems about sets of mass particles are considered in which moments of the masses play a primary role. For a continuous distribution of mass as in Definition II, similar problems arise, where the following concepts are found to be the proper generalizations of those met with systems of mass

---

* On the basis of the discussion related to Figure 82, we are accepting the following result, referred to as the *mean value theorem for an integral.* "*If $f$ is continuous, there exists $\xi$ such that $a \leq \xi \leq b$ and $\int_a^b f(x)dx = f(\xi)(b - a)$.*"

particles. In the statements below, the notational setting of Definition II is employed.

$$\left\{\begin{matrix} \textit{Moment of the mass} \\ \textit{distribution about the origin} \end{matrix}\right\} = \int_a^b x\delta(x)dx. \tag{8}$$

*The center of mass, $P:(\bar{x})$, is that point for which*

$$\bar{x} = \frac{\int_a^b x\delta(x)dx}{\int_a^b \delta(x)dx}. \tag{9}$$

In (9), the denominator is the *total mass, m,* of the distribution. Hence, from (9),

$$m\bar{x} = \int_a^b x\delta(x)dx. \tag{10}$$

In (10), $m\bar{x}$ is the moment with respect to the origin *if all of the mass were concentrated at the center of mass $P:(\bar{x})$.* Hence, this moment is stated, in (10), to be equal to the moment of the continuously distributed mass.

We shall not consider physical properties associated with (8) and (9). Our interest in them is due to the fact that, in mathematical statistics, the right-hand sides of (8) and (9) are taken as a basis for the definitions of fundamental parameters.

## ★ Exercise 51

*Mass is distributed continuously on the specified interval of the x-axis, with the given density function $\delta(x)$. Find (a) the total mass; (b) the average density of mass on the interval.*

1.  On $\{2 \le x \le 7\}$; $\delta(x) = 4x - 4$.
2.  On $\{-3 \le x \le 2\}$; $\delta(x) = 7 - 2x + x^2$.
3.  On $\{-1 \le x \le 3\}$; $\delta(x) = 5 - x + \dfrac{x^2}{5}$.
4.  On $\{-4 \le x \le 1\}$; $\delta(x) = 4 - x + x^2$.

5–8.  In Problems 1–4, respectively, find the center of mass.

## ★ 84.   Continuous random variables

Let $r$ represent any outcome of a random experiment, and let $T$ be the sample space consisting of all of these outcomes. With $T$ as a finite set, in Chapter 7 we defined a *random variable*, $X$, on $T$ as a real-valued function whose domain is $T$. That is, to each outcome $r$ in $T$, there corresponds a single number $x = X(r)$. Let $V$ be the range of $X$:

$$V = \{x \mid x = X(r), \textit{for all } r \textit{ in } T\}.* \tag{1}$$

* In (1), we read: " *V is the set of all numbers x such that $x = X(r)$, for all r in T.*"

When $T$ is a finite set of $n$ outcomes, $V$ consists of at most $n$ numbers, because only distinct values $x = X(r)$ are listed in (1).

In more extensive treatments of probability in mathematical statistics, sample spaces must be considered which are *not* finite. Thus, a sample space $T$ might consist of an endless set of outcomes $\{r_1, r_2, r_3, \cdots\}$. This set is said to be *countably infinite*, because the outcomes are in a one-to-one correspondence with the set of all positive integers, as seen from the subscripts. Or, it may be possible to establish a one-to-one correspondence between the outcomes of $T$ and all numbers on a finite interval $\{c \leqq x \leqq d\}$ of the number scale. In such a case, we say that $T$ is an *infinite* set but is *not* countably infinite.

The definition given in Chapter 7 for a random variable on a finite sample space $T$ applies unchanged when $T$ is an infinite set. If this occurs, and $T$ is not merely countably infinite, the range $V$ of the random variable $X$ may be an interval, finite or infinite.* We shall assume that $V$ is a finite interval, $V = \{a \leqq x \leqq b\}$. $V$ is the set of all values of $x$ such that $x = X(r)$, for all $r$ in $T$. We shall discuss limited aspects of probability as defined for this case. Thus, we make the following assumption:

$$X \text{ is a random variable on an infinite sample space } T, \text{ and} \atop \text{the range of } X \text{ is an interval } V = \{a \leqq x \leqq b\}. \tag{2}$$

In Chapter 7, where the sample space was finite, probabilities concerning values of a random variable $X$ were determined as consequences of corresponding probabilities in the sample space $T$. In cases where (2) applies, usually it is desirable to define probabilities about sets of values of $X$ in $V$ without mention of probabilities for $T$. Or, $T$ is studied from the probability viewpoint by obtaining results relating entirely to the *new sample space* $V$. Hence, hereafter, $T$ will *not be involved*, and we shall not mention any outcomes in $T$. Thus, we may simplify the notation by referring to a value simply of "$X$" instead of to a value of "$X(r)$."

ILLUSTRATION 1.   Consider a statistical study of the diameters of trees of a certain variety after five years of growth. We idealize the problem, and decide to act as if there are so many trees being measured that their diameters will range over all numbers from 0 to some number $h$. (As an approximation to this ideal, a very large number of trees would be measured.) Let $x$ inches be the diameter of a tree. With $x = X(r)$ for any tree $r$, we have a random variable $X$ whose domain is $\{0 \leqq x \leqq h\}$, where $h$ is subject to realistic estimation. Then, we would wish to have meaning for such a phrase as "*the probability that* $3 \leqq X \leqq 4$."

NOTE 1.   In Section 83, we considered *mass* on a line, thought of perhaps as a wire having mass but negligible diameter. We conceived of mass

---

* With our limited treatment of calculus, we cannot consider the infinite case.

being spread out on the line. If we think of "*probability*" as a "*probability mass*," a discussion very similar to that in Section 83 for "*mass*" can be expected in the remainder of this section.

We decide to define probability for a random variable $X$, with domain $V = \{a \leq x \leq b\}$, by specifying the probability of all events of a certain simple type. Also we shall assume that Theorem II of page 156 applies in the case of probabilities which we shall introduce.

Visualize a total probability of magnitude 1 spread over the interval $V$ for the random variable in (2). Then, the following definition applies. We let $P$ be the probability function for subsets of $V$.

DEFINITION III.    *A function $f(x)$ with domain $V = \{a \leq x \leq b\}$ will be called the* **probability density function** *for the random variable $X$, whose domain is $V$, in case $f$ is a continuous\* function and the following conditions are satisfied:*

$$f(x) \geq 0 \quad on \quad V; \tag{3}$$

$$\int_a^b f(x)dx = 1; \tag{4}$$

*for any $x_1$ and $x_2$ on $V$, with $x_1 \leq x_2$,*

$$P(x_1 \leq X \leq x_2) = \int_{x_1}^{x_2} f(x)dx. \tag{5}$$

On the left in (5), we may read, in expanded form, "*the probability that the value of the random variable $X$ will satisfy $x_1 \leq X \leq x_2$.*" When $X$ has a density function satisfying Definition III, we refer to $X$ as a **continuous random variable**. We speak of the density function $f(x)$ establishing a *continuous probability distribution* over the interval $V$.

With "*probability of $X$ being on an interval*" taking the place of "*mass over an interval*," from (5) on page 240 we obtain the following result.

*If $x_1$ and $x_2$ are on $V$ and $x_1 < x_2$, then there exists $\xi$ such that $x_1 \leq \xi \leq x_2$ and*

$$P(x_1 \leq X \leq x_2) = f(\xi)(x_2 - x_1). \tag{6}$$

From (5) with $x_1 = a$ and $x_2 = b$, and from (4),

$$P(a \leq X \leq b) = \int_a^b f(x)dx = 1. \tag{7}$$

---

\* In more extensive discussions of probability, discontinuous density functions are admitted.

With $x_1 = a$ and $x_2 = x$ in (5),*

$$P(a \leq X \leq x) = \int_a^x f(t)dt, \; or \tag{8}$$

$$P(X \leq x) = \int_a^x f(t)dt. \tag{9}$$

If $x_1 = x_2$, the condition $x_1 \leq X \leq x_2$ is equivalent to $X = x_1$. Then, from (5),

$$P(X = x_1) = \int_{x_1}^{x_1} f(t)dt = 0.$$

Thus, our definition for probability implies that *the probability of any particular value of X is zero.* Nevertheless, we permit reference to $f(x)$ as "*the probability density at point x on V.*" Only *intervals* of the domain of $X$ have nonzero probability.

DEFINITION IV.   *Let* $F(x) = P(X \leq x)$. *Then F is called the* **probability distribution function** *for X.*

From (9), we have

$$F(x) = \int_a^x f(t)dt. \tag{10}$$

Hence, by (2) on page 233, $F$ has a derivative and

$$F'(x) = f(x). \tag{11}$$

Or, *the probability density function is the derivative of the distribution function.* Recall that a derivative is an *instantaneous rate of change.* Hence, if $x$ is increasing, on account of (11) we can refer to $f(x_0)$ as the instantaneous rate of increase of the "*cumulative*" probability $F(x)$ at $x = x_0$.

EXAMPLE 1.   Determine the constant $k$ so that the function $f(x) = k(1 + 2x)$ is a probability density function for a random variable $X$ with the domain $\{1 \leq x \leq 4\}$. Then find $P(2 \leq X \leq 3)$ and the distribution function for $X$.

*Solution.*   *1.*   If $f$ is a probability density function, we must have

$$\int_1^4 f(x)dx = 1, \quad or \quad k\int_1^4 (1 + 2x)dx = 1;$$

$$k(x + x^2)\Big]_1^4 = 1, \quad or \quad 18k = 1; \quad k = \tfrac{1}{18}.$$

Hence, the density function is $f(x) = \tfrac{1}{18}(1 + 2x)$.

*2.*   $P(2 \leq X \leq 3) = \int_2^3 \tfrac{1}{18}(1 + 2x)dx = \tfrac{1}{18}(x + x^2)\Big]_2^3 = \tfrac{1}{3}.$

*3.*   $F(x) = \int_1^x \tfrac{1}{18}(1 + 2t)dt = \tfrac{1}{18}(t + t^2)\Big]_1^x = \tfrac{1}{18}x + \tfrac{1}{18}x^2 - \tfrac{1}{9}.$

* In the integral, we change the dummy variable to $t$ for clarity later.

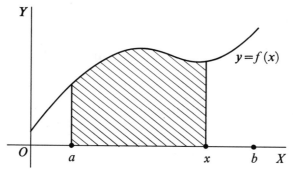

*Fig. 83*

If $f(x)$ is the probability density function for a random variable $X$ with the domain $V = \{a \leq x \leq b\}$, let the curve, $W$, in Figure 83 be the graph of $y = f(x)$. We have

$$F(x) = P(X \leq x) = \int_a^x f(x)dx. \qquad (12)$$

Hence, in Figure 83, $P(X \leq x)$ is the *area* of the ruled region.

EXAMPLE 2. Verify that the function $f(x)$ defined as follows is the probability density function for some random variable $X$ with the domain $\{0 \leq X \leq 4\}$. Then obtain formulas defining the distribution function $F$. Also, draw a graph of $y = f(x)$.

$$\begin{cases} f(x) = \dfrac{x}{10} & \text{if} \quad 0 \leq x \leq 2; \qquad (13) \\[2mm] f(x) = \dfrac{1}{5}(x - 1) & \text{if} \quad 2 \leq x \leq 4. \qquad (14) \end{cases}$$

*Solution.* *1.* A graph of $y = f(x)$ on $\{0 \leq x \leq 4\}$ with an expanded vertical scale is the curve $OAB$ consisting of line segments in Figure 84.

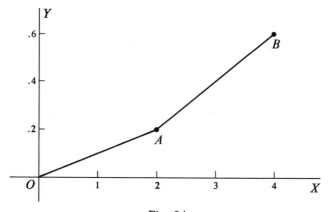

*Fig. 84*

From (13) and (14),

$$\int_0^4 f(x)dx = \int_0^2 f(x)dx + \int_2^4 f(x)dx = \int_0^2 \frac{1}{10} x dx + \int_2^4 \left(\frac{1}{5} x - \frac{1}{5}\right)dx;$$

$$\int_0^4 f(x)dx = \frac{1}{20} x^2 \Big]_0^2 + \left(\frac{1}{10} x^2 - \frac{1}{5} x\right)\Big]_2^4$$

$$= \frac{1}{5} + \frac{16}{10} - \frac{4}{5} - \frac{4}{10} + \frac{2}{5} = 1.$$

Hence, $f$ is acceptable as a density function.

2.  From (10), $\qquad\qquad\qquad\qquad F(x) = \int_0^x f(t)dt.$

If $x \geq 2$, from (13) and (14), $\qquad\qquad F(x) = \int_0^2 f(t)dt + \int_2^x f(t)dt$

$$= \frac{1}{5} + \int_2^x \frac{1}{5}(t - 1)dt = \frac{1}{5} + \left(\frac{1}{10} t^2 - \frac{1}{5} t\right)\Big]_2^x$$

$$= \frac{1}{10} x^2 - \frac{1}{5} x + \frac{1}{5} - \frac{2}{5} + \frac{2}{5}; \quad or$$

$$F(x) = \frac{1}{10} x^2 - \frac{1}{5} x + \frac{1}{5} = \frac{1}{10}(x^2 - 2x + 2), \qquad if\ x \geq 2.$$

From (13), if $x \leq 2$, $\qquad\qquad F(x) = \int_0^x f(t)dt = \int_0^x \frac{1}{10} t dt;$

$$F(x) = \frac{1}{20} t^2 \Big]_0^x, \qquad or \qquad F(x) = \frac{1}{20} x^2 \qquad if\ 0 \leq x \leq 2.$$

Hence, we have the following result:

$$F(x) = \begin{cases} \dfrac{1}{20} x^2, & if\ 0 \leq x \leq 2; \\[2mm] \dfrac{1}{10}(x^2 - 2x + 2), & if\ 2 \leq x \leq 4. \end{cases} \qquad (15)$$

## ★ Exercise 52

(a) *Find the constant $k$ so that the function $f(x)$ is acceptable as a probability density function for a random variable $X$ with the specified domain $V$.* (b) *Obtain the requested probability.* (c) *Calculate the corresponding distribution function $F(x)$.* (d) *Draw graphs of $y = f(x)$ and $y = F(x)$ on separate coordinate systems.*

1.  $f(x) = k$; $V = \{2 \leq x \leq 5\}$; find $P(3 \leq x \leq 3.5)$.
2.  $f(x) = kx$; $V = \{1 \leq x \leq 3\}$; find $P(2 \leq X \leq 2.5)$.
3.  $f(x) = kx^2$; $V = \{2 \leq x \leq 4\}$; find $P(2.5 \leq X \leq 3)$.

4.  $f(x) = k(x + 2)$; $V = \{1 \leq x \leq 4\}$; find $P(2 \leq X \leq 3.5)$.
5.  $f(x) = k(1 - x)$; $V = \{0 \leq x \leq 1\}$; find $P(.4 \leq X \leq .5)$.
6.  $f(x) = \begin{cases} kx \text{ if } 0 \leq x \leq 2 \\ 2k \text{ if } 2 \leq x \leq 6 \end{cases}$; $V = \{0 \leq x \leq 6\}$.  Find $P(1.5 \leq X \leq 2.5)$.
7.  $f(x) = \begin{cases} 3k \text{ if } 0 \leq x \leq 3 \\ k(6 - x) \text{ if } 3 \leq x \leq 6 \end{cases}$; $V = \{0 \leq x \leq 6\}$.
    Find $P(2 \leq X \leq 4)$.
8.  $f(x) = \begin{cases} kx \text{ if } 0 \leq x \leq 1 \\ k(-x + 2) \text{ if } 1 \leq x \leq 2 \end{cases}$; $V = \{0 \leq x \leq 2\}$.
    Find $P(.5 \leq X \leq 1.5)$.

## ★ 85.  Moments and the mean for a continuous probability distribution

Let $X$ be a continuous random variable with the range $V = \{a \leq x \leq b\}$ and probability density function $f(x)$. Then, the mean $\mu$, of $X$, or the "*expected value*" of $X$ is defined as follows.

$$\mu = \int_a^b xf(x)dx. \tag{1}$$

An appropriate discussion, which is outside the scope of this text, would show that (1) is the natural generalization of $E(X)$ as introduced for a random variable $X$ on a finite sample space. Also, observe that (1) is obtained from the expression for the *center of mass*, $\bar{x}$, in (9) on page 241, if $\delta(x)$ is replaced by $f(x)$ where $\int_a^b f(x)dx = 1$. Thus, $\mu$ can be thought of as a "*center of probability mass.*"

In statistics, fundamental importance is associated with various moments of the probability distribution which are defined as follows.

*The **k**th moment, $\mu_k$, of $X$ with respect to the origin:*

$$\mu_k = \int_a^b x^k f(x)dx. \tag{2}$$

*The **variance**, $\sigma^2$, of $X$, or its second moment with respect to the point $x = \mu$:*

$$\sigma^2 = \int_a^b (x - \mu)^2 f(x)dx. \tag{3}$$

In (2), when $k = 1$, we write $\mu$ instead of $\mu_1$; that is, $\mu_1$ is the mean $\mu$ as defined previously in (1). The positive square root, $\sigma$, of $\sigma^2$ from (3) is called the **standard deviation**\* of $X$.

* For contact between $\sigma^2$ and $\sigma$, as just defined, and similarly named parameters $s_x^2$ and $s_x$ for a sample of $n$ values of $X$ as discussed later in Chapter 11, see texts on mathematical statistics.

In stating the definitions in (1)–(3), our primary objective was to emphasize that integration is a basic tool in the formulation of mathematical statistics as it applies to continuous random variables. In any complete treatment of the foundations of statistics, the range of the random variable $X$ would be the infinite interval $\{-\infty < x < \infty\}$, with corresponding integrals involving $\int_{-\infty}^{\infty}$ instead of $\int_{a}^{b}$ as in this text. Integrals over an infinite interval are referred to as *improper integrals*, and cannot be treated in this text.

Problems are provided for those who desire practice in calculating $\mu$ or $\sigma^2$.

EXAMPLE 1.  For the random variable $X$ of Example 1 on page 244, find the mean and the variance.

*Solution.*  The domain of $X$ is $V = \{1 \le x \le 4\}$ and $f(x) = \frac{1}{18}(1 + 2x)$. Hence,

$$\mu = \int_{1}^{4} \tfrac{1}{18}x(1 + 2x)dx = 2.75.$$

$$\sigma^2 = \tfrac{1}{18}\int_{1}^{4}(x - 2.75)^2(1 + 2x)dx$$

$$= \tfrac{1}{18}\int_{1}^{4}(2x^3 - 10x^2 + \tfrac{77}{8}x + \tfrac{121}{16})dx; \quad or,$$

$$\sigma^2 = \tfrac{1}{18}(\tfrac{1}{2}x^4 - \tfrac{10}{3}x^3 + \tfrac{77}{16}x^2 + \tfrac{121}{16}x)\Big]_{1}^{4} = \tfrac{1}{18}(12.375) = .6875.$$

## ★ Exercise 53

*1–5.*  In Exercise 52, find $\mu$ and $\sigma^2$ for the random variable $X$ with the probability density function in Problems 1, 2, 3, 4, and 8, respectively. The results from Exercise 52 may be used.

# 10 | MATRICES, DETERMINANTS, AND SYSTEMS OF LINEAR EQUATIONS

### 86.   Matrix addition and multiplication by scalars

In specifying data, frequently it is natural to arrange it in rows and columns.

ILLUSTRATION 1.   The goals made by six members of a hockey team in four successive games are listed as follows, where each column gives the goals of a particular player in the four games, and a row corresponds to each game.

$$\begin{bmatrix} 0 & 0 & 1 & 0 & 1 & 0 \\ 1 & 0 & 1 & 1 & 1 & 0 \\ 0 & 1 & 0 & 1 & 1 & 0 \\ 1 & 1 & 0 & 0 & 1 & 0 \end{bmatrix} \tag{1}$$

If $m$ and $n$ are integers, an $m \times n$ (read "$m$ by $n$") **matrix** $W$ of numbers is defined as an array of $mn$ numbers, each called an *element* of $W$, arranged in $m$ rows with $n$ columns. Thus, the array in (1) is a $4 \times 6$ matrix. In case $m = n$, then $W$ is called a *square matrix*. If $W$ is an $m \times n$ matrix, we refer to "$m \times n$" as the *dimensions* of $W$. If $W$ consists of a single row, then $W$ is called a *row matrix*, or a *row vector*. If $W$ consists of a single column, then $W$ is called a *column matrix*, or a *column vector*. Matrices may be considered whose elements are not numbers. However, in this text, as a rule the elements of any matrix will be numbers. We shall introduce various operations on matrices involving language similar to that used in ordinary algebra. Hence, to avoid ambiguity, sometimes it will be convenient to refer to a number as a **scalar**, to distinguish it from a matrix.

ILLUSTRATION 2.    The following array is a $2 \times 3$ matrix.

$$\mathbf{W} = \begin{bmatrix} w_{11} & w_{12} & w_{13} \\ w_{21} & w_{22} & w_{23} \end{bmatrix}. \tag{2}$$

We shall use capital Roman letters in bold face type to represent matrices. If $\mathbf{W}$ represents a matrix, as in (2), we may use the corresponding lower case letter, $w$, with subscripts for the elements of $\mathbf{W}$. In such a case, as a rule, the *first* subscript will be the number of the *row*, and the *second* will be the number of the *column* of the matrix where the element is located. This notation is illustrated in (2). We may write simply $\mathbf{W} = [w_{ij}]$ when the dimensions of $\mathbf{W}$ are known, or $\mathbf{W} = [w_{ij}]_{m \times n}$ to show the dimensions.

Let $T$ be the set of all matrices of fixed dimensions $m \times n$. We proceed to introduce operations on the matrices of $T$ as a basis for what may be termed an "*algebra*" of matrices.

The **zero matrix** of any dimensions $m \times n$ will be represented by $\mathbf{O}$, and is defined as a matrix where each element is 0. To indicate dimensions, $m \times n$, we may write $\mathbf{O}_{m \times n}$. Thus,

$$\mathbf{O}_{2 \times 3} = \begin{bmatrix} 0 & 0 & 0 \\ 0 & 0 & 0 \end{bmatrix}.$$

DEFINITION I.    *Let all matrices which are mentioned be of dimensions* $m \times n$. *Then, if* $\mathbf{A} = [a_{ij}]$ *and* $\mathbf{B} = [b_{ij}]$,

$$\mathbf{A} = \mathbf{B} \quad \textit{means that} \quad a_{ij} = b_{ij}; \tag{3}$$

$$\left. \begin{array}{l} \textit{the } \textbf{sum} \textit{ of } \mathbf{A} \textit{ and } \mathbf{B}, \textit{ represented by } (\mathbf{A} + \mathbf{B}), \textit{ is defined} \\ \textit{by } \mathbf{A} + \mathbf{B} = [(a_{ij} + b_{ij})]; \end{array} \right\} \tag{4}$$

$$\textit{if } r \textit{ is any scalar, then } r\mathbf{A} = [ra_{ij}]; \tag{5}$$

$$-\mathbf{B} = (-1)\mathbf{B}. \tag{6}$$

**To add** two matrices $\mathbf{A}$ and $\mathbf{B}$, will mean to find their sum $(\mathbf{A} + \mathbf{B})$. We agree that $(\mathbf{A} - \mathbf{B})$ will mean $[\mathbf{A} + (-\mathbf{B})]$, and shall refer to $(\mathbf{A} - \mathbf{B})$ as the *difference* of $\mathbf{A}$ and $\mathbf{B}$.

ILLUSTRATION 3.

$$\begin{bmatrix} 1 & 3 & 2 \\ -1 & 2 & -4 \end{bmatrix} + 3 \begin{bmatrix} -2 & 4 & 0 \\ 3 & -5 & 6 \end{bmatrix} =$$

$$\begin{bmatrix} 1 & 3 & 2 \\ -1 & 2 & -4 \end{bmatrix} + \begin{bmatrix} -6 & 12 & 0 \\ 9 & -15 & 18 \end{bmatrix} = \begin{bmatrix} -5 & 15 & 2 \\ 8 & -13 & 14 \end{bmatrix}.$$

$$\begin{bmatrix} 2 & -7 \\ -3 & 5 \end{bmatrix} + (-1) \cdot \begin{bmatrix} 2 & -7 \\ -3 & 5 \end{bmatrix} = \begin{bmatrix} 2 & -7 \\ -3 & 5 \end{bmatrix} + \begin{bmatrix} -2 & 7 \\ 3 & -5 \end{bmatrix} = \mathbf{O}.$$

Similarly, as above, if **A** is any matrix, then

$$\mathbf{A} + (-1)\mathbf{A} = \mathbf{O}, \quad or \quad \mathbf{A} - \mathbf{A} = \mathbf{O}. \tag{7}$$

Hence, we say that $-\mathbf{A}$ is the **additive inverse** (or, the **negative**) of **A**.

Let **A** and **B** be any matrices of dimensions $m \times n$, and let $c$ and $d$ be scalars. In the next exercise, on the basis of (3)–(6), the student may verify the following simple results:

$$c\mathbf{O} = \mathbf{O}; \quad c(d\mathbf{A}) = (cd)\mathbf{A}; \quad 0(\mathbf{A}) = \mathbf{O}; \tag{8}$$

$$(1)\mathbf{A} = \mathbf{A}; \quad (c + d)\mathbf{A} = c\mathbf{A} + d\mathbf{A}; \quad c(\mathbf{A} + \mathbf{B}) = c\mathbf{A} + c\mathbf{B}. \tag{9}$$

## Exercise 54

*Obtain the result as a single matrix.*

1. $\begin{bmatrix} 2 & 3 \\ -1 & 4 \end{bmatrix} - 3 \begin{bmatrix} 2 & -3 \\ 5 & 4 \end{bmatrix}.$ 

2. $3 \begin{bmatrix} 2 & -1 \\ -2 & 4 \end{bmatrix} - 2 \begin{bmatrix} -2 & 1 \\ 3 & 4 \end{bmatrix}.$

3. $5 \begin{bmatrix} 2 & 3 & 1 \\ -1 & 2 & 5 \end{bmatrix} - \begin{bmatrix} 1 & 4 & 6 \\ -2 & 3 & -1 \end{bmatrix}.$

4. $2 \begin{bmatrix} -1 & 3 \\ 2 & 4 \end{bmatrix}.$ 

5. $5 \begin{bmatrix} 3 \\ -2 \end{bmatrix} - 2 \begin{bmatrix} 1 \\ 4 \end{bmatrix}.$

6. $-3[2 \quad -1 \quad 5] + 2[0 \quad -4 \quad 2].$ 

7. $3[-2 \quad 0 \quad 1 \quad 4].$

8. $-3 \begin{bmatrix} -1 & 0 & -2 \\ -4 & 2 & 3 \\ 2 & 3 & 2 \end{bmatrix} + 4 \begin{bmatrix} 0 & -1 & 3 \\ -2 & 0 & 6 \\ 3 & -2 & 4 \end{bmatrix}.$

9. $5 \begin{bmatrix} 3 \\ 4 \\ -1 \end{bmatrix} - 3 \begin{bmatrix} 2 \\ -3 \\ 4 \end{bmatrix} - \begin{bmatrix} x \\ y \\ z \end{bmatrix}.$

*Find the solutions of the equations in the variables x and y, or in x, y, and z.*

10. $[x \quad 2y] = [3 \quad -5].$ 

11. $[x \quad (y - 2)] = [3 \quad x].$

12. $[x \quad (y + 1)] = [(2 - y) \quad 3x].$

13. $-[y \quad (x - y) \quad 2z] = [3 \quad (x + z) \quad -y].$

14. $[(2 + 3x) \quad (y - 2) \quad z] = [(y + 2z) \quad (x + 3) \quad 2].$

15. Prove that matrix addition is *commutative* and *associative*. That is, if **A**, **B**, and **C** are matrices of the same dimensions, prove that

$$\mathbf{A} + \mathbf{B} = \mathbf{B} + \mathbf{A}; \quad \mathbf{A} + (\mathbf{B} + \mathbf{C}) = (\mathbf{A} + \mathbf{B}) + \mathbf{C}.$$

16. (For $2 \times 3$ matrices.) If $r$ and $s$ are scalars, while **A** and **B** are matrices of the same dimensions, prove that

$$r(s\mathbf{A}) = s(r\mathbf{A}) = (rs)\mathbf{A};$$
$$r\mathbf{A} + s\mathbf{A} = (r + s)\mathbf{A};$$
$$r\mathbf{A} + r\mathbf{B} = r(\mathbf{A} + \mathbf{B}).$$

## 87.   Linear systems in triangular form

Any system of $n$ linear equations in $n$ variables is equivalent to a system of the following standard form, written for the case $n = 3$, with $(x_1, x_2, x_3)$ as the variables.

$$(\text{I}) \begin{cases} a_{11}x_1 + a_{12}x_2 + a_{13}x_3 = c_1, & (1) \\ a_{21}x_1 + a_{22}x_2 + a_{23}x_3 = c_2, & (2) \\ a_{31}x_1 + a_{32}x_2 + a_{33}x_3 = c_3. & (3) \end{cases}$$

EXAMPLE 1.   Solve:

$$(\text{II}) \begin{cases} x - 3y - 2z = 11, & (4) \\ 3x - y - 2z = 13, & (5) \\ x - y - 6z = 11. & (6) \end{cases}$$

*Solution.*   *1.*   Subtract (4) from (5):          $2x + 2y = 2.$          (7)

Multiply by 3 in (5):                        $9x - 3y - 6z = 39.$          (8)

Subtract, (6) from (8):                        $8x - 2y = 28.$          (9)

Add, (7) and (9):                                $10x = 30.$          (10)

Thus, system (II) is equivalent to the following system:

$$(\text{III}) \begin{cases} 10x \qquad = 30, & (11) \\ 8x - 2y \quad = 28, & (12) \\ x - y - 6z = 11. & (13) \end{cases}$$

*2.*   From (11), $x = 3$. With $x = 3$ in (12), we obtain $24 - 2y = 28$, or $y = -2$. If $x = 3$ and $y = -2$ in (13), then $5 - 6z = 11$ or $z = -1$. The solution of (II) is $(x = 3, y = -2, z = -1)$.

In (II), the coefficients of the variables in the order $(x, y, z)$ form a $3 \times 3$ square matrix, given at the left below, which is called the **coefficient matrix** for (II). When the constant terms on the right in (I) are joined as a fourth column to the preceding matrix, this yields a $3 \times 4$ matrix, at the right below, which is called the **augmented matrix** for (II).

$$\begin{bmatrix} 1 & -3 & -2 \\ 3 & -1 & -2 \\ 1 & -1 & -6 \end{bmatrix}; \qquad \begin{bmatrix} 1 & -3 & -2 & 11 \\ 3 & -1 & -2 & 13 \\ 1 & -1 & -6 & 11 \end{bmatrix}. \qquad (14)$$

We shall verify that the sequence of operations which led from system (II) to (III) is equivalent to a corresponding sequence of operations of the following types applied to the augmented matrix of (II). These matrix operations yield the matrix of (III).

(*i*)   *Change the order of the rows of the augmented matrix in any manner.*

(*ii*)   *Change the order of the columns of the coefficient matrix in any manner.*

(*iii*)   *Multiply any row of the augmented matrix by a constant, not zero.*

(*iv*)   *After* (*iii*) *is applied to any two rows, add them, or subtract one from the other, to obtain a replacement for either one of the rows.*

If any one of (*i*)–(*iv*) is applied to the augmented matrix of a given system of equations, we observe that the result is the augmented matrix for a new system which is *equivalent to the given system*. Thus, (*i*) is equivalent to merely changing the order in which the equations are written; (*ii*) is equivalent to changing the order in which terms in the variables are written in standard form; (*iii*) is equivalent to multiplying both sides of an equation of the system by a constant; (*iv*) is equivalent to adding corresponding sides of two equations, or subtracting sides of one equation from corresponding sides of another equation.

NOTE 1.   In a square matrix, its elements in the diagonal from the upper left-hand corner to the lower right-hand corner are referred to as the **main diagonal** of the matrix. Thus, in the coefficient matrix at the left in (14), the main diagonal is $\{1, -1, -6\}$.

Instead of the solution given for Example 1, we may obtain a convenient system like (III) as follows, by use of (*i*)–(*iv*) as applied to the augmented matrix.

*Solution of Example* 1 *by matrix operations.   1.*   We write the augmented matrix as at the right in (14). Instead of saying "*eliminate z*," we say "*manipulate the augmented matrix by use of* (*i*)–(*iv*) *to obtain zeros in two rows in the* 3d *column from the left.*" To do this, in (14):

*Subtract elements of the* 1st *row from those of the* 2d *row; then multiply the elements of the* 1st *row by* 3; *subtract the results* (*kept in mind and not written*) *from the elements of the* 3d *row. These operations give:*

$$\begin{bmatrix} 1 & -3 & -2 & 11 \\ 2 & 2 & 0 & 2 \\ 1 & -1 & -6 & 11 \end{bmatrix}; \quad then \quad \begin{bmatrix} 1 & -3 & -2 & 11 \\ 2 & 2 & 0 & 2 \\ -2 & 8 & 0 & -22 \end{bmatrix}. \quad (15)$$

*2.*   In (15) at the right, move the 1st row to the bottom. Then interchange the first two columns:

$$\begin{bmatrix} 2 & 2 & 0 & 2 \\ -2 & 8 & 0 & -22 \\ 1 & -3 & -2 & 11 \end{bmatrix}; \quad then \quad \begin{bmatrix} 2 & 2 & 0 & 2 \\ 8 & -2 & 0 & -22 \\ -3 & 1 & -2 & 11 \end{bmatrix}. \quad (16)$$

In (16), add the elements of the 2d row to those of the 1st row:

$$\begin{bmatrix} 10 & 0 & 0 & -20 \\ 8 & -2 & 0 & -22 \\ -3 & 1 & -2 & 11 \end{bmatrix}. \quad (17)$$

*3.* Write the system whose augmented matrix is (17). Since the first two columns were interchanged in (16), the order of the variables now is $(y, x, z)$.

$$\text{(IV)} \begin{cases} 10y & = -20, & (18) \\ 8y - 2x & = -22, & (19) \\ -3y + x - 2z = & 11. & (20) \end{cases}$$

From (18), $y = -2$; then, from (19), $x = 3$; then, from (20), $z = -1$.

A square matrix is said to be in *triangular form* if all of the elements *above* (or, *below*) the main diagonal are zeros. In (17), observe that we obtained an augmented matrix where the coefficient matrix is in triangular form. Hence, it is said that the final system (III) or (IV) is in **triangular form**. For any system (I), if the method of either solution of Example 1 leads to a contradictory equation such as $k = 0$ where $k$ is a constant not zero, this indicates that the system is inconsistent. If the method leads to an identity such as $0 = 0$ as one of the final equations, this indicates that the given system, of $n$ equations, is equivalent to only $(n - 1)$ equations. Then, at least one of the variables can be given any value, and corresponding values of the other variables can be found to form a solution of the system. Thus, it would have infinitely many solutions.

Suppose that the preceding matrix method of solution is used for a system (I). Then, the method leads to a single solution of the system if all elements in the main diagonal of the coefficient matrix in triangular form are not zero.

**Summary.** *To change the augmented matrix of a system of n linear equations in n variables to a form where the coefficient matrix is in triangular form.*

(1) *Manipulate rows by use of operations (iii) and (iv) to obtain 0 in the nth column, 1st row. Repeat, to obtain 0 in all places in the nth column above the last row.*

(2) *Use operations (iii) and (iv) to obtain 0 in the (n − 1)th column in all rows except the last two rows. Continue in this fashion until each element becomes 0 above the main diagonal in the coefficient matrix.*

In use of the Summary, it may happen that operations (*i*) and (*ii*) can be employed to shorten the work.

## Exercise 55

*Solve the system by manipulation of its augmented matrix.*

*1.* $x + 2y = 3,$
$\quad 3x + 5y = 10.$

*2.* $4x + 3y = 2,$
$\quad 5x + y = -3.$

3.  $x - 3y + z = 7$,
    $2x + y - 2z = -1$,
    $2x - 3y + z = 9$.

4.  $3x - 2y + z = -10$,
    $-x + 3y - z = 7$,
    $2x - y - 4z = 3$.

5.  $3x - 4y - 3z = -9$,
    $x + 3y - z = 10$,
    $2x + y = -1$.

6.  $2y + 5z = 1$,
    $3x - y + 2z = 16$,
    $-2x - 3y - z = -3$.

7.  $2x + y - 3z = 2$,
    $2y - 4x + z = 9$,
    $z - 2x - y = 0$.

8.  $x - 3y + 2z = -1$,
    $3z + 2x - 6y = -4$,
    $3y - 3x + z = 9$.

9.  $2y - 9x + 2z = 4$,
    $z - 4y - 6x = 10$,
    $3x - 3z - 6y = 2$.

10. $\frac{2}{3}x - \frac{1}{2}y + z = 2$,
    $-\frac{1}{3}x + \frac{3}{2}y + 2z = 4$,
    $x - 2y - 3z = -4$.

11. $2x - y + 3z = 4$,
    $3x + 2y - z = 5$,
    $5x + 8y - 9z = 12$.

12. $x - 2y + z = 4$,
    $3x + y - 2z = 5$,
    $4x - y - z = 9$.

## 88.  Determinants of order two

Consider the system

$$(I) \begin{cases} ax + by = e, \text{ and} & (1) \\ cx + dy = f, & (2) \end{cases}$$

for the variables $x$ and $y$, where $\{a, b, c, d, e, f\}$ are any constants. Hereafter, we shall omit "*and*" as in (1), but "*and*" is understood to be implied in the notation for systems of equations. In (I), the matrix, **R**, of coefficients of the variables, and the augmented matrix, **S**, are as follows:

$$\mathbf{R} = \begin{bmatrix} a & b \\ c & d \end{bmatrix}; \qquad \mathbf{S} = \begin{bmatrix} a & b & e \\ c & d & f \end{bmatrix}. \qquad (3)$$

From Example 5 on page 85, we recall that the solution of (I) is as follows:

$$x = \frac{de - bf}{ad - bc} \qquad and \qquad y = \frac{af - ce}{ad - bc}. \qquad (4)$$

The symmetrical nature of the numerators and the denominator in (4) led mathematicians to introduce the following concept.

DEFINITION II.   *The* **determinant** *of the matrix* **R** *is denoted by the symbol at the left below, and is defined by*

$$|\mathbf{R}| = ad - bc, \qquad or \qquad \begin{vmatrix} a & b \\ c & d \end{vmatrix} = ad - bc. \qquad (5)$$

At the right in (5), on mentioning the elements of **R** by rows, we read "*the determinant of* $(a, b; c, d)$ *is* $(ad - bc)$." In (5), $|\mathbf{R}|$ is said to be a determinant of the 2d order, because **R** is a $2 \times 2$ matrix.

ILLUSTRATION 1.   From (5), $\begin{vmatrix} 2 & -5 \\ -3 & 7 \end{vmatrix} = (2)(7) - (-3)(-5) = -1.$

In view of (5), we may rewrite (4) as follows:

$$x = \frac{\begin{vmatrix} e & b \\ f & d \end{vmatrix}}{\begin{vmatrix} a & b \\ c & d \end{vmatrix}}; \qquad y = \frac{\begin{vmatrix} a & e \\ c & f \end{vmatrix}}{\begin{vmatrix} a & b \\ c & d \end{vmatrix}}. \tag{6}$$

In (6), we have proved the following theorem for the case $n = 2$. Later, after defining a determinant of order 3, we shall prove the theorem for $n = 3$ by a method making it evident that the theorem is easily proved for any value of the positive integer $n$.

THEOREM I.   *In a system of n linear equations in n variables, arranged in standard form* [illustrated by (1)], *suppose that the determinant of the matrix,* **R**, *of coefficients of the variables is not zero. Then, the system has a single solution, where the value of each variable is equal to a fraction obtained as follows:*

($\alpha$)   *The denominator is* $|\mathbf{R}|$.

($\beta$)   *The numerator is the determinant of the matrix obtained from* **R** *by replacing, in it, the column of coefficients of the variable by the column of constant terms in the augmented matrix for the system.*

EXAMPLE 1.   Solve by use of Theorem I: $\begin{cases} 2x - 3y = 8, & (7) \\ 5x + 4y = -2. & (8) \end{cases}$

*Solution.*   From (6),

$$x = \frac{\begin{vmatrix} 8 & -3 \\ -2 & 4 \end{vmatrix}}{\begin{vmatrix} 2 & -3 \\ 5 & 4 \end{vmatrix}} = \frac{26}{23}; \qquad y = \frac{\begin{vmatrix} 2 & 8 \\ 5 & -2 \end{vmatrix}}{\begin{vmatrix} 2 & -3 \\ 5 & 4 \end{vmatrix}} = -\frac{44}{23}.$$

In (6), if the denominator determinant is zero, then (6) does not apply. In such a case, a corresponding discussion is necessary to determine whether equations (1) and (2) are inconsistent or dependent.

Theorem I is referred to as **Cramer's rule**, in honor of the Swiss mathematician CRAMER (1704–1752) who first formulated the result in the Western World. The result was also obtained at about the same time by Japanese mathematicians.

# Exercise 56

*Solve by use of determinants if possible.*

1. $x + y = 3,$
   $2x - 3y = 11.$

2. $y - x = 4,$
   $4y - 2x = 4.$

3. $x + 2y = 3,$
   $3x + 5y = 10.$

4. $4x + 3y = 2,$
   $5x + y = -3.$

5. $2y - 3x = 8,$
   $6x - 4y = 5.$

6. $3x + 2y = 9,$
   $4y - 18 = -6x.$

7. $2x - 3y = 7,$
   $2x - y = 1.$

8. $5y - 4 = 0,$
   $3x + 4y + 1 = 0.$

9. $2x + 3y = 0,$
   $5x - 2y = 0.$

10. $y + 3x = 2,$
    $x - 5y = 0.$

11. $3x - 5 = 0,$
    $2x + 5y = 4.$

12. $3x - y = 4,$
    $2y - 6x = 9.$

13. $6x - 5y = 3,$
    $4y - 9x = 5.$

14. $3x - 5y = 2,$
    $2x + 3y = -5.$

## 89. Determinants of order three

If **H** is any $3 \times 3$ matrix, let "$|\mathbf{H}|$" represent "*the determinant of* **H**," whose value has yet to be defined:

$$\mathbf{H} = \begin{bmatrix} A_1 & B_1 & C_1 \\ A_2 & B_2 & C_2 \\ A_3 & B_3 & C_3 \end{bmatrix}; \qquad |\mathbf{H}| = \begin{vmatrix} A_1 & B_1 & C_1 \\ A_2 & B_2 & C_2 \\ A_3 & B_3 & C_3 \end{vmatrix}. \qquad (1)$$

In order that certain later definitions will apply to $2 \times 2$ matrices as well as $3 \times 3$ matrices, and to corresponding determinants, we agree to refer also to $1 \times 1$ matrices, such as $[A]$, where only one element is involved. Also, we then define the determinant of $[A]$ as simply $A$;* that is, $|[A]| = A$. Although we intend to restrict illustrations of the next two definitions of this chapter principally to the cases of square matrices of dimensions $2 \times 2$ and $3 \times 3$, the definitions will be stated for $n \times n$ matrices, where $n$ is any positive integer greater than 1.

**DEFINITION III.** *In an $n \times n$ matrix* **H**, *suppose that the row and column of any particular element E is blotted out, leaving a matrix* **S**. *Then* $|\mathbf{S}|$ *is called the* **minor** *of E in* $|\mathbf{H}|$. *If E is in row i and column j of* **H**, *and* $M = |\mathbf{S}|$, *then the* **cofactor**, *K, of E is defined by*

$$(\text{cofactor}) = (-1)^{i+j}(\text{minor}), \quad or \quad K = (-1)^{i+j}M. \qquad (2)$$

* In a notation for a determinant, such as "$|\mathbf{H}|$", the student should avoid confusing it with use of vertical rules as in $|-4|$ to represent the "*absolute value*" of a number.

ILLUSTRATION 1.  Consider    $\mathbf{H} = \begin{bmatrix} 2 & -1 & 3 \\ -2 & 4 & 5 \\ 3 & 1 & 4 \end{bmatrix}.$

Then, in $|\mathbf{H}|$, the minor $M$ and cofactor $K$ of the element 5, in (*row* $i = 2$, *column* $j = 3$), are given by

$$M = \begin{vmatrix} 2 & -1 \\ 3 & 1 \end{vmatrix} = 5 \quad and \quad K = (-1)^{2+3} \begin{vmatrix} 2 & -1 \\ 3 & 1 \end{vmatrix} = -(2 + 3) = -5.$$

DEFINITION IV.   *Let* $\mathbf{H}$ *be an* $n \times n$ *matrix, and let* $\{e_1, e_2, \cdots, e_n\}$ *be the elements in any row, or in any column of* $\mathbf{H}$, *with* $\{K_1, K_2, \cdots, K_n\}$ *as the cofactors of* $\{e_1, e_2, \cdots, e_n\}$. *Then, the determinant of* $\mathbf{H}$ *is defined by*

$$|\mathbf{H}| = e_1 K_1 + e_2 K_2 + \cdots + e_n K_n. \tag{3}$$

ILLUSTRATION 2.   By use of (3), with cofactors of the 2d column used below, we obtain

$$\begin{vmatrix} 2 & -1 & 3 \\ -2 & 4 & 5 \\ 3 & 1 & 4 \end{vmatrix}$$

$$= (-1)^{1+2}(-1) \cdot \begin{vmatrix} -2 & 5 \\ 3 & 4 \end{vmatrix} + (-1)^{2+2}(4) \cdot \begin{vmatrix} 2 & 3 \\ 3 & 4 \end{vmatrix} + (-1)^{3+2}(1) \cdot \begin{vmatrix} 2 & 3 \\ -2 & 5 \end{vmatrix}$$

$$= + (-8 - 15) + 4(8 - 9) - (10 + 6) = -43,$$

where we used (5) on page 255 in computing the determinants of order 2.

ILLUSTRATION 3.   By use of (3), we expand the following determinant according to the elements and cofactors of the 1st column. The minors of $\{A_1, A_2, A_3\}$ must be multiplied, respectively, by $(-1)^{1+1}$ or $+1$; $(-1)^{1+2}$ or $-1$; $(-1)^{1+3}$ or $+1$.

$$\begin{vmatrix} A_1 & B_1 & C_1 \\ A_2 & B_2 & C_2 \\ A_3 & B_3 & C_3 \end{vmatrix}$$

$$= A_1 \begin{vmatrix} B_2 & C_2 \\ B_3 & C_3 \end{vmatrix} - A_2 \begin{vmatrix} B_1 & C_1 \\ B_3 & C_3 \end{vmatrix} + A_3 \begin{vmatrix} B_1 & C_1 \\ B_2 & C_2 \end{vmatrix}$$

$$= A_1(B_2 C_3 - B_3 C_2) - A_2(B_1 C_3 - B_3 C_1) + A_3(B_1 C_2 - B_2 C_1)$$

$$= A_1 B_2 C_3 - A_1 B_3 C_2 - A_2 B_1 C_3 + A_2 B_3 C_1 + A_3 B_1 C_2 - A_3 B_2 C_1. \tag{4}$$

In Definition IV, $|\mathbf{H}|$ is called a determinant of the $n$th **order** because $\mathbf{H}$ is a matrix of dimensions $n \times n$. In (3), a determinant of order $n$ is defined in terms of determinants $\{K_1, K_2, \cdots, K_n\}$ of order $(n - 1)$. Without reference to Definition IV, a determinant of the 2d order is defined in (5) on page 255. Hence, by (3), determinants of order $n = 3$ are well defined since determinants of order $n = 2$ have been defined. Then, with $n = 4$, determinants of order $n = 4$ are well defined, because then (3) involves determinants of order $n = 3$. In this way determinants of order $n$ are well defined by (3) because determinants of order $(n - 1)$ are well defined. Thus, (3) defines determinants of all orders.

We omit proving that the value obtained for $|\mathbf{H}|$ in (3) is the same, regardless of the row or column $\{e_1, e_2, \cdots, e_n\}$ which was used. This fact will be verified partially in later examples when $n = 3$. Various other theorems about determinants of order $n$ will be stated and used without proof, but will be verified partially when $n = 3$. In advanced algebra, such proofs are given most conveniently on the basis of a different definition for $|\mathbf{H}|$ than we are using. Then, our defining equation (3) becomes a *theorem*.

NOTE 1.   In the Western world, determinants were invented in 1693 by the German mathematician GOTTFRIED WILHELM LEIBNIZ (1646–1716), who was also mentioned in connection with calculus. However, determinants were invented at least ten years earlier by SEKI-KOWA (1642–1708), the great Japanese mathematician. His work had no influence on contemporary mathematicians outside of Japan.

Suppose that each element of some row (or column) of an $n \times n$ matrix $\mathbf{H}$ is 0. If this row (or column) is used to provide $\{e_1, e_2, \cdots, e_n\}$ in (3), then each term on the right in (3) is 0, and hence $|\mathbf{H}| = 0$.

The following result will be useful later.

THEOREM II.   *If each element of a row (or column) of an $n \times n$ matrix $\mathbf{H}$ has r as a factor, and if $\mathbf{W}$ is the new matrix obtained from $\mathbf{H}$ on removing the factor r from each of the elements mentioned, then $|\mathbf{H}| = r|\mathbf{W}|$.*

To prove Theorem II informally, suppose that (with $n = 3$), a row of $\mathbf{H}$ consists of the elements $\{ru_1, ru_2, ru_3\}$. If these are used as $\{e_1, e_2, e_3\}$ in (3), then

$$|\mathbf{H}| = ru_1 K_1 + ru_2 K_2 + ru_3 K_3 = r(u_1 K_1 + u_2 K_2 + u_3 K_3),$$

where $(u_1 K_1 + u_2 K_2 + u_3 K_3) = |\mathbf{W}|$, with $\mathbf{W}$ as described in Theorem II.

ILLUSTRATION 4.   By Theorem II,

$$\begin{vmatrix} 3k & -5 \\ 2k & 4 \end{vmatrix} = k \begin{vmatrix} 3 & -5 \\ 2 & 4 \end{vmatrix},$$

which can be checked by expanding each of the determinants.

## Exercise 57

*Compute each determinant. Notice the desirability of expanding by co-factors of a row or column where one or more zeros occur. Carry out the work at least twice, using different rows or columns.*

1.  $\begin{vmatrix} -1 & 3 & 0 \\ 2 & -1 & 2 \\ -4 & 3 & 5 \end{vmatrix}$.   2.  $\begin{vmatrix} 2 & -1 & 3 \\ 4 & 2 & -2 \\ -3 & 1 & 5 \end{vmatrix}$.   3.  $\begin{vmatrix} -4 & 2 & 3 \\ 3 & 0 & 2 \\ 1 & 4 & 6 \end{vmatrix}$.

4.  $\begin{vmatrix} -3 & 1 & -2 \\ 2 & 0 & 4 \\ -1 & 2 & 3 \end{vmatrix}$.   5.  $\begin{vmatrix} -2 & 2 & -1 \\ 3 & -3 & 2 \\ 0 & 5 & 4 \end{vmatrix}$.   6.  $\begin{vmatrix} -1 & 2 & 4 \\ 3 & -2 & 5 \\ 6 & 4 & 0 \end{vmatrix}$.

7.  Expand $|\mathbf{H}|$ of (1) on page 257 by cofactors of the 1st row; of the 2d column. Compare with the result in Illustration 3 on page 258.

8.  In (1) on page 257, interchange the rows and columns in $\mathbf{H}$ to obtain the new matrix $\mathbf{W}$, called the **transpose** of $\mathbf{H}$:

$$\mathbf{W} = \begin{bmatrix} A_1 & A_2 & A_3 \\ B_1 & B_2 & B_3 \\ C_1 & C_2 & C_3 \end{bmatrix}.$$

Then expand $|\mathbf{W}|$ and verify that $|\mathbf{W}| = |\mathbf{H}|$, as given in (4) on page 258. On this basis, without added proof, we state the following theorem:

*If the rows and columns in a square matrix* $\mathbf{H}$ *are interchanged to obtain a new matrix* $\mathbf{W}$, *then* $|\mathbf{H}| = |\mathbf{W}|$.

As a consequence of the preceding result, for every theorem about a determinant referring to its *rows*, there is a corresponding theorem referring to its *columns*.

9.  In (1) on page 257, suppose that $(A_1 = B_1, A_2 = B_2, A_3 = B_3)$. Expand $|\mathbf{H}|$ for this case and verify that $|\mathbf{H}| = 0$. On this basis, without added proof, we state the following theorem:

*If two* **rows** *(or* **columns***) of a square matrix* $\mathbf{H}$ *are identical, then* $|\mathbf{H}| = 0$.

## 90.  Computation of determinants of higher orders

If the order of a determinant is $n \geq 3$, usually it is best to employ the following result before expanding by use of cofactors. Theorem III may be used to obtain a new form for the given determinant where *all elements except one in some row or column are zeros.*

THEOREM III.  *In a square matrix* **H**, *suppose that, to each element of a certain column (or row) there is added a constant c times the corresponding element of another column (or row), to obtain a new matrix* **W**. *Then* $|\mathbf{H}| = |\mathbf{W}|$.

The proof of Theorem III depends on various other properties of determinants which we shall not mention.* Hence we accept Theorem III without proof.

ILLUSTRATION 1.    By use of Theorem III, we shall calculate the determinant at the left below, by first changing it to a new form where *only one element is not zero* in the 1st row (any row or column would do as well). To obtain the zeros in a *row*, we operate on *columns* as follows:

(*i*)    *On scratch paper, multiply the elements of the* 3d *column by* $-3$ *to obtain* $(3, -12, -15)$; *add these to the elements of the* 1st *column, to obtain* $(0, -7, -13)$ *as the new* 1st *column (we do not change the* 3d *column).*

(*ii*)    *Multiply the elements of the* 3d *column by* 2 *to obtain* $(-2, 8, 10)$; *add these to the elements of the* 2d *column, to obtain* $(0, 6, 13)$ *as the new* 2d *column. (We do not change the* 3d *column.)*

Operations (*i*) and (*ii*) give a new form which we then expand by cofactors of the 1st row:

$$\begin{vmatrix} -3 & 2 & -1 \\ 5 & -2 & 4 \\ 2 & 3 & 5 \end{vmatrix} = \begin{vmatrix} 0 & 0 & -1 \\ -7 & 6 & 4 \\ -13 & 13 & 5 \end{vmatrix} = (-1)\begin{vmatrix} -7 & 6 \\ -13 & 13 \end{vmatrix} = 13.$$

In (*i*) and (*ii*), notice the convenience of having used a *key element* $\pm 1$ as the base for operations.

The standard content in the remainder of the chapter will be restricted to use of determinants of order $n \leqq 3$. However, supplementary problems involving determinants of order $n > 3$ will be available. Hence, the following illustration may be of interest.

★ILLUSTRATION 2.    To calculate the following determinant $D$, we first arrange to get elements $\pm 1$ in the 1st *column*. To do this, in sequence, we subtract the elements of 3d *row* from elements of 4th *row*; then add elements of 2d *row* to those of 3d *row*; then add elements of 1st *row* to those of 2d *row*:

$$D = \begin{vmatrix} 2 & 3 & -4 & 5 \\ -3 & 5 & 2 & -4 \\ 4 & 2 & 3 & 6 \\ 5 & 6 & 5 & 7 \end{vmatrix} = \begin{vmatrix} 2 & 3 & -4 & 5 \\ -1 & 8 & -2 & 1 \\ 1 & 7 & 5 & 2 \\ 1 & 4 & 2 & 1 \end{vmatrix}.$$

* For proofs leading to the proof of Theorem III, see texts on advanced algebra.

To arrange for three zeros in 1st *column*, we operate on *rows*. Multiply the elements of 2d row by 2 to obtain $(-2, 16, -4, 2)$, and add these to elements of 1st row to get $(0, 19, -8, 7)$ as new 1st row; add elements of 2d row to elements of 3d row to get $(0, 15, 3, 3)$ as new 3d row; add elements of 2d row to elements of 4th row to get $(0, 12, 0, 2)$ as new 4th row. Then expand by cofactors of the 1st column:

$$D = \begin{vmatrix} 0 & 19 & -8 & 7 \\ -1 & 8 & -2 & 1 \\ 0 & 15 & 3 & 3 \\ 0 & 12 & 0 & 2 \end{vmatrix} = (-1)(-1)\begin{vmatrix} 19 & -8 & 7 \\ 15 & 3 & 3 \\ 12 & 0 & 2 \end{vmatrix}.$$

Remove factor 3 from 2d row and 2 from 3d row, with these factors placed as multipliers of the new determinant, as specified by Theorem II on page 259. Then expand by cofactors of the last row.

$$D = (3 \cdot 2)\begin{vmatrix} 19 & -8 & 7 \\ 5 & 1 & 1 \\ 6 & 0 & 1 \end{vmatrix}$$

$$= 6(6)\begin{vmatrix} -8 & 7 \\ 1 & 1 \end{vmatrix} + 6\begin{vmatrix} 19 & -8 \\ 5 & 1 \end{vmatrix} = -540 + 354 = -186.$$

## Exercise 58

*1–6.* In Problems 1–6, respectively, of Exercise 57 on page 260, calculate the determinant by first using Theorem III on page 261 to obtain a new form where there are at least two zeros in some row or column.

*Calculate the determinant as directed for Problems 1–6.*

7. $\begin{vmatrix} 2 & 4 & 5 \\ -3 & 2 & 4 \\ 5 & -3 & -2 \end{vmatrix}.$

8. $\begin{vmatrix} 7 & 3 & -4 \\ 2 & -2 & 5 \\ -3 & 4 & 6 \end{vmatrix}.$

★9. $\begin{vmatrix} 3 & -2 & 6 & 5 \\ 2 & 3 & -3 & 4 \\ -1 & -4 & 2 & 3 \\ 4 & 5 & 4 & 7 \end{vmatrix}.$

★10. $\begin{vmatrix} 5 & -4 & 3 & -2 \\ -3 & 2 & 4 & 5 \\ 2 & 3 & -5 & 4 \\ 6 & -5 & 7 & 3 \end{vmatrix}.$

## 91. Solution of a system of three linear equations by determinants

Recall the following expansion from (4) on page 258.

$$\begin{vmatrix} A_1 & B_1 & C_1 \\ A_2 & B_2 & C_2 \\ A_3 & B_3 & C_3 \end{vmatrix} = \tag{1}$$

$$A_1(B_2C_3 - B_3C_2) - A_2(B_1C_3 - B_3C_1) + A_3(B_1C_2 - B_2C_1). \tag{2}$$

On expanding the following determinant by use of cofactors of the 2d column, we obtain

$$\begin{vmatrix} A_1 & D_1 & C_1 \\ A_2 & D_2 & C_2 \\ A_3 & D_3 & C_3 \end{vmatrix} = \tag{3}$$

$$- D_1(A_2C_3 - A_3C_2) + D_2(A_1C_3 - A_3C_1) - D_3(A_1C_2 - A_2C_1). \tag{4}$$

We shall use (2) and (4) later in this section.

Suppose that the method of solution used in Example 1 on page 252 is employed for solving the following system.

$$(\mathbf{I}) \begin{cases} A_1x + B_1y + C_1z = D_1, & (5) \\ A_2x + B_2y + C_2z = D_2, & (6) \\ A_3x + B_3y + C_3z = D_3. & (7) \end{cases}$$

Then, if the denominator in the result below is not zero, it is found that, in the solution of (I), the value obtained for $y$ is

$$y = \frac{- D_1(A_2C_3 - A_3C_2) + D_2(A_1C_3 - A_3C_1) - D_3(A_1C_2 - A_2C_1)}{A_1(B_2C_3 - B_3C_2) - A_2(B_1C_3 - B_3C_1) + A_3(B_1C_2 - B_2C_1)}, \tag{8}$$

On comparing (8) with (2) and (4), it is found that (8) can be written

$$y = \frac{\begin{vmatrix} A_1 & D_1 & C_1 \\ A_2 & D_2 & C_2 \\ A_3 & D_3 & C_3 \end{vmatrix}}{\begin{vmatrix} A_1 & B_1 & C_1 \\ A_2 & B_2 & C_2 \\ A_3 & B_3 & C_3 \end{vmatrix}}. \tag{9}$$

In (9), we have verified that the value of $y$ is given as specified by Cramer's rule on page 256 when applied to system (I). Similarly, it can be shown that the values of $x$ and $z$ in the solution of (I) are given by fractions with determinants in the numerators and denominators as specified by Cramer's rule.

We accept the preceding discussion then as proof of Cramer's rule for the case of a system of three linear equations in three variables. Without proof at this time, we also accept Cramer's rule for a system of four equations. Later in the chapter, a method will be met which can be used to prove Cramer's rule conveniently for a system of $n$ equations.

EXAMPLE 1.    Solve:

$$\begin{cases} x - 3y - 2z = 11, & (10) \\ 3x - y - 2z = 13, & (11) \\ x - y - 6z = 11. & (12) \end{cases}$$

*Solution.*    *1.*    The determinant, $V$, of the matrix of coefficients of the variables is

$$V = \begin{vmatrix} 1 & -3 & -2 \\ 3 & -1 & -2 \\ 1 & -1 & -6 \end{vmatrix} = -40. \tag{13}$$

*2.*    From Cramer's rule:

$$x = \frac{\begin{vmatrix} 11 & -3 & -2 \\ 13 & -1 & -2 \\ 11 & -1 & -6 \end{vmatrix}}{\begin{vmatrix} 1 & -3 & -2 \\ 3 & -1 & -2 \\ 1 & -1 & -6 \end{vmatrix}}; \quad y = \frac{\begin{vmatrix} 1 & 11 & -2 \\ 3 & 13 & -2 \\ 1 & 11 & -6 \end{vmatrix}}{\begin{vmatrix} 1 & -3 & -2 \\ 3 & -1 & -2 \\ 1 & -1 & -6 \end{vmatrix}}; \quad z = etc. \tag{14}$$

In (14), we find that the numerator of the fraction for $x$ is equal to $-120$. Hence $x = -120/(-40) = 3$. The numerator for $y$ is equal to 80, so that $y = 80/(-40) = -2$; $z = 40/(-40) = -1$.

### Exercise 59

*1–11.*    In Problems 1–11, respectively, of Exercises 55 on page 254, first compute the determinant of the matrix of the coefficients of the variables. Keep a record of the value of this determinant for use later in Exercises 61 and 62. If the determinant is not zero, use Cramer's rule to solve the system of equations.

★*12.*    Solve by use of determinants:

$$\begin{cases} 3v - w - 2z + 10 = 0, \\ 4u + v - 4w - z = 0, \\ u - v + 4z = 15, \\ 3u - 2v - w + 2z = 13. \end{cases}$$

## ★92.  Multiplication of matrices

For present purposes, it is desirable to use the following standard form for a system of three linear equations in the variables $(x_1, x_2, x_3)$, with $a_{ij}$ as the constant which is the coefficient of $x_j$ in the $i$th equation, and $c_i$ as the constant term in that equation.

$$(\mathbf{I})\begin{cases} a_{11}x_1 + a_{12}x_2 + a_{13}x_3 = c_1, & (1) \\ a_{21}x_1 + a_{22}x_2 + a_{23}x_3 = c_2, & (2) \\ a_{31}x_1 + a_{32}x_2 + a_{33}x_3 = c_3. & (3) \end{cases}$$

We may abbreviate (I) by writing*

$$\sum\nolimits_{j=1}^{3} a_{ij}x_j = c_i; \qquad (i = 1, 2, 3). \tag{4}$$

Let $\mathbf{A} = [a_{ij}]$, the $3 \times 3$ matrix of coefficients of the variables in (I). Also, let

$$\mathbf{X} = \begin{bmatrix} x_1 \\ x_2 \\ x_3 \end{bmatrix} \quad and \quad \mathbf{C} = \begin{bmatrix} c_1 \\ c_2 \\ c_3 \end{bmatrix}, \tag{5}$$

where $\mathbf{X}$ and $\mathbf{C}$ are $3 \times 1$ matrices, or *column* matrices. In terms of the concept of matrix multiplication which we shall introduce, the left-hand side of (4) becomes the matrix product $\mathbf{AX}$, and (4) can be written.

$$\mathbf{AX} = \mathbf{C}. \tag{6}$$

Thus, the following terminology has an immediate pertinent application.

DEFINITION V.  *Let* $\mathbf{A} = [a_{ij}]$ *be an* $m \times n$ *matrix, and* $\mathbf{B} = [b_{ij}]$ *be an* $n \times s$ *matrix. Then, the* **product** $\mathbf{AB}$ *is an* $m \times s$ *matrix whose element in* (*row i, column k*) *is obtained as follows:*

$$\left.\begin{array}{l} \textit{multiply each element, in order, in the ith row of A by the} \\ \textit{corresponding element, in order, in the kth column of B,} \\ \textit{and add the results.} \end{array}\right\} \tag{7}$$

Briefly, we recall (7) by saying that we obtain $\mathbf{AB}$ by multiplying "*rows of* $\mathbf{A}$ *by columns of* $\mathbf{B}$."

ILLUSTRATION 1.    $\begin{bmatrix} 2 & -3 & 1 \\ -4 & 2 & 3 \end{bmatrix} \cdot \begin{bmatrix} -3 & 2 \\ 4 & -1 \\ 5 & 3 \end{bmatrix} = \begin{bmatrix} -13 & 10 \\ 35 & -1 \end{bmatrix},$

because

$2(-3) + (-3)(4) + (1)(5) = -13; \qquad 2(2) + (-3)(-1) + (1)(3) = 10;$

$(-4)(-3) + (2)(4) + (3)(5) = 35; \qquad (-4)(2) + (2)(-1) + (3)(3) = -1.$

* See page 277 for introduction to summation notation.

ILLUSTRATION 2.   By use of Definition V, the equation

$$\begin{bmatrix} 2 & 4 & 1 \\ -3 & 2 & 5 \\ 1 & -2 & 3 \end{bmatrix} \cdot \begin{bmatrix} x \\ y \\ z \end{bmatrix} = \begin{bmatrix} -2 \\ 4 \\ 7 \end{bmatrix} \qquad (8)$$

specifies the equality of a 3 × 1 column matrix on the left and the 3 × 1 matrix on the right. By use of (7) on the left in (8), we obtain

$$\begin{bmatrix} (2x + 4y + z) \\ (-3x + 2y + 5z) \\ (x - 2y + 3z) \end{bmatrix} = \begin{bmatrix} -2 \\ 4 \\ 7 \end{bmatrix}. \qquad (9)$$

By the definition of equality for matrices, (9) means that:

$$\begin{cases} 2x + 4y + z = -2, \\ -3x + 2y + 5z = 4, \\ x - 2y + 3z = 7. \end{cases}$$

## ★ Exercise 60

*Obtain the product.*

1. $\begin{bmatrix} 2 & 4 \\ -3 & 1 \end{bmatrix} \cdot \begin{bmatrix} -1 & 3 \\ 2 & 1 \end{bmatrix}.$    2. $\begin{bmatrix} -2 & 4 \\ 3 & 0 \end{bmatrix} \cdot \begin{bmatrix} 3 & -1 \\ 0 & 2 \end{bmatrix}.$

3. $\begin{bmatrix} -1 & 2 \\ -3 & 4 \end{bmatrix} \cdot \begin{bmatrix} 2 & 0 \\ -2 & 4 \end{bmatrix}.$    4. $\begin{bmatrix} 1 & 0 \\ 0 & 1 \end{bmatrix} \cdot \begin{bmatrix} 3 & 5 \\ -4 & 7 \end{bmatrix}.$

5. $\begin{bmatrix} 2 & 4 \\ -3 & 1 \end{bmatrix} \cdot \begin{bmatrix} 5 \\ -2 \end{bmatrix}.$    6. $\begin{bmatrix} -1 & 3 \\ 2 & -4 \end{bmatrix} \cdot \begin{bmatrix} 2 \\ 6 \end{bmatrix}.$

7. $\begin{bmatrix} 2 & 1 & -2 \\ -3 & 0 & 3 \\ 4 & 2 & 1 \end{bmatrix} \cdot \begin{bmatrix} -1 & 2 & 3 \\ 3 & 4 & 2 \\ -1 & 0 & 4 \end{bmatrix}.$

8. $\begin{bmatrix} 0 & 3 & 2 \\ 2 & 1 & 0 \\ 1 & 4 & 6 \end{bmatrix} \cdot \begin{bmatrix} -2 & 1 & -2 \\ 0 & 4 & 0 \\ 3 & 0 & 5 \end{bmatrix}.$

9. $\begin{bmatrix} 1 & 0 & 0 \\ 0 & 1 & 0 \\ 0 & 0 & 1 \end{bmatrix} \cdot \begin{bmatrix} 3 & 8 & 5 \\ 7 & 4 & 9 \\ 9 & 6 & 4 \end{bmatrix} ; \quad \begin{bmatrix} 3 & 8 & 5 \\ 7 & 4 & 9 \\ 9 & 6 & 4 \end{bmatrix} \cdot \begin{bmatrix} 1 & 0 & 0 \\ 0 & 1 & 0 \\ 0 & 0 & 1 \end{bmatrix}.$

10. $\begin{bmatrix} -2 & 3 & 0 \\ 1 & 0 & -1 \\ 4 & 2 & 4 \end{bmatrix} \cdot \begin{bmatrix} 1 & 3 & 0 \\ 1 & 2 & -1 \\ 1 & 5 & 2 \end{bmatrix}.$

11. $\begin{bmatrix} 2 & -3 & 4 \\ 5 & 2 & -1 \\ -2 & 3 & 2 \end{bmatrix} \cdot \begin{bmatrix} -2 \\ 3 \\ 4 \end{bmatrix}.$      12. $\begin{bmatrix} 3 & 2 & 5 \\ 1 & -3 & 4 \\ -1 & 2 & -3 \end{bmatrix} \cdot \begin{bmatrix} -5 \\ 3 \\ 2 \end{bmatrix}.$

*Write the given system of equations without use of any matrix, and solve the system.*

13. $\begin{bmatrix} 2 & -3 \\ 1 & 2 \end{bmatrix} \cdot \begin{bmatrix} x \\ y \end{bmatrix} = \begin{bmatrix} 3 \\ 5 \end{bmatrix}.$      14. $\begin{bmatrix} 1 & 2 \\ -3 & 1 \end{bmatrix} \cdot \begin{bmatrix} x \\ y \end{bmatrix} = \begin{bmatrix} 4 \\ 5 \end{bmatrix}.$

*Only write the system of equations without use of a matrix.*

15. $\begin{bmatrix} -2 & 4 & 0 \\ 3 & -1 & 3 \\ 1 & 2 & 2 \end{bmatrix} \cdot \begin{bmatrix} x \\ y \\ z \end{bmatrix} = \begin{bmatrix} -2 \\ 3 \\ 5 \end{bmatrix}.$

16. $\begin{bmatrix} 3 & 5 & -1 \\ -1 & 0 & 2 \\ 2 & 4 & 6 \end{bmatrix} \cdot \begin{bmatrix} x_1 \\ x_2 \\ x_3 \end{bmatrix} = \begin{bmatrix} 1 \\ -2 \\ 4 \end{bmatrix}.$

17–19.  In each of Problems 1–3 in Exercise 55 on page 254, write the system of equations in the form illustrated above in Problems 15–16.

20.  A certain college maintains three intercollegiate sports ($S_1$, $S_2$, $S_3$). For each sport, the seasonal costs in dollars per athlete of transportation, hotel accommodations on trips, training table at home, uniforms, and laundry of uniforms are, respectively, the elements in a row of the $3 \times 5$ matrix **A** below. The number of athletes in the sport corresponding to any one of these rows is the element in the corresponding place in the vector **X** below. Calculate **XA**. What does each element of **XA** represent?

$$\mathbf{A} = \begin{bmatrix} 100 & 200 & 30 & 120 & 25 \\ 40 & 0 & 10 & 50 & 10 \\ 75 & 150 & 20 & 75 & 20 \end{bmatrix}; \qquad \mathbf{X} = [40 \quad 6 \quad 30].$$

21.  A manufacturer of food for cats will prepare a mixture of compounds $\{C_1, C_2, C_3\}$. The percentages of carbohydrates, fats, and proteins in $C_1$ are, respectively, the elements in the first row of the following matrix **A**, in $C_2$ are the second row, and in $C_3$ are the third row. The numbers of pounds of $\{C_1, C_2, C_3\}$ to be used are, respectively, the elements of the vector **X**. Calculate **XA**, and tell what its elements represent.

$$\mathbf{A} = \begin{bmatrix} 25\% & 10\% & 30\% \\ 25\% & 60\% & 10\% \\ 5\% & 20\% & 30\% \end{bmatrix}. \qquad \mathbf{X} = [200 \quad 300 \quad 100].$$

*22.*  With $\mathbf{A} = \begin{bmatrix} 3 & 2 \\ -4 & 5 \end{bmatrix}$ and $\mathbf{B} = \begin{bmatrix} 1 & 4 \\ 5 & 7 \end{bmatrix}$, calculate $\mathbf{AB}$ and $\mathbf{BA}$. To state that matrix multiplication for square matrices is *commutative* would imply that $\mathbf{AB} = \mathbf{BA}$ for *all* square matrices of given dimensions $n \times n$. Is such multiplication commutative?

## ★ 93.  Inverse of a square matrix

At a more advanced mathematical level, the results of this section are met for $n \times n$ matrices, where $n$ is any positive integer. We shall present the content for the case of $3 \times 3$ matrices. The corresponding discussion for $2 \times 2$ matrices can be inferred easily. The exercises will involve only $2 \times 2$ and $3 \times 3$ matrices. Let $\mathbf{A}$ represent any $3 \times 3$ matrix, where $a_{ij}$ is the element of $\mathbf{A}$ in (*row i, column j*):

$$\mathbf{A} = [a_{ij}], \qquad or \qquad \mathbf{A} = \begin{bmatrix} a_{11} & a_{12} & a_{13} \\ a_{21} & a_{22} & a_{23} \\ a_{31} & a_{32} & a_{33} \end{bmatrix}. \tag{1}$$

A matrix $\mathbf{A}$ is said to be a **diagonal matrix** if each element is zero outside of the main diagonal. The **unit diagonal matrix**, $\mathbf{U}$, is that matrix having 1 as each element in the main diagonal, with each other element zero.

ILLUSTRATION 1.   The unit diagonal $2 \times 2$ and $3 \times 3$ matrices are

$$\begin{bmatrix} 1 & 0 \\ 0 & 1 \end{bmatrix} \qquad and \qquad \begin{bmatrix} 1 & 0 & 0 \\ 0 & 1 & 0 \\ 0 & 0 & 1 \end{bmatrix}. \tag{2}$$

In Problem 9 of Exercise 60, the student met an illustration of the fact that, if $\mathbf{U}$ is the $n \times n$ unit diagonal matrix, and $\mathbf{A}$ is any $n \times n$ matrix, then $\mathbf{UA} = \mathbf{AU} = \mathbf{A}$. It is easy to verify this for the matrix $\mathbf{A}$ of (1). Below, recall that all matrices in our discussion are $n \times n$ matrices, for a fixed value of $n$ (with $n = 3$ in our work).

DEFINITION VI.   *A matrix* $\mathbf{B}$ *is said to be* **AN inverse** *of a matrix* $\mathbf{A}$ *in case* $\mathbf{AB} = \mathbf{BA} = \mathbf{U}$, *where* $\mathbf{U}$ *is the unit diagonal matrix.*

In a problem of the next exercise, the student will have an opportunity to prove that, if $\mathbf{A}$ has an inverse $\mathbf{B}$, and if $\mathbf{C}$ is any matrix such that $\mathbf{CA} = \mathbf{U}$, or $\mathbf{AC} = \mathbf{U}$, then $\mathbf{C} = \mathbf{B}$. That is, *the inverse of* $\mathbf{A}$ *is unique, if the inverse exists.* Hereafter, let $\mathbf{A}^{-1}$, read "$\mathbf{A}$, *inverse*," represent the inverse of $\mathbf{A}$ when $\mathbf{A}$ has an inverse (which is *not* always the case).

In Definition VI, the conditions $\mathbf{AB} = \mathbf{BA} = \mathbf{U}$ treat $\mathbf{A}$ and $\mathbf{B}$ alike. Hence, if $\mathbf{B}$ is an inverse of $\mathbf{A}$ then $\mathbf{A}$ is an inverse of $\mathbf{B}$.

The following result will be proved later.

THEOREM IV.   *For any matrix* $\mathbf{A}$ *in* (1), *if* $|\mathbf{A}| \neq 0$ *then* $\mathbf{A}^{-1}$ *exists, and*

$$\mathbf{A}^{-1} = \frac{1}{|\mathbf{A}|}\begin{bmatrix} A_{11} & A_{21} & A_{31} \\ A_{12} & A_{22} & A_{32} \\ A_{13} & A_{23} & A_{33} \end{bmatrix}, \tag{3}$$

*where* $A_{ij}$ *is the cofactor of* $a_{ij}$ *in* $|\mathbf{A}|$.

Because of the definition of multiplication of a matrix by a scalar in (5) on page 250, (3) can be written as follows:

$$\mathbf{A}^{-1} = \left[\frac{A_{ij}}{|\mathbf{A}|}\right]_{(j\,for\,row,\,i\,for\,column)}. \tag{4}$$

Usually, we shall prefer to use (3) rather than (4). In the matrix at the right in (3), observe that each *row* consists of the cofactors of the elements in the corresponding *column* of $\mathbf{A}$. Thus, the matrix at the right in (3) is the *transpose**\* of the matrix $[A_{ij}]$ of cofactors of the elements of $\mathbf{A} = [a_{ij}]$. The right-hand side of (4) is undefined if $|\mathbf{A}| = 0$, when Theorem IV does not apply. An advanced treatment beyond the scope of this text shows that, if $|\mathbf{A}| = 0$, then $\mathbf{A}$ has no inverse.

EXAMPLE 1.   Calculate $\mathbf{A}^{-1}$ if $\mathbf{A} = \begin{bmatrix} 2 & -1 & 3 \\ -2 & 4 & 5 \\ 3 & 1 & 4 \end{bmatrix}$ and verify that

$\mathbf{AA}^{-1} = \mathbf{A}^{-1}\mathbf{A} = \mathbf{U}$.

*Solution.   1.* First we compute $|\mathbf{A}| = -43$. Hence, $\mathbf{A}^{-1}$ exists. With $\mathbf{A}$ thought of in the notation $\mathbf{A} = [a_{ij}]$, the cofactors of the first *column* of $\mathbf{A}$ are as follows:

$$A_{11} = \begin{vmatrix} 4 & 5 \\ 1 & 4 \end{vmatrix} = 11; \quad A_{21} = -\begin{vmatrix} -1 & 3 \\ 1 & 4 \end{vmatrix} = 7; \quad A_{31} = \begin{vmatrix} -1 & 3 \\ 4 & 5 \end{vmatrix} = -17.$$

Thus, the first *row* in the matrix from (3) is $\{11, 7, -17\}$. Similarly, we obtain the other rows, and (3) gives

$$\mathbf{A}^{-1} = -\frac{1}{43}\begin{bmatrix} 11 & 7 & -17 \\ 23 & -1 & -16 \\ -14 & -5 & 6 \end{bmatrix}. \tag{5}$$

\* See Problem 8 on page 260.

*2.* On applying matrix multiplication, we obtain

$$\mathbf{A}\mathbf{A}^{-1} = -\frac{1}{43}\begin{bmatrix} 2 & -1 & 3 \\ -2 & 4 & 5 \\ 3 & 1 & 4 \end{bmatrix} \cdot \begin{bmatrix} 11 & 7 & -17 \\ 23 & -1 & -16 \\ -14 & -5 & 6 \end{bmatrix} \tag{6}$$

$$= \frac{1}{43}\begin{bmatrix} 43 & 0 & 0 \\ 0 & 43 & 0 \\ 0 & 0 & 43 \end{bmatrix} = \begin{bmatrix} 1 & 0 & 0 \\ 0 & 1 & 0 \\ 0 & 0 & 1 \end{bmatrix} = \mathbf{U}_{3 \times 3}. \tag{7}$$

For instance, in the product of matrices in (6), the element in (*row* 2, *column* 2), for (7) is obtained by multiplying, in turn, each element of row 2 in **A** by the corresponding element of column 2 at the right, or

$$(-2)(7) + (4)(-1) + (5)(-5) = -14 - 4 - 25 = -43.$$

The element in the product matrix in (*row* 3, *column* 1) is

$$(3)(11) + (1)(23) + (4)(-14) = 33 + 23 - 56 = 0.$$

Similarly, it may be verified that $\mathbf{A}^{-1}\mathbf{A} = \mathbf{U}_{3 \times 3}$.

In the next section, the concept of an inverse matrix will be used in connection with Cramer's rule. At that time, it will be sufficient to know that Theorem IV is true.

★*Proof of Theorem* IV *for the matrix* $\mathbf{A} = [a_{ij}]_{3 \times 3}$. *I.* In $|\mathbf{A}|$, the cofactors of the elements form the following new matrix **H**, where $A_{ij}$ is the cofactor of $a_{ij}$ in $|\mathbf{A}|$:

$$\mathbf{H} = \begin{bmatrix} A_{11} & A_{12} & A_{13} \\ A_{21} & A_{22} & A_{23} \\ A_{31} & A_{32} & A_{33} \end{bmatrix}. \tag{9}$$

The transpose of **H** is

$$\mathbf{H}' = \begin{bmatrix} A_{11} & A_{21} & A_{31} \\ A_{12} & A_{22} & A_{32} \\ A_{13} & A_{23} & A_{33} \end{bmatrix}. \tag{10}$$

*2.* Consider formation of the product

$$\mathbf{A}\mathbf{H}' = \begin{bmatrix} a_{11} & a_{12} & a_{13} \\ a_{21} & a_{22} & a_{23} \\ a_{31} & a_{32} & a_{33} \end{bmatrix} \cdot \begin{bmatrix} A_{11} & A_{21} & A_{31} \\ A_{12} & A_{22} & A_{32} \\ A_{13} & A_{23} & A_{33} \end{bmatrix}. \tag{11}$$

*3.* In $\mathbf{A}\mathbf{H}'$, the element in row 2 and column 2 is

$$a_{21}A_{21} + a_{22}A_{22} + a_{23}A_{23} = |\mathbf{A}|, \tag{12}$$

because the left-hand side is the expansion of $|\mathbf{A}|$ by the elements and co-factors of the 2d row of **A**. Similarly, each element in the main diagonal for $\mathbf{A}\mathbf{H}'$ is $|\mathbf{A}|$.

*4.* In **AH′**, the element in row 2 and column 3 is

$$a_{21}A_{31} + a_{22}A_{32} + a_{23}A_{33}. \tag{13}$$

The expansion of $|\mathbf{A}|$ by the elements and cofactors of row 3 is

$$|\mathbf{A}| = a_{31}A_{31} + a_{32}A_{32} + a_{33}A_{33}. \tag{14}$$

Observe that (13) is obtained from (14) on replacing the elements of the 3d row of **A** by the elements of the 2d row. Hence, (13) is the expansion of the determinant obtained from $|\mathbf{A}|$ by replacing its 3d row by the 2d row, or

$$\begin{vmatrix} a_{11} & a_{12} & a_{13} \\ a_{21} & a_{22} & a_{23} \\ a_{21} & a_{22} & a_{23} \end{vmatrix} = a_{21}A_{31} + a_{22}A_{32} + a_{23}A_{33},$$

which is *zero* because two rows above are *identical* (see Problem 9 on page 260). Hence, in (13), the element of the product **AH′** in row 2 and column 3 is 0. Similarly, each element *not* in the main diagonal of **AH′** is zero. Therefore,

$$\mathbf{AH'} = \begin{bmatrix} |\mathbf{A}| & 0 & 0 \\ 0 & |\mathbf{A}| & 0 \\ 0 & 0 & |\mathbf{A}| \end{bmatrix}.$$

*5.* We wish to prove that, with $\mathbf{A}^{-1}$ as in (3), we obtain $\mathbf{AA}^{-1} = \mathbf{A}^{-1}\mathbf{A} = \mathbf{U}$. From (3), $\mathbf{A}^{-1} = \mathbf{H'}/|\mathbf{A}|$. Hence

$$\mathbf{AA}^{-1} = \frac{\mathbf{AH'}}{|\mathbf{A}|} = \frac{\begin{bmatrix} |\mathbf{A}| & 0 & 0 \\ 0 & |\mathbf{A}| & 0 \\ 0 & 0 & |\mathbf{A}| \end{bmatrix}}{|\mathbf{A}|} = \begin{bmatrix} 1 & 0 & 0 \\ 0 & 1 & 0 \\ 0 & 0 & 1 \end{bmatrix} = \mathbf{U}.$$

Similarly, we may show that $\mathbf{A}^{-1}\mathbf{A} = \mathbf{U}$. Therefore, $\mathbf{A}^{-1}$ of (3) is the inverse of $|\mathbf{A}|$.

## ★ Exercise 61

*Obtain the inverse $\mathbf{A}^{-1}$ for the matrix $\mathbf{A}$ which is given, provided that $\mathbf{A}^{-1}$ exists. Then form the products $\mathbf{AA}^{-1}$ and $\mathbf{A}^{-1}\mathbf{A}$ to verify the result.*

*1.* $\begin{bmatrix} 3 & -2 \\ 4 & 5 \end{bmatrix}.$   *2.* $\begin{bmatrix} -2 & 1 \\ 3 & -1 \end{bmatrix}.$   *3.* $\begin{bmatrix} -3 & 1 \\ 4 & -1 \end{bmatrix}.$   *4.* $\begin{bmatrix} 2 & 5 \\ -2 & -5 \end{bmatrix}.$

*5–15.* Let **A** be the matrix of the coefficients of the variables in Problems 1–11, respectively, of Exercise 55 on page 254. Retain $\mathbf{A}^{-1}$ for use in the next exercise.

*16.* Suppose that the $n \times n$ matrix **A** has an inverse **B**, as described in Definition VI on page 268. Also, assume that **C** is an $n \times n$ matrix such that $CA = U_{n \times n}$, the unit diagonal matrix. By right-multiplication with **B**, prove that **C = B**. If **AC = U**, also prove that **C = B**.

## ★94.   Solution of linear systems by use of an inverse matrix

Let the normal form for a system of three linear equations in the variables $(x_1, x_2, x_3)$ be

$$(I) \begin{cases} a_{11}x_1 + a_{12}x_2 + a_{13}x_3 = c_1, & (1) \\ a_{21}x_1 + a_{22}x_2 + a_{23}x_3 = c_2, & (2) \\ a_{31}x_1 + a_{32}x_2 + a_{33}x_3 = c_3, & (3) \end{cases}$$

where the coefficients $a_{ij}$ and the right-hand members $c_i$ are constants. Let

$$\mathbf{A} = \begin{bmatrix} a_{11} & a_{12} & a_{13} \\ a_{21} & a_{22} & a_{23} \\ a_{31} & a_{32} & a_{33} \end{bmatrix}; \quad \mathbf{X} = \begin{bmatrix} x_1 \\ x_2 \\ x_3 \end{bmatrix}; \quad \mathbf{C} = \begin{bmatrix} c_1 \\ c_2 \\ c_3 \end{bmatrix}. \quad (4)$$

Then system (I) can be written

$$\mathbf{AX = C}. \quad (5)$$

Assume that $|\mathbf{A}| \neq 0$, so that the inverse $\mathbf{A}^{-1}$ exists. We shall prove that the solution of (I) is given by

$$\begin{bmatrix} x_1 \\ x_2 \\ x_3 \end{bmatrix} = \frac{1}{|\mathbf{A}|} \begin{bmatrix} A_{11} & A_{21} & A_{31} \\ A_{12} & A_{22} & A_{32} \\ A_{13} & A_{23} & A_{33} \end{bmatrix} \cdot \begin{bmatrix} c_1 \\ c_2 \\ c_3 \end{bmatrix}. \quad (6)$$

*Proof of* (6).   In (5), "left-multiply" by the matrix $\mathbf{A}^{-1}$ on each side, to obtain

$$\mathbf{A}^{-1}(\mathbf{AX}) = \mathbf{A}^{-1}\mathbf{C}, \quad or \quad (\mathbf{A}^{-1}\mathbf{A})\mathbf{X} = \mathbf{A}^{-1}\mathbf{C}, \quad or \quad \mathbf{UX} = \mathbf{A}^{-1}\mathbf{C}, \quad (7)$$

where **U** is the unit diagonal $3 \times 3$ matrix. In writing $\mathbf{A}^{-1}(\mathbf{AX}) = (\mathbf{A}^{-1}\mathbf{A})\mathbf{X}$, we assumed without proof the fact that *matrix multiplication obeys the associative law*. Since $\mathbf{UX = X}$, from (7) we obtain

$$\mathbf{X = A^{-1}C}, \quad (8)$$

which is a compact form of (6).

On the right in (6), the product of the $3 \times 3$ matrix and the $3 \times 1$ matrix yields a $3 \times 1$ matrix whose elements, when divided by $|\mathbf{A}|$, are the values of $(x_1, x_2, x_3)$, respectively. The 1st row $(A_{11}, A_{21}, A_{31})$, when applied to the column $(c_1, c_2, c_3)$, gives $x_1$; the 2d row $(A_{12}, A_{22}, A_{32})$, when applied to $(c_1, c_2, c_3)$, gives $x_2$; etc. Thus,

$$x_1 = \frac{c_1 A_{11} + c_2 A_{21} + c_3 A_{31}}{|A|}; \quad x_2 = \frac{c_1 A_{12} + c_2 A_{22} + c_3 A_{32}}{|A|}; \text{ etc.} \quad (9)$$

The numerator for $x_1$ in (9) is the expansion of the following determinant by cofactors of its first column:

$$\begin{vmatrix} c_1 & a_{12} & a_{13} \\ c_2 & a_{22} & a_{23} \\ c_3 & a_{32} & a_{33} \end{vmatrix}$$

Thus, the expression for $x_1$ in (9) is the same as specified by Cramer's rule for system (I). Similarly, the values of $x_2$ and $x_3$ in (9) are those specified by Cramer's rule. Hence, that rule has been proved for system (I).

EXAMPLE 1.   Solve:
$$\textbf{(II)} \begin{cases} 2x - y + 3z = 1, & (10) \\ x + 2y - z = 3, & (11) \\ -x + 3y - 2z = -2. & (12) \end{cases}$$

*Solution.*   *1.*   The matrix, **A**, of coefficients of the variables in (II), and $|A|$ are as follows:

$$\mathbf{A} = \begin{bmatrix} 2 & -1 & 3 \\ 1 & 2 & -1 \\ -1 & 3 & -2 \end{bmatrix}; \quad |A| = 10. \quad (13)$$

From (13), we find that
$$\mathbf{A}^{-1} = \frac{1}{10} \begin{bmatrix} -1 & 7 & -5 \\ 3 & -1 & 5 \\ 5 & -5 & 5 \end{bmatrix}. \quad (14)$$

*2.*   With $\mathbf{X} = \begin{bmatrix} x \\ y \\ z \end{bmatrix}$, by use of (8) we obtain

$$\begin{bmatrix} x \\ y \\ z \end{bmatrix} = \frac{1}{10} \begin{bmatrix} -1 & 7 & -5 \\ 3 & -1 & 5 \\ 5 & -5 & 5 \end{bmatrix} \cdot \begin{bmatrix} 1 \\ 3 \\ -2 \end{bmatrix} = \begin{bmatrix} 3 \\ -1 \\ -2 \end{bmatrix}. \quad (15)$$

To verify (15): the sum of the products of the elements in the 1st row of the $3 \times 3$ matrix and corresponding elements of the column vector with elements $(1, 3, -2)$ is

$$(-1)(1) + 7(3) + (-5)(-2), \quad or \quad -1 + 21 + 10 = 30.$$

For the second element of the result in (15):

$$3(1) + (-1)(3) + 5(-2) = 3 - 3 - 10 = -10; \ etc.$$

From (15), the solution of (II) is ($x = 3$, $y = -1$, $z = -2$).

## ★ Exercise 62

*Obtain the inverse (if it exists) of the matrix of coefficients of the variables in the system of equations, or take the result for this inverse from a problem in Exercise 61. Then, with the system in the notation* $\mathbf{AX} = \mathbf{C}$, *obtain the solution by matrix multiplication by* $\mathbf{A}^{-1}$.

*1–11.*   The systems in Problems 1–11, respectively, in Exercise 55 on page 254.

# 11 | INTRODUCTION TO LEAST SQUARE APPROXIMATION

## 95. Nature of the applications

Consider an experiment where the true measure $H$ of some measurable quantity is desired. Suppose that estimates $\{x_1, x_2, \cdots, x_n\}$ for the measure are obtained experimentally, and that some number $\bar{x}$ is to be specified as the "*best*" corresponding approximation to $H$. Then, the sense in which "*best*" is used must be defined. Frequently, the interpretation is "*best in the sense of least square approximation*," which we shall describe for certain situations in this chapter. In all fields of physical and social science, approximations similar to the preceding simplified illustration are involved. More elaborate problems of approximation occur when an unknown function is to be determined on the basis of observed data. We shall discuss this type of problem for the case of a linear function in one variable.

ILLUSTRATION 1.   The table gives the average, $y$, in \$10's of the highest and lowest values of the industrial component of the Dow-Jones index number for prices of stocks on the New York Stock Exchange for certain years, $t$, where $t = 0$ is 1954 and the unit for $t$ is one year. The corresponding points $(t, y)$ are shown as dots in Figure 85 on page 276. In economics, the "*best fitting line* $y = at + b$" for this set of points is called the "*trend line*" for the data. In a later section, the student will obtain this line with "*best*" meaning "*best in the sense of least squares*." The trend line is $HK$ in Figure 85. In such a problem, a best fitting linear function $f(t) = at + b$ is required for the given data, thought of as showing values for an unknown function $f(t)$.

| $y =$ | 34 | 49 | 47 | 51 | 63 | 67 | 71 | 83 | 87 | 91 |
|---|---|---|---|---|---|---|---|---|---|---|
| $t =$ | 0 | 2 | 3 | 4 | 5 | 7 | 9 | 10 | 12 | 14 |

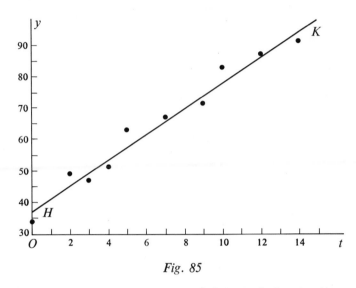

*Fig. 85*

In the field of statistics, a large part of the basis for the theory of correlation involves use of least square approximation. Thus, at the most basic level, the *lines of regression* in a study of two related variables $x$ and $y$ are defined as best fitting lines in the sense of least squares.

The typical application of least square approximation involves elaborate numerical computation, which can be done efficiently with the aid of a modern electronic computing machine, or other devices for calculation. In this chapter, only simplified illustrations of actual situations will be met in the associated problems. Fortunately, however, these simplified versions will provide acquaintance with the principles involved.

## 96.   The minimum of a quadratic function

The theoretical basis for all of the methods presented in this chapter is the following property of a quadratic function of a single variable $z$. The property can be proved by simple algebra, and the result is implied in statement (II) of page 67 about the graph of a quadratic function. Also, the property was met in problems of Chapter 8. On account of the present importance of the result, we shall prove it again by use of calculus.

THEOREM I.   *If a, b, and c are constants and a > 0, the function* $F(z) = az^2 + bz + c$ *has its minimum value when* $z = -b/2a$.

*Proof.   1.*   In $F(z)$, the domain for $z$ is the set of all real numbers.

Hence, if $F(z)$ has a minimum at any point $z = z_0$, then $F'(z_0) = 0$. We obtain

$$F'(z) = 2az + b = 2a\left[z - \left(-\frac{b}{2a}\right)\right], \tag{1}$$

and $F'(z) = 0$ when and only when $z = -b/2a$. Thus, $-b/2a$ is the only critical value of $z$ for maxima or minima.

2.  From (1), if $z < -b/2a$ then $[z - (-b/2a)]$ is *negative*, and hence $F'(z) < 0$, because $a > 0$. If $z > -b/2a$, then $F'(z) > 0$. Hence, by the tests for extremes on page 205, $F(z)$ has a *minimum* at $z = -b/2a$.

Geometrically, Theorem I states the following familiar fact: *If $a > 0$, then $z = -b/2a$ at the vertex or lowest point of the parabola which is the graph of $y = F(z)$ in a zy-plane.*

ILLUSTRATION 1.   The minimum value of the function $f(z) = 3z^2 - 5z + 7$ is attained when $z = -(-5)/6$ or $z = 5/6$. Hence, the minimum value of $f(z)$ is $f(\frac{5}{6}) = 3(\frac{25}{36}) - \frac{25}{6} + 7 = 59/12$.

## 97.   The sigma notation for sums

We use capital sigma, $\sum$, the sign of summation, to abbreviate sums of notationally similar terms. Thus, we write

$$a_1 + a_2 + \cdots + a_n = \sum_{i=1}^{n} a_i, \tag{1}$$

where the right-hand side is read "*the sum of $a_i$ from $i = 1$ to $i = n$.*" In (1), $i$ is called the *index* or *variable of summation*, and we think of $\sum$ as abbreviating the word *sum*.

ILLUSTRATION 1.     $\sum_{i=1}^{5} x_i = x_1 + x_2 + x_3 + x_4 + x_5.$

Also,     $\sum_{j=1}^{5} x_j = x_1 + x_2 + x_3 + x_4 + x_5.$

Notice that the letter, $i$ or $j$, used as the variable of summation is immaterial. The *domain* of this variable is the important feature.

ILLUSTRATION 2.   For any positive integer $n$,

$$\sum_{i=1}^{n} (x_i - c) = (x_1 - c) + (x_2 - c) + \cdots + (x_n - c) \tag{2}$$

$$= \sum_{i=1}^{n} x_i - nc,$$

because there are $n$ numbers $c$ on the right in (2). As a special case,

$$\sum_{i=1}^{3} (x_i - c) = (x_1 - c) + (x_2 - c) + (x_3 - c) = \left[\sum_{i=1}^{3} x_i\right] - 3c.$$

ILLUSTRATION 3.    $\sum_{i=1}^{3} (x_i + c)^2 =$    (3)

$$\sum_{i=1}^{3} (x_i^2 + 2cx_i + c^2) = \sum_{i=1}^{3} x_i^2 + 2c \sum_{i=1}^{3} x_i + 3c^2,$$

because (3) abbreviates

$$(x_1^2 + 2cx_1 + c^2) + (x_2^2 + 2cx_2 + c^2) + (x_3^2 + 2cx_3 + c^2).$$

## 98.  Arithmetic mean and variance

Consider a variable $x$ whose domain is a set $D$ of $n$ numbers, $D = \{x_1, x_2, \cdots, x_n\}$. For contact with statistics, we may think of $D$ as a sample of $n$ values of a random variable $X$. The distribution of such a set of numbers on a number scale is investigated by studying various functions of the $x$'s. We shall introduce just two of these functions, the *mean* and the *variance*.

DEFINITION I.    *Let $\{x_1, x_2, \cdots, x_n\}$ be a sample of $n$ values of a random variable $X$. Then, the* **arithmetic mean,** *$\bar{x}$, of the sample is defined as the sum of the numbers in the sample divided by $n$, or*

$$\bar{x} = \frac{\sum_{i=1}^{n} x_i}{n}.$$    (1)

ILLUSTRATION 1.    The arithmetic mean of 2, 5, 9, 16 is

$$\bar{x} = \tfrac{1}{4}(2 + 5 + 9 + 16) = 8.$$    (2)

If $v$ and $w$ are any numbers, the **deviation** of $w$ from $v$ is defined as $(w - v)$.

THEOREM II.    *The sum of the deviations of $\{x_1, x_2, \cdots, x_n\}$ from their arithmetic mean is 0.*

*Proof.*    The deviation of $x_i$ from $\bar{x}$ is $(x_i - \bar{x})$. Hence, the sum, $T$, of the deviations of all of the $x_i$'s from $\bar{x}$ is

$$T = \sum_{i=1}^{n} (x_i - \bar{x}) = (x_1 - \bar{x}) + (x_2 - \bar{x}) + \cdots + (x_n - \bar{x})$$

$$= \sum_{i=1}^{n} x_i - n\bar{x} = \sum_{i=1}^{n} x_i - n \frac{\sum_{i=1}^{n} x_i}{n}$$

$$= \sum_{i=1}^{n} x_i - \sum_{i=1}^{n} x_i = 0.$$

ILLUSTRATION 2.    In Illustration 1, the deviations of the $x_i$'s from $\bar{x}$ are:

$$(2 - 8); \quad (5 - 8); \quad (9 - 8); \quad (16 - 8);$$

$$(2 - 8) + (5 - 8) + (9 - 8) + (16 - 8) = 32 - 32 = 0.$$

THEOREM III.  *The sum of the squares of the deviations of n given numbers $(x_1, x_2, \cdots, x_n)$ from their arithmetic mean, $\bar{x}$, is less than the sum of the squares of such deviations from any number not equal to $\bar{x}$.*

*Proof.*  1.  Let $F(z) = \sum_{i=1}^{n} (x_i - z)^2$.  Thus,  $F$  is the sum of the squares of the deviations of the $x$'s from the number $z$. Theorem III states that $F(z)$ has its *least value* when $z = \bar{x}$. We wish to prove this fact.

2.  We expand $(x_i - z)^2$ and obtain

$$F(z) = \sum_{i=1}^{n} (x_i^2 - 2x_i z + z^2).  \tag{3}$$

For any positive integer $n$, from (3) we find that

$$F(z) = \sum_{i=1}^{n} x_i^2 - 2z \sum_{i=1}^{n} x_i + nz^2.  \tag{4}$$

3.  By Theorem I, $F(z)$ in (4) has its minimum value if and only if

$$z = -\frac{-2 \sum_{i=1}^{n} x_i}{2n} = \frac{\sum_{i=1}^{n} x_i}{n} = \bar{x},$$

which proves Theorem III.

We may rephrase Theorem III as follows.

*If $\{x_1, x_2, \cdots, x_n\}$ are considered as experimentally determined estimates of an unknown number z, then the best approximation to z in the sense of least squares is $z = \bar{x}$.*

Hereafter, in summation notation, if the *domain* of the index of summation is well known, we may omit showing it on $\sum$. For instance, instead of writing $\sum_{i=1}^{n} x_i y_i$, we may write simply $\sum x_i y_i$. Or, we may abbreviate further and write $\sum xy$, which is read "*the sum of all products xy.*" Such abbreviations are common in statistical literature.

DEFINITION II.  *The* **variance***, $s_x^2$, of a sample $\{x_1, x_2, \cdots, x_n\}$ of values of X is the arithmetic mean of the squares of the deviations of the x's from their arithmetic mean. Or,*

$$\textbf{variance} = s_x^2 = \frac{\sum_{i=1}^{n} (x_i - \bar{x})^2}{n}.  \tag{5}$$

By reference to Theorem III, we observe that $s_x^2$ is the *minimum* of $\sum (x_i - z)^2$, divided by $n$. The positive square root, $s_x$, of $s_x^2$ is called the **standard deviation** of $\{x_1, x_2, \cdots, x_n\}$, or

$$s_x = \sqrt{\frac{\sum (x_i - \bar{x})^2}{n}}.  \tag{6}$$

NOTE 1.    Sometimes, the arithmetic mean of $\{x_1, x_2, \cdots, x_n\}$ is called simply the *mean* of $x$.

In (5), the numerator is

$$\sum_{i=1}^{n} (x_i^2 - 2\bar{x}x_i + \bar{x}^2) = \sum x_i^2 - 2\bar{x} \sum x_i + n\bar{x}^2. \tag{7}$$

Since $\bar{x} = \sum x_i/n$, then $\sum x_i = n\bar{x}$. Hence, from (7),

$$s_x^2 = \frac{\sum x_i^2 - 2n\bar{x}\bar{x} + n\bar{x}^2}{n}, \text{ or}$$

$$s_x^2 = \frac{\sum x_i^2}{n} - \bar{x}^2. \tag{8}$$

Formula (8) is convenient for calculating $s_x^2$.

In our limited consideration of samples of values of a random variable $X$, we shall employ the *variance* instead of its square root, the standard deviation.

From (5), it is seen that $s_x$, or $s_x^2$, will be *relatively small* if the deviations of the $x_i$'s from $\bar{x}$ are *small*, so that the $x_i$'s cluster closely about their mean $\bar{x}$ on a number scale. If the $x_i$'s are widely scattered about $\bar{x}$ on the number scale, then $s_x$ is relatively large. Hence, the variance of a set of numbers can be used as a measure of their dispersion.

EXAMPLE 1.    Find the mean and variance of the following set of values of $x$:    $\{6.2, 6.5, 6.4, 6.1, 6.0, 5.9, 6.3\}$.

*Solution 1.*    $\bar{x} = \dfrac{6.2 + 6.5 + 6.4 + 6.1 + 6.0 + 5.9 + 6.3}{7} = 6.2.$

2.    The values of $(x_i - \bar{x})$ for the data are

$$\{0, .3, .2, -.1, -.2, -.3, .1\}.$$

Hence, by (5),    $s_x^2 = \dfrac{0 + .09 + .04 + .01 + .04 + .09 + .01}{7} = .04.$

Then, $s_x = \sqrt{.04} = .02$, which is relatively small compared to the numbers in the data. Hence we decide that the $x$'s are clustered closely about their arithmetic mean.

## 99.    Frequency distributions of values of a variable

Suppose that the data consist of values $\{x_1, x_2, \cdots, x_k\}$ of a variable $x$, with $x_i$ repeated $f_i$ times. Such data are viewed best in tabular form as follows, and are referred to as a *frequency distribution* of values of $x$. We think of the data as a special case of the setting in Section 98, with $x_i$ *repeated* as often as

| $x =$ | $x_1$ | $x_2$ | $x_3$ | $\cdots$ | $x_k$ |
|---|---|---|---|---|---|
| FREQUENCY | $f_1$ | $f_2$ | $f_3$ | $\cdots$ | $f_k$ |

(1)

indicated by its frequency $f_i$. Thus, in the expression for the arithmetic mean $\bar{x}$ of (1), we add $x_i$ a total of $f_i$ times, which gives $f_i x_i$ below. The number of values for $x$, with $x_i$ counted $f_i$ times, is the total frequency $\sum f_i$ from (1). Hence,

$$\bar{x} = \frac{\sum f_i x_i}{\sum f_i}. \tag{2}$$

ILLUSTRATION 1.   Let the data consist of the numbers $\{5, 5, 5, 7, 7, 7, 7, 9, 6, 6\}$, or 5 with frequency $f_1 = 3$, 7 with frequency $f_2 = 4$, etc. Then, the arithmetic mean is

$$\bar{x} = \frac{3(5) + 4(7) + 9 + 2(6)}{10} = 6.4.$$

Similarly as for (2), the variance $s_x^2$ for (1) is obtained as follows:

$$s_x^2 = \frac{\sum f_i (x_i - \bar{x})^2}{\sum f_i}. \tag{3}$$

ILLUSTRATION 2.   In Illustration 1,

$$s_x^2 = \frac{3(1.4)^2 + 4(.6)^2 + (2.6)^2 + 2(.4)^2}{10} = 1.44.$$

With data $\{x_1, x_2, \cdots, x_k\}$, sometimes it is said that each $x_i$ has a certain *weight* (or, *measure of importance*) $f_i$, where $f_i$ is not necessarily an integer. Then, in (2), $\bar{x}$ is called the *weighted average* of the $x$'s.

ILLUSTRATION 3.   Suppose that the numbers in the data $\{-5, 3, 4, 7\}$ are assigned the weights $\{2, 4, 2.5, 3\}$, respectively. Then, the weighted average, $\bar{x}$, of the given numbers is

$$\bar{x} = \frac{2(-5) + 4(3) + 2.5(4) + 3(7)}{11.5} = 2.9.$$

## Exercise 63

*Find the minimum value of the function.*

1.   $5z^2 + 12z - 4.$         2.   $2z^2 - 8z + 6.$         3.   $z^2 + 10z - 5.$

*Expand the sum. Compute it if possible.*

4.   $\displaystyle\sum_{i=1}^{3} i^3.$       5.   $\displaystyle\sum_{j=1}^{5} 2j.$       6.   $\displaystyle\sum_{k=1}^{4} k^2.$       7.   $\displaystyle\sum_{h=1}^{5} (2h - 1).$

8. $\displaystyle\sum_{i=1}^{5} x_i y_i^2.$    9. $\displaystyle\sum_{i=1}^{7} x_i^2.$    10. $\displaystyle\sum_{k=1}^{4} 5k.$    11. $\displaystyle\sum_{i=1}^{4} (x_i + y_i).$

12. $\displaystyle\sum_{i=1}^{3} (2x_i - 5).$    13. $\displaystyle\sum_{k=1}^{4} (v_i + 3).$    14. $\displaystyle\sum_{i=1}^{3} (x_i + c)^2.$

15. If $\{x_1, x_2, \cdots, x_6\}$ are $\{-1, 2, 3, 5, -2, 6\}$, compute

$$\sum_{i=1}^{6} x_i; \qquad \sum_{i=1}^{6} x_i^2; \qquad \sum_{i=1}^{6} (x_i - 3)^2.$$

*Find the arithmetic mean and the variance for the given set of values of x.*
*Verify that* $\sum (x_i - \bar{x}) = 0$. *Also, use* (8) *on page* 280.

16. $\{8, 7, 4, 2, -4, 1\}$.                    17. $\{24, 27, 30, 26, 33, 34\}$.
18. $\{107, 101, 106, 99, 97, 108\}$.          19. $\{-14, -4, -10, -12, 5, -1\}$.
20. $\{0, 7, 23, 4, 63, 29\}$.                  21. $\{1, 1, 3, 3, 2, 2, 7, 7, 7, 8, 6, 9, 9\}$.

*Find the weighted average of the numbers.*

22. $(3, 5, 6, 8)$, with weights $(4, 7, 9, 15)$.
23. $(2, 3, 9, 7)$, with weights $(8, 6, 7, 5)$.
24. $(.3, .5, .4, .0, .7)$, with weights $(4, 2, 3, 6, 2)$.
25. $(2, 4, 5, 1, 8)$, with weights $(3, \frac{1}{2}, \frac{2}{3}, \frac{4}{3}, 3)$. What integral weights would give the same final result for the weighted mean?
26. Find the average height for the group of men described in the table. Use $5'$ as a *"new origin,"* and work first in inches.

| HEIGHT | 5'10" | 5'9" | 5'8" | 5'7" |
|---|---|---|---|---|
| NUMBER OF MEN | 39 | 20 | 35 | 40 |

HINT.    Total frequency is 134. With $x$ as height in inches, first let $y_i = x_i - 60$, and find all $y_i$. Then, with $n = 134$,

$$\sum_{i=1}^{n} y_i = \left[\sum_{i=1}^{n} x_i\right] - 60(134); \qquad \frac{\sum y}{134} = \frac{\sum x}{134} - 60; \qquad or \qquad \bar{y} = \bar{x} - 60.$$

Find $\bar{y}$ and then $\bar{x} = \bar{y} + 60$. This device is referred to as use of a *new origin* $(x = 60)$ because $y = 0$ when $x = 60$. Use of a new origin to reduce the size of numbers may simplify the arithmetic in problems where $\bar{x}$ or $s_x^2$ is requested for a frequency distribution.

27. Find the mean weight for the group described in the table. Use 130 pounds as a new origin.

| WEIGHT (LB.) | 125 | 130 | 135 | 140 | 145 |
|---|---|---|---|---|---|
| NUMBER OF PEOPLE | 16 | 20 | 31 | 28 | 40 |

28. Find the mean price at which wheat sold on a day when the indicated numbers of bushels were sold at the specific prices, in cents. Use 160 cents as a new origin.

| PRICE | 160 | 162 | 165 | 167 |
|---|---|---|---|---|
| BUSHELS (1,000,000's) | 25 | 21 | 18 | 14 |

29. Find the mean score on an examination in a class when the indicated numbers of students received the specified scores.

| SCORE | 60 | 65 | 70 | 75 | 80 | 85 | 90 |
|---|---|---|---|---|---|---|---|
| NUMBER OF STUDENTS | 25 | 21 | 18 | 28 | 31 | 16 | 11 |

## 100.  Least square solution of systems of linear equations

In the system of equations

$$(I) \begin{cases} a_1x + b_1y = c_1, & (1) \\ a_2x + b_2y = c_2, & (2) \\ a_3x + b_3y = c_3, & (3) \end{cases}$$

in the variables $x$ and $y$, suppose that the constants $\{a_i, b_i, c_i\}$ are chosen at random. Then, it would be very unusual if (I) had a solution. Thus, as a rule there would be a single solution for system [(1), (2)], obtained as in Chapter 10, but it would be an accident if this solution also satisfied (3). That is, a system of *three* linear equations in *two* variables usually is inconsistent. Similarly, a system of $k$ equations in $n$ variables as a rule is inconsistent if $k > n$.

Let us refer to (I) as if it involved $n$ equations in $x$ and $y$ with $n > 2$, and assume that (I) is inconsistent. Then, although there is no pair $(x = u, y = v)$ which satisfies all equations of (I) *exactly*, we propose finding $(u, v)$ so that $(x = u, y = v)$ will be the "*best possible approximation*" to a solution of (I) where "*best*" must be defined.

For any values of $(x, y)$ in (I), let

$$r_1 = a_1x + b_1y - c_1; \quad r_2 = a_2x + b_2y - c_2; \quad r_3 = a_3x + b_3y - c_3. \quad (4)$$

If a pair $(x, y)$ is a solution of (I), then $r_1 = r_2 = r_3 = 0$. Otherwise, we shall consider $\{r_1, r_2, r_3\}$ as a set of measures of the extent to which the pair $(x, y)$ *fails* to satisfy the equations in (I). We shall call $\{r_1, r_2, r_3\}$ the *residuals* for (I) corresponding to the pair $(x, y)$ used in (4). The following definition of a "*best approximation to a solution*" of (I) is designed to produce residuals whose absolute values as a whole are small. In (4), the residuals are seen to be functions of the variables $(x, y)$.

DEFINITION III.  *A pair $(x = \alpha, y = \beta)$ is called a best approxima-tion "in the sense of least squares" to a solution of a system of n linear equations in x and y in case the sum of the squares of the residuals has its least value when $(x = \alpha, y = \beta)$.*

Any system (I), with $n$ equations, as met in this text will have a single best solution $(\alpha, \beta)$ as just defined, and then will be called THE solution of (I) in the sense of least squares.

EXAMPLE 1.    Solve (I) in the sense of least squares.

*Solution.    1.*    Let $f(x, y) = r_1^2 + r_2^2 + r_3^2$. From (4),

$$r_i^2 = a_i^2 x^2 + b_i^2 y^2 + c_i^2 - 2a_i c_i x - 2b_i c_i y + 2a_i b_i xy, \qquad (5)$$

where we have $i = 1, 2,$ and 3 from (4). On adding in (5) for $i = 1, 2,$ and 3, we obtain

$$f(x, y) =$$
$$x^2 \sum a_i^2 + y^2 \sum b_i^2 + \sum c_i^2 - 2x \sum a_i c_i - 2y \sum b_i c_i + 2xy \sum a_i b_i. \qquad (6)$$

We wish to find a pair of numbers $(x, y)$ so that $f(x, y)$ will have its *least* value (if there is such a value).

2.    In $f(x, y)$, for the moment think of $y$ as a *constant*. Then $f(x, y)$ is a quadratic function of $x$ as the only variable:

$$f(x, y) = x^2 \sum a^2 + 2x(y \sum ab - \sum ac) + (\textit{other terms}), \qquad (7)$$

where the "*other terms*" do not involve $x$. By Theorem I on page 276, $f(x, y)$ has its minimum value just when

$$x = -\frac{y \sum ab - \sum ac}{\sum a^2}, \qquad \text{or} \qquad x \sum a^2 + y \sum ab = \sum ac. \qquad (8)$$

3.    Similarly, if $x$ is held fast with a constant value, $f(x, y)$ becomes a quadratic function of $y$, and assumes its minimum value just when

$$y = -\frac{x \sum ab - \sum bc}{\sum b^2}, \qquad \text{or} \qquad x \sum ab + y \sum b^2 = \sum bc. \qquad (9)$$

Hence, if $(x, y)$ is the solution of (I) in the sense of least squares, it is *necessary* for $(x, y)$ to satisfy both of [(8), (9)], or $(x, y)$ should be a solution of the system

$$\text{(II)} \begin{cases} x \sum a^2 + y \sum ab = \sum ac, & (10) \\ x \sum ab + y \sum b^2 = \sum bc. & (11) \end{cases}$$

*4.* We announce now that the solution $(x = \alpha, y = \beta)$, *if* it exists, for (II) will be called the solution of (I) *in the sense of least squares.* We have only proved that, **IF** such a solution of (I) exists, then we obtain $(x = \alpha, y = \beta)$ by solving (II). We should also prove that any solution of (II) **IS** the solution of (I) as stated. The proof of this *"sufficiency"* of (II) as a condition for the least square solution requires use of calculus beyond the scope of this text.

With (II) accepted as the defining equations for the solution of (I) in the sense of least squares, we have the following routine.

**Summary.** *Solution of a system of n linear equations in m variables, where* $n > m$.

(I)    *Let x be any one of the variables. Multiply both sides of each equation by the coefficient of x in it, and add the corresponding sides of all of the equations. Call the result the* **normal equation** *corresponding to x. In this manner, obtain a normal equation corresponding to each of the m variables.*

(II)   *Solve the system of m normal linear equations in the m variables, to obtain the solution of the given system in the sense of least squares.*

The student should verify that (10) is the normal equation for $x$ as obtained from (I), and (11) is the normal equation for $y$.

NOTE 1.    A more advanced discussion would show that the determinant of the matrix of coefficients of $x$ and $y$ in (II) is not zero, and hence (II) has a unique solution if the set $\{a_1, a_2, \cdots\}$ is not proportional to $\{b_1, b_2, \cdots\}$.

EXAMPLE 2.    Solve for $x$ and $y$ by the method of least squares.

$$\text{(III)} \begin{cases} x + 2y = 10, & (12) \\ -x + y = 4, & (13) \\ -2x + 6y = 7. & (14) \end{cases}$$

*Solution.    1.* Multiply by 1 in (12), by $-1$ in (13), by $-2$ in (14), and then add corresponding sides, to find the normal equation corresponding to $x$:

$$\left.\begin{array}{l} x + 2y = 10. \\ x - y = -4. \\ 4x - 12y = -14. \end{array}\right\} \quad \text{(add):} \quad 6x - 11y = -8. \quad (15)$$

Similarly, the normal equation for $y$ is

$$-11x + 41y = 66. \quad (16)$$

*2.* The solution of system [(15), (16)], as obtained by use of determinants, is $(x = 3.18, y = 2.46)$, which is the solution of (III) in the sense of least squares.

NOTE 2.   In any application of the Summary, it is essential *not to multiply any one of the equations by a constant k where $|k| \neq 1$*. It can be verified that multiplication in any equation by $k$ with $|k| \neq 1$ would be analogous to *weighting* this equation by a weight $|k|$ whereas each unchanged equation, in a sense, has only weight 1. Thus, no given equation may be cleared of fractions before applying the Summary. Hence, in solving a system of linear equations by the method of least squares, we take the equations unaltered, except possibly by transposing terms. In a future geometrical example involving curve fitting, it will be seen that the preceding restriction is natural and essential for the application.

## Exercise 64

*Solve for the variables by the method of least squares.*

1.   $3x - y = 3,$
     $x - y = -5,$
     $x + 2y = 6.$

2.   $-4x + 3y = 4,$
     $2x - y = 5,$
     $3x - 2y = 3.$

3.   $2x + 3z = 2,$
     $x - 3z = 4,$
     $3x = 7,$
     $2x + 3z = -3.$

4.   $3x - 2y = 4,$
     $2x + 5y = 2,$
     $-x + 3y = 5,$
     $-2x + y = -4.$

5.   $2x - y + 3z = -1,$
     $x + 2y - z = 3,$
     $3x - y + 2z = 5,$
     $-x + 3y - z = -4,$
     $2x - y = 5.$

6.   $2u - v + 3w = 2,$
     $u + 2v - w = 4,$
     $-u + 3v + 2w = 5,$
     $3u - v = -2,$
     $-2u - 3v + 4w = -3.$

## 101.   Curve fitting in the sense of least squares

Consider $n$ given points

$$(x_1, y_1), (x_2, y_2), \cdots, (x_n, y_n), \tag{1}$$

in an $xy$-plane. Think of (1) as giving the values, $\{y_i\}$, of an unknown function of $x$ for the indicated values $\{x_i\}$ of $x$. Then, in a wide range of applications in the physical and social sciences, the following type of problem arises.

*To obtain a function $f(x)$ of some specified type so that the graph of $y = f(x)$ will be the "best" fitting curve of its type for the given points.*

In the typical case, as in this section, "*best*" is interpreted to mean "*best in the sense of least square approximation.*" We shall define the sense involved, and then consider the method in detail for the important case where the type function $f(x)$ is linear. If a best fitting function $f(x)$ is determined, then the relation $y = f(x)$ may be referred to as an *empirical formula* for $y$ in terms of $x$.

**DEFINITION IV.**  *To say that an equation $y = f(x)$ of a specified type defines a "best fitting curve for a set of points (1) in an xy-plane" has the following meaning:*

> *The sum of the squares of the distances measured parallel to the y-axis between the given points and the graph of $y = f(x)$ has the least value possible with a function f of the specified type.* (2)

In Definition IV, we may refer to $f(x)$ as the *best fitting function* for the values of $y$ given in (1). In any application of Definition IV in this text, we shall be led to a single function $f(x)$, which then will be referred to as THE best fitting function of its type *"in the sense of least squares."* Usually, we shall omit the reference to least squares.

We proceed to discuss the linear case of Definition IV, that is, the case where $f(x) = ax + b$, with $a$ and $b$ as constants and $a \neq 0$. If $n = 2$ in (1), an exact fit is possible if $x_1 \neq x_2$, where the result $y = ax + b$ would be found by use of the point-slope form for a line on page 56. Now assume that $n > 2$. An exact fit for the points in (1) by use of $y = ax + b$ would be possible only under the unusual circumstances where the points are *collinear*, which we assume is not the case. Let us think of $a$ and $b$ having any values, with the graph, $L$, of $y = ax + b$ as shown in Figure 86, and with $P_i : (x_i, y_i)$ somewhere in the plane. When $x = x_i$, let $\hat{y}_i = ax_i + b$ represent the ordinate on $L$, with $Q : (x_i, \hat{y}_i)$ as the corresponding point on $L$ having the same abscissa as $P_i$. Let $d_i = |\overline{P_i Q_i}|$. Then we have

$$d_i = |y_i - \hat{y}_i|, \qquad where \qquad \hat{y}_i = ax_i + b. \qquad (3)$$

In (3), $d_i$ is a function of $a$ and $b$.

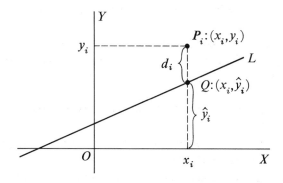

Fig. 86

The defining condition (2) specifies that the following function $G(a, b)$ should be a *minimum* when $(a, b)$ have the values which produce the best fitting function $f(x)$:

$$G(a, b) = (y_1 - \hat{y}_1)^2 + (y_2 - \hat{y}_2)^2 + \cdots + (y_n - \hat{y}_n)^2. \tag{4}$$

Since $\hat{y}_i = ax_i + b$, from (4) we obtain $y_i - \hat{y}_i = y_i - ax_i - b$, and

$$G(a, b) =$$
$$(y_1 - ax_1 - b)^2 + (y_2 - ax_2 - b)^2 + \cdots + (y_n - ax_n - b)^2. \tag{5}$$

Now consider the following companion details, which it is natural to think of in connection with the problem being considered. We wish the line $L$, which is the graph of $y = ax + b$, to yield a value for $y$ as near as possible to $y_1$ when $x = x_1$. If $P_1:(x_1, y_1)$ *were on* $L$, then $(x = x_1, y = y_1)$ would satisfy the equation $y = ax + b$, or $y_1 = ax_1 + b$. Similarly, $y_i = ax_i + b$ would be true *if* $P_i:(x_i, y_i)$ *were on* $L$. The most desirable result would be that *all* points in (1) would be on $L$, or that the following system of $n$ equations would be satisfied:

$$(\text{I}) \begin{cases} y_1 = ax_1 + b, \\ y_2 = ax_2 + b, \\ \quad\vdots \\ y_n = ax_n + b. \end{cases}$$

It is admitted that, with $n > 2$, system (I) *cannot be expected to be consistent.* However, we may propose obtaining *the best solution of* (I) *for* $(a, b)$ *in the sense of least squares.* This solution, as defined in Section 100, yields values for $(a, b)$ such that the sum of the squares of the residuals $\{r_i\}$ is a minimum, where

$$r_i = y_i - ax_i - b. \tag{6}$$

*Notice, now, that* $\sum r_i^2$ *is precisely* $G(a, b)$ *in* (5). Hence we reach the following conclusion, which may be thought of as a fortunate coincidence associated with $G(a, b)$.

> *The values of a and b in the best fitting line* $y = ax + b$ *for the n points in* (1) *form the solution in the sense of least squares for system* (I). $\qquad$ (7)

**Summary.** *To obtain the best fitting line* $y = ax + b$ *for a given set of n points in the xy-plane.*

(I) *Substitute the coordinates of each point for* $(x, y)$ *in* $y = ax + b$, *to obtain n linear equations in the unknown numbers a and b.*

(II) *Solve the preceding system of equations for* $(a, b)$ *by the method of least squares.*

EXAMPLE 1.   Find the best fitting line $y = ax + b$ for the points $\{(3, 1), (5, 2), (6, 5)\}$.

*Solution.   1.*   On substituting $(x = 3, y = 1)$, $(x = 5, y = 2)$, and $(x = 6, y = 5)$ in $y = ax + b$, the following system of three equations is obtained.

$$(\text{II}) \begin{cases} 1 = 3a + b, \\ 2 = 5a + b, \\ 5 = 6a + b. \end{cases}$$

We solve (II) for $a$ and $b$ by the method of least squares.

2.   The normal equations for $x$ and for $y$, respectively, as obtained from (II) are as follows.

$$(\text{III}) \begin{cases} 70a + 14b = 43, \\ 14a + \phantom{0}3b = 8. \end{cases}$$

The solution of (III) is $(a = 1.21, b = -3.00)$. Hence an equation for the best fitting line is $y = 1.21x - 3.00$. The line, $L$, and the given points are shown in Figure 87.

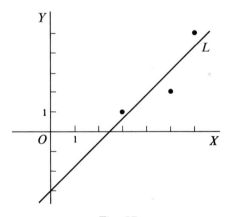

*Fig. 87*

Suppose that the type form for $y = f(x)$ in (2) is $y = ax^2 + bx + c$, where $a \neq 0$. Then, a best fitting parabola is described by Definition IV. To find such a curve, the routine of the Summary would be changed by use of $y = ax^2 + bx + c$ instead of $y = ax + b$. Then, for $n$ given points in (1), a system of $n$ linear equations in the unknown numbers $(a, b, c)$ would be obtained. The solution of this system in the sense of least squares, as in Section 100, then would give the coefficients $\{a, b, c\}$ for the parabola which gives the best fit for the given points in (1). Similarly we could consider obtaining the best fitting polynomial $f(x) = a_0 + a_1x + \cdots + a_kx^k$ of degree $k$ for $n$ given points. We shall restrict our applications to the case where $f(x) = ax + b$.

## 102.    Trend line for a time series

We refer to a set of statistical data as a **time series** if the data consist of the values of some variable $y$ for a set of values of the time, $t$, where $t$ is the number of time units counting from some specified instant.

ILLUSTRATION 1.    The first line of the following table gives the total amount of life insurance, $y$, in dollars, in force on the lives of residents of the United States in various years, $t$. The unit for $y$ is \$10,000,000,000, and for $t$ is one year, with $t = 0$ as the year 1957. Thus, with $t = 2$, the table shows that the total insurance in force in 1959 was \$540,000,000,000, with accuracy to two digits. A graph of this time series consists of the eleven black dots in Figure 88. We recognize that $y$ is a function of $t$, say $y = f(t)$, where the domain of $t$ consists of all real numbers, negative in the past and positive after 1957, on an interval whose length is of no importance here. The function values in the table are merely a convenient sample of the set of *all* values of $f$ because, at any instant, the assets have a certain size. Hence, it would be proper to draw a continuous curve through the eleven black dots in Figure 88 as the graph of $y = f(t)$, although this would be inconvenient for present purposes.

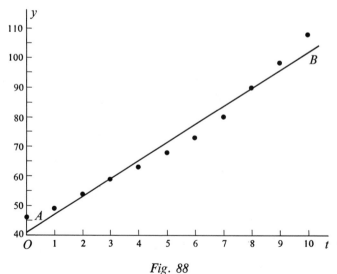

*Fig. 88*

| $y =$ | 46 | 49 | 54 | 59 | 63 | 68 | 73 | 80 | 90 | 98 | 108 |
|-------|----|----|----|----|----|----|----|----|----|----|-----|
| $t =$ | 0 | 1 | 2 | 3 | 4 | 5 | 6 | 7 | 8 | 9 | 10 |

Any time series is a set of values of some function, $f$, of the time $t$. Thus, in a time series, we deal with an equation $y = f(t)$, where the values of $f$ are given for a sequence of $n$ values of $t$, say $(t_1, t_2, t_3, \cdots, t_n)$, which we may assume are arranged in order of increasing magnitude. If we let $y_i = f(t_i)$, any time series can be defined by a table of corresponding values of $y$ and $t$, as follows. An extremely large percentage of the statistical data of economics and other social sciences arises in this form.

| $y =$ | $y_1$ | $y_2$ | $y_3$ | $\cdots$ | $y_n$ |
|-------|-------|-------|-------|----------|-------|
| $t =$ | $t_1$ | $t_2$ | $t_3$ | $\cdots$ | $t_n$ |

(1)

**DEFINITION V.**   *The* **trend line** *for a time series* (1) *is the line of best fit in a ty-plane for the graph of the time series.*

ILLUSTRATION 2.   In Figure 88, line $AB$ is the trend line for the time series of Illustration 1. The line was found by use of the method of Section 101. The student will obtain this trend line in a problem of the next exercise. An equation for $AB$ is $y = 6.05t + 41.4$.

The trend line for a time series $y = f(t)$ frequently is used to forecast the values of $f(t)$ at *future* dates. Naturally, the accuracy of such a forecast depends on how closely the trend line approximates the data. Use of past experience to forecast future values of a variable is spoken of as **extrapolation**.

EXAMPLE 1.   By use of the trend line of Illustration 2, estimate the amount of insurance that will be in force in 1970.

*Solution.*   For 1970, $t = 13$. Hence, we use $t = 13$ in $y = 6.05t + 41.4$ from Illustration 2, and obtain $y = 13(6.05) + 41.4 = 120$.

If the trend line provides a good fit for the points representing a time series, it is said to exhibit a *linear trend*. If this is not the case, it may be possible to obtain a good fit for the graph of the series by use of a curve which is *not* a line. This possibility gives rise to a search for a curve of best fit for the time series where the equation of the curve, $y = f(t)$, involves a function $f$ of any variety* which the investigator may choose to use.

* For curve fitting by use of power and exponential functions, see pages 413–417, in *College Algebra*, 4th *Edition*, by William L. Hart; D. C. Heath and Company, publishers.

## Exercise 65

*Find the best fitting line y = ax + b for the points (x, y).*

1.

| x = | 3 | 4 | 7 | 8 |
|---|---|---|---|---|
| y = | 2 | 5 | 4 | 8 |

2.

| x = | −3 | 0 | 2 | −2 |
|---|---|---|---|---|
| y = | 1 | 2 | 5 | −2 |

3.

| x = | 2 | −3 | 0 | 5 | 5 |
|---|---|---|---|---|---|
| y = | −1 | −2 | 1 | 2 | 4 |

4.

| x = | 0 | −2 | 3 | 3 | 1 |
|---|---|---|---|---|---|
| y = | −2 | −2 | 3 | 1 | 1 |

*Find the trend line for the time series.*

5. The data in Illustration 1 on page 290.
6. The table gives the density of population, *y* people, per square mile of land area in the United States in various years, *t*, where the unit for *t* is 10 years, with 1860 as $t = 0$. From the line obtained, estimate the density of population in 1970.

| y = | 11 | 13 | 17 | 21 | 26 | 31 | 36 | 41 | 44 | 51 | 60 |
|---|---|---|---|---|---|---|---|---|---|---|---|
| t = | 0 | 1 | 2 | 3 | 4 | 5 | 6 | 7 | 8 | 9 | 10 |

7. Statistics gathered by the Bureau of Labor Statistics of the United States Department of Labor show the following average weekly earnings to the nearest dollar, *y*, of manufacturing workers in various years, *t*. The unit for *t* is one year and 1958 is $t = 0$. From the line obtained, estimate the weekly earnings in 1968.

| y = | 83 | 88 | 90 | 92 | 97 | 99 | 103 | 108 | 112 | 115 |
|---|---|---|---|---|---|---|---|---|---|---|
| t = | 0 | 1 | 2 | 3 | 4 | 5 | 6 | 7 | 8 | 9 |

8. The table gives the Consumer's Price Index Number, *y*, of the United States Department of Labor to the nearest unit for a sequence of years, *t*. The unit for *t* is 3 years, and 1940 is $t = 0$. From the line obtained, estimate *y* for 1970.

| y = | 49 | 60 | 68 | 83 | 92 | 93 | 101 | 104 | 108 | 116 |
|---|---|---|---|---|---|---|---|---|---|---|
| t = | 0 | 1 | 2 | 3 | 4 | 5 | 6 | 7 | 8 | 9 |

9.  The table gives the number of bachelor's degrees, $y$ thousands, conferred by colleges of the United States in certain years, $t$, where 1954 is $t = 0$ and the unit for $t$ is one year.

| $y =$ | 293 | 311 | 366 | 395 | 420 | 502 | 556 |
|-------|-----|-----|-----|-----|-----|-----|-----|
| $t =$ | 0   | 2   | 4   | 6   | 8   | 10  | 12  |

10. The table gives the average number, $y$, in 1,000,000's, of employees in nonagricultural establishments in the United States for various years, $t$. The unit for $t$ is two years, and 1952 is $t = 0$.

| $y =$ | 49 | 49 | 52 | 51 | 54 | 56 | 58 | 64 |
|-------|----|----|----|----|----|----|----|----|
| $t =$ | 0  | 1  | 2  | 3  | 4  | 5  | 6  | 7  |

11. The table shows the median annual income, $y$, in \$100's, for families in the United States for certain years, $t$. The unit for $t$ is one year and 1957 is $t = 0$.

| $y =$ | 50 | 51 | 54 | 56 | 57 | 60 | 62 | 66 | 70 | 74 |
|-------|----|----|----|----|----|----|----|----|----|----|
| $t =$ | 0  | 1  | 2  | 3  | 4  | 5  | 6  | 7  | 8  | 9  |

12. Find the best fitting parabola $y = ax^2 + bx + c$ for the set of points. Plot them and the resulting parabola on the same coordinate system.

| $x =$ | $-3$ | $-1$ | 1 | 3 | 4 | 6 | 7 |
|-------|------|------|---|---|---|---|---|
| $y =$ | 3    | 2    | 1 | 2 | 5 | 3 | 6 |

## 103.  Introduction to correlation

As the basis for a problem, let the data be the following set of corresponding values of two related variables

$$(x_1, y_1), (x_2, y_2), \cdots, (x_n, y_n), \tag{1}$$

with arithmetic means $(\bar{x}, \bar{y})$, and standard deviations $s_x$ and $s_y$. Assume that $s_x \neq 0$ and $s_y \neq 0$. From the definition of the variance $s_x^2$ in (5) on page 279, the conditions $s_x \neq 0$ and $s_y \neq 0$ imply that the $x$'s are not identical and the $y$'s are not identical. Let the data (1) be plotted as points in an $xy$-plane.

DEFINITION VI.   *The **line of regression of** y **on** x is the best fitting line with the equation $y = ax + b$ for the points (1) in the sense of least squares, with distances from the line measured perpendicular to the x-axis. The **line of regression of** x **on** y is the best fitting line $x = cy + d$ for the points (1) in the sense of least squares, with distances from the line measured perpendicular to the y-axis.*

By Definition VI, the line of regression of $y$ on $x$ is the best fitting line which is found by applying the method of Section 101 to the data (1). The line of regression of $x$ on $y$ for (1) is the line found by applying Section 101 with the roles of $x$ and $y$ interchanged.

From Section 101, it is verified that the coefficients $(a, b)$ in the line of regression of $y$ on $x$ are the least square solution of the system (I) below. The coefficients $(c, d)$ in the line of regression of $x$ on $y$ are the least square solution of system (II) below.

$$(\text{I}) \begin{cases} y_1 = ax_1 + b, \\ y_2 = ax_2 + b, \\ \quad\vdots \\ y_n = ax_n + b. \end{cases} \qquad (\text{II}) \begin{cases} x_1 = cy_1 + d, \\ x_2 = cy_2 + d, \\ \quad\vdots \\ x_n = cy_n + d. \end{cases}$$

From (I) and (II), separately, the systems of normal equations whose solutions give $(a, b)$, and $(c, d)$ are as follows:

*Line of regression of y on x,*        $y = ax + b$:

$$(\text{III}) \begin{cases} \sum xy = a \sum x^2 + b \sum x, & (2) \\ \sum y = a \sum x + nb. & (3) \end{cases}$$

*Line of regression of x on y,*        $x = cy + d$:

$$(\text{IV}) \begin{cases} \sum xy = c \sum y^2 + d \sum y, & (4) \\ \sum x = c \sum y + nd. & (5) \end{cases}$$

EXAMPLE 1.   Find the lines of regression for the following data:

| $x =$ | $-2$ | $-1$ | $-1$ | 0 | 4 | 2 | 3 | 4 | 5 | 6 |
|-------|------|------|------|---|---|---|---|---|---|---|
| $y =$ | 5 | 5 | 3 | 4 | 2 | 4 | 2 | 1 | 1 | 3 |

*Solution.    1.*   With $n = 10$ in (2)–(5), the following sums are needed, as obtained from the data.

$$\sum x = 20; \quad \sum y = 30; \quad \sum xy = 31; \quad \sum x^2 = 112; \quad \sum y^2 = 110.$$

Equations (2)–(5) yield the following systems.

$$(V) \begin{cases} 31 = 112a + 20b, \\ 30 = 20a + 10b. \end{cases} \qquad (VI) \begin{cases} 31 = 110c + 30d, \\ 20 = 30c + 10d. \end{cases}$$

2.   From (V), $(a = -.40, b = 3.80)$. From (VI), $(c = -1.45, d = 6.35)$. Hence we obtain the following lines:

*Line of regression, y on x:* $\qquad\qquad y = -.40x + 3.80.$ $\qquad\qquad$ (6)

*Line of regression, x on y:* $\qquad\qquad x = -1.45y + 6.35.$ $\qquad\qquad$ (7)

The graphs of (6) and (7) are shown in Figure 89, with the data marked by black dots.

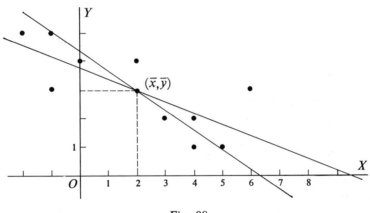

*Fig. 89*

THEOREM IV.   *The lines of regression for data* (1) *intersect at the point* $(\bar{x}, \bar{y})$ (*which we shall call the* **mean point** *for the data*).

*Proof.*   On dividing by $n$ in (3), we obtain

$$\frac{\Sigma y}{n} = a \frac{\Sigma x}{n} + b, \qquad or \qquad \bar{y} = a\bar{x} + b. \qquad (8)$$

Hence $(x = \bar{x}, y = \bar{y})$ satisfies the equation $y = ax + b$ of the line of regression of $y$ on $x$. Similarly, on dividing by $n$ in (5), we obtain $\bar{x} = c\bar{y} + d$, so that $(x = \bar{x}, y = \bar{y})$ satisfies the equation of the line of regression of $x$ on $y$. Hence, the lines of regression intersect at $(\bar{x}, \bar{y})$.

ILLUSTRATION 1.   In Example 1, $\bar{x} = 2$ and $\bar{y} = 3$. In Figure 89, the lines of regression intersect at $(2, 3)$.

NOTE 1.   A third line of best fit can be defined for (1) as follows. Let $L$ be called a *geometrically best fitting line*, in the sense of least squares, for the points (1) in case the sum of the squares of the *perpendicular distances* from $L$ to the points is a minimum. By somewhat elaborate details it can be proved that $L$ exists, passes through the mean point $(\bar{x}, \bar{y})$, and lies in the smaller angles formed by the lines of regression.

Figure 89 exhibits a special case of the fact that, usually, the lines of regression do not coincide. Also, since a line of regression is a line of best fit, in one of two senses, it is clear that, if all points in (1) lie on a line $L$, then $L$ is the line of regression of $y$ on $x$, and also of $x$ on $y$. In this case, there exist constants $\{u, v, w\}$ such that each point $(x_i, y_i)$ of (1) is on the line $ux + vy = w$. Then, it is said that the data exhibit *perfect correlation* between $x$ and $y$.

As a measure of the extent to which data (1) approximate the ideal of perfect correlation, the following number $r$ is introduced:

$$r = \frac{\sum (x_i - \bar{x})(y_i - \bar{y})}{\sqrt{[\sum (x_i - \bar{x})^2][\sum (y_i - \bar{y})^2]}}. \tag{9}$$

In (9), $r$ is called the **coefficient of correlation** of $x$ and $y$. Let $nW_y$ be *the sum of the squares of the distances measured parallel to the y-axis between the points* (1) *and the line of regression of y on x.* Let $nW_x$ be *the sum of the squares of the distances measured parallel to the x-axis between the points* (1) *and the line of regression of x on y.* Then, in statistics, it is proved that

$$W_y = s_y^2(1 - r^2); \qquad W_x = s_x^2(1 - r^2). \tag{10}$$

THEOREM V.  *For any data* (1),               $|r| \leq 1.$

*Proof.* By definition, $W_y \geq 0$ or $s_y^2(1 - r^2) \geq 0$. Hence $1 - r^2 \geq 0$. Or, $r^2 \leq 1$ and thus $|r| \leq 1$. Another proof not based on (10) is suggested in a supplementary problem of the next exercise.

Note that $W_y$ and $W_x$ are natural measures of the closeness with which the respective lines of regression fit the points of (1). When $|r|$ is small, then $W_y$ and $W_x$ are near their largest possible values. When $|r|$ is near 1, then $W_y$ and $W_x$ are relatively near zero, and hence the data closely approximate perfect correlation. Our preceding remarks lead us to the following conclusion.

*The value of r for a set of data* (1) *may be taken as a measure of the extent to which the data satisfy a linear relation ux + vy = w.*

With $r = \pm 1$, there is perfect correlation. When $|r|$ is small, there is a pronounced departure from perfect correlation.

In a problem of the next exercise, suggestions are given for proving the following facts:

*The slope of the line of regression of y on x is $rs_y/s_x$, and of x on y is $s_y/rs_x$.*

If $r > 0$, it is said that there is *positive correlation* between $x$ and $y$. Then the lines of regression slope upward to the right, and there is a tendency for $y$ to increase if $x$ increases in (1). If $r < 0$, it is said that there is *negative correlation* between $x$ and $y$. Then the lines of regression slope downward to the right, and there is a tendency for $y$ to decrease if $x$ increases in (1).

NOTE 2.   Brief methods for computation of $r$ are developed in statistics. Also, the computation can be programmed conveniently on modern computing machines. In the next exercise, the problems are limited as to data in order to avoid excessive arithmetic in the absence of computing devices. To obtain $r$ by use of (9), first compute $\bar{x}$ and $\bar{y}$; then tabulate all of $(x_i - \bar{x})$, $(y_i - \bar{y})$, their squares, and their product.

ILLUSTRATION 2.   In Example 1, $r = -.76$, showing negative correlation.

## Exercise 66

*Find the lines of regression and the coefficient of correlation for the data. Show the points and the lines of regression in a figure. Verify that the lines intersect at the mean point.*

1–4.   The data in Problems 1–4, respectively, of Exercise 65 on page 292. Notice that one of the lines of regression was found in Exercise 65.

5.

| $x =$ | $-6$ | $-4$ | $-1$ | 2 | 4 | 5 | 5 | 7 | 6 |
|-------|------|------|------|---|---|---|---|---|---|
| $y =$ | $-2$ | $-3$ | $-1$ | 2 | 3 | 2 | 4 | 6 | 7 |

*Suppose that, in two examinations in a course, students* I–X *received the indicated scores. Compute the coefficient of correlation of the grades on the two examinations. Were the grades positively correlated, with a significantly large coefficient of correlation?*

6.

| STUDENT | I | II | III | IV | V | VI | VII | VIII | IX | X |
|---------|---|----|----|----|----|----|----|------|----|----|
| EXAM. 1 | 76 | 83 | 62 | 73 | 61 | 60 | 81 | 66 | 67 | 71 |
| EXAM. 2 | 91 | 92 | 72 | 82 | 71 | 68 | 96 | 74 | 78 | 86 |

7.

| STUDENT | I | II | III | IV | V | VI | VII | VIII | IX | X |
|---------|---|----|----|----|----|----|----|------|----|----|
| EXAM. 1 | 80 | 78 | 68 | 79 | 94 | 76 | 98 | 85 | 72 | 90 |
| EXAM. 2 | 93 | 62 | 69 | 62 | 59 | 48 | 68 | 60 | 65 | 74 |

★8.  In the line of regression of $y$ on $x$ found on page 294, prove that $a = rs_y/s_x$ by expanding the sum in the numerator of (9) on page 296, and using (5) and (8) of Section 98. Similarly, prove that $c = rs_x/s_y$ in the line of regression of $x$ on $y$ on page 294.

★9.  With the data in (1) on page 293, let

$$H(\lambda) = \sum [(x_i - \bar{x}) + \lambda(y_i - \bar{y})]^2.$$

Assume that $(x_i - \bar{x}) + \lambda(y_i - \bar{y}) \neq 0$ with any value of $\lambda$, for all values of $i$. Then, notice that, for the $n$ assigned points, the equation $H(\lambda) = 0$ has no real solution. Use this fact and the quadratic formula to prove that

$$[\sum (x_i - \bar{x})(y_i - \bar{y})]^2 < [\sum (x_i - \bar{x})^2][\sum (y_i - \bar{y})^2],$$

and then prove that $r^2 < 1$. Also, if $(x_i - \bar{x}) + \lambda(y_i - \bar{y}) = 0$ for some value of $\lambda$, and all values of $i$, prove that $|r| = 1$.

TABLE I—POWERS AND ROOTS    *299*

| No. | Sq. | Sq. Root | Cube | Cube Root | No. | Sq. | Sq. Root | Cube | Cube Root |
|---|---|---|---|---|---|---|---|---|---|
| 1 | 1 | 1.000 | 1 | 1.000 | 51 | 2,601 | 7.141 | 132,651 | 3.708 |
| 2 | 4 | 1.414 | 8 | 1.260 | 52 | 2,704 | 7.211 | 140,608 | 3.733 |
| 3 | 9 | 1.732 | 27 | 1.442 | 53 | 2,809 | 7.280 | 148,877 | 3.756 |
| 4 | 16 | 2.000 | 64 | 1.587 | 54 | 2,916 | 7.348 | 157,464 | 3.780 |
| 5 | 25 | 2.236 | 125 | 1.710 | 55 | 3,025 | 7.416 | 166,375 | 3.803 |
| 6 | 36 | 2.449 | 216 | 1.817 | 56 | 3,136 | 7.483 | 175,616 | 3.826 |
| 7 | 49 | 2.646 | 343 | 1.913 | 57 | 3,249 | 7.550 | 185,193 | 3.848 |
| 8 | 64 | 2.828 | 512 | 2.000 | 58 | 3,364 | 7.616 | 195,112 | 3.871 |
| 9 | 81 | 3.000 | 729 | 2.080 | 59 | 3,481 | 7.681 | 205,379 | 3.893 |
| 10 | 100 | 3.162 | 1,000 | 2.154 | 60 | 3,600 | 7.746 | 216,000 | 3.915 |
| 11 | 121 | 3.317 | 1,331 | 2.224 | 61 | 3,721 | 7.810 | 226,981 | 3.936 |
| 12 | 144 | 3.464 | 1,728 | 2.289 | 62 | 3,844 | 7.874 | 238,328 | 3.958 |
| 13 | 169 | 3.606 | 2,197 | 2.351 | 63 | 3,969 | 7.937 | 250,047 | 3.979 |
| 14 | 196 | 3.742 | 2,744 | 2.410 | 64 | 4,096 | 8.000 | 262,144 | 4.000 |
| 15 | 225 | 3.873 | 3,375 | 2.466 | 65 | 4,225 | 8.062 | 274,625 | 4.021 |
| 16 | 256 | 4.000 | 4,096 | 2.520 | 66 | 4,356 | 8.124 | 287,496 | 4.041 |
| 17 | 289 | 4.123 | 4,913 | 2.571 | 67 | 4,489 | 8.185 | 300,763 | 4.062 |
| 18 | 324 | 4.243 | 5,832 | 2.621 | 68 | 4,624 | 8.246 | 314,432 | 4.082 |
| 19 | 361 | 4.359 | 6,859 | 2.668 | 69 | 4,761 | 8.307 | 328,509 | 4.102 |
| 20 | 400 | 4.472 | 8,000 | 2.714 | 70 | 4,900 | 8.367 | 343,000 | 4.121 |
| 21 | 441 | 4.583 | 9,261 | 2.759 | 71 | 5,041 | 8.426 | 357,911 | 4.141 |
| 22 | 484 | 4.690 | 10,648 | 2.802 | 72 | 5,184 | 8.485 | 373,248 | 4.160 |
| 23 | 529 | 4.796 | 12,167 | 2.844 | 73 | 5,329 | 8.544 | 389,017 | 4.179 |
| 24 | 576 | 4.899 | 13,824 | 2.884 | 74 | 5,476 | 8.602 | 405,224 | 4.198 |
| 25 | 625 | 5.000 | 15,625 | 2.924 | 75 | 5,625 | 8.660 | 421,875 | 4.217 |
| 26 | 676 | 5.099 | 17,576 | 2.962 | 76 | 5,776 | 8.718 | 438,976 | 4.236 |
| 27 | 729 | 5.196 | 19,683 | 3.000 | 77 | 5,929 | 8.775 | 456,533 | 4.254 |
| 28 | 784 | 5.291 | 21,952 | 3.037 | 78 | 6,084 | 8.832 | 474,552 | 4.273 |
| 29 | 841 | 5.385 | 24,389 | 3.072 | 79 | 6,241 | 8.888 | 493,039 | 4.291 |
| 30 | 900 | 5.477 | 27,000 | 3.107 | 80 | 6,400 | 8.944 | 512,000 | 4.309 |
| 31 | 961 | 5.568 | 29,791 | 3.141 | 81 | 6,561 | 9.000 | 531,441 | 4.327 |
| 32 | 1,024 | 5.657 | 32,768 | 3.175 | 82 | 6,724 | 9.055 | 551,368 | 4.344 |
| 33 | 1,089 | 5.745 | 35,937 | 3.208 | 83 | 6,889 | 9.110 | 571,787 | 4.362 |
| 34 | 1,156 | 5.831 | 39,304 | 3.240 | 84 | 7,056 | 9.165 | 592,704 | 4.380 |
| 35 | 1,225 | 5.916 | 42,875 | 3.271 | 85 | 7,225 | 9.220 | 614,125 | 4.397 |
| 36 | 1,296 | 6.000 | 46,656 | 3.302 | 86 | 7,396 | 9.274 | 636,056 | 4.414 |
| 37 | 1,369 | 6.083 | 50,653 | 3.332 | 87 | 7,569 | 9.327 | 658,503 | 4.431 |
| 38 | 1,444 | 6.164 | 54,872 | 3.362 | 88 | 7,744 | 9.381 | 681,472 | 4.448 |
| 39 | 1,521 | 6.245 | 59,319 | 3.391 | 89 | 7,921 | 9.434 | 704,969 | 4.465 |
| 40 | 1,600 | 6.325 | 64,000 | 3.420 | 90 | 8,100 | 9.487 | 729,000 | 4.481 |
| 41 | 1,681 | 6.403 | 68,921 | 3.448 | 91 | 8,281 | 9.539 | 753,571 | 4.498 |
| 42 | 1,764 | 6.481 | 74,088 | 3.476 | 92 | 8,464 | 9.592 | 778,688 | 4.514 |
| 43 | 1,849 | 6.557 | 79,507 | 3.503 | 93 | 8,649 | 9.644 | 804,357 | 4.531 |
| 44 | 1,936 | 6.633 | 85,184 | 3.530 | 94 | 8,836 | 9.695 | 830,584 | 4.547 |
| 45 | 2,025 | 6.708 | 91,125 | 3.557 | 95 | 9,025 | 9.747 | 857,375 | 4.563 |
| 46 | 2,116 | 6.782 | 97,336 | 3.583 | 96 | 9,216 | 9.798 | 884,736 | 4.579 |
| 47 | 2,209 | 6.856 | 103,823 | 3.609 | 97 | 9,409 | 9.849 | 912,673 | 4.595 |
| 48 | 2,304 | 6.928 | 110,592 | 3.634 | 98 | 9,604 | 9.899 | 941,192 | 4.610 |
| 49 | 2,401 | 7.000 | 117,649 | 3.659 | 99 | 9,801 | 9.950 | 970,299 | 4.626 |
| 50 | 2,500 | 7.071 | 125,000 | 3.684 | 100 | 10,000 | 10.000 | 1,000,000 | 4.642 |

| N | 0 | 1 | 2 | 3 | 4 | 5 | 6 | 7 | 8 | 9 |
|---|---|---|---|---|---|---|---|---|---|---|
| 10 | .0000 | 0043 | 0086 | 0128 | 0170 | 0212 | 0253 | 0294 | 0334 | 0374 |
| 11 | .0414 | 0453 | 0492 | 0531 | 0569 | 0607 | 0645 | 0682 | 0719 | 0755 |
| 12 | .0792 | 0828 | 0864 | 0899 | 0934 | 0969 | 1004 | 1038 | 1072 | 1106 |
| 13 | .1139 | 1173 | 1206 | 1239 | 1271 | 1303 | 1335 | 1367 | 1399 | 1430 |
| 14 | .1461 | 1492 | 1523 | 1553 | 1584 | 1614 | 1644 | 1673 | 1703 | 1732 |
| 15 | .1761 | 1790 | 1818 | 1847 | 1875 | 1903 | 1931 | 1959 | 1987 | 2014 |
| 16 | .2041 | 2068 | 2095 | 2122 | 2148 | 2175 | 2201 | 2227 | 2253 | 2279 |
| 17 | .2304 | 2330 | 2355 | 2380 | 2405 | 2430 | 2455 | 2480 | 2504 | 2529 |
| 18 | .2553 | 2577 | 2601 | 2625 | 2648 | 2672 | 2695 | 2718 | 2742 | 2765 |
| 19 | .2788 | 2810 | 2833 | 2856 | 2878 | 2900 | 2923 | 2945 | 2967 | 2989 |
| 20 | .3010 | 3032 | 3054 | 3075 | 3096 | 3118 | 3139 | 3160 | 3181 | 3201 |
| 21 | .3222 | 3243 | 3263 | 3284 | 3304 | 3324 | 3345 | 3365 | 3385 | 3404 |
| 22 | .3424 | 3444 | 3464 | 3483 | 3502 | 3522 | 3541 | 3560 | 3579 | 3598 |
| 23 | .3617 | 3636 | 3655 | 3674 | 3692 | 3711 | 3729 | 3747 | 3766 | 3784 |
| 24 | .3802 | 3820 | 3838 | 3856 | 3874 | 3892 | 3909 | 3927 | 3945 | 3962 |
| 25 | .3979 | 3997 | 4014 | 4031 | 4048 | 4065 | 4082 | 4099 | 4116 | 4133 |
| 26 | .4150 | 4166 | 4183 | 4200 | 4216 | 4232 | 4249 | 4265 | 4281 | 4298 |
| 27 | .4314 | 4330 | 4346 | 4362 | 4378 | 4393 | 4409 | 4425 | 4440 | 4456 |
| 28 | .4472 | 4487 | 4502 | 4518 | 4533 | 4548 | 4564 | 4579 | 4594 | 4609 |
| 29 | .4624 | 4639 | 4654 | 4669 | 4683 | 4698 | 4713 | 4728 | 4742 | 4757 |
| 30 | .4771 | 4786 | 4800 | 4814 | 4829 | 4843 | 4857 | 4871 | 4886 | 4900 |
| 31 | .4914 | 4928 | 4942 | 4955 | 4969 | 4983 | 4997 | 5011 | 5024 | 5038 |
| 32 | .5051 | 5065 | 5079 | 5092 | 5105 | 5119 | 5132 | 5145 | 5159 | 5172 |
| 33 | .5185 | 5198 | 5211 | 5224 | 5237 | 5250 | 5263 | 5276 | 5289 | 5302 |
| 34 | .5315 | 5328 | 5340 | 5353 | 5366 | 5378 | 5391 | 5403 | 5416 | 5428 |
| 35 | .5441 | 5453 | 5465 | 5478 | 5490 | 5502 | 5514 | 5527 | 5539 | 5551 |
| 36 | .5563 | 5575 | 5587 | 5599 | 5611 | 5623 | 5635 | 5647 | 5658 | 5670 |
| 37 | .5682 | 5694 | 5705 | 5717 | 5729 | 5740 | 5752 | 5763 | 5775 | 5786 |
| 38 | .5798 | 5809 | 5821 | 5832 | 5843 | 5855 | 5866 | 5877 | 5888 | 5899 |
| 39 | .5911 | 5922 | 5933 | 5944 | 5955 | 5966 | 5977 | 5988 | 5999 | 6010 |
| 40 | .6021 | 6031 | 6042 | 6053 | 6064 | 6075 | 6085 | 6096 | 6107 | 6117 |
| 41 | .6128 | 6138 | 6149 | 6160 | 6170 | 6180 | 6191 | 6201 | 6212 | 6222 |
| 42 | .6232 | 6243 | 6253 | 6263 | 6274 | 6284 | 6294 | 6304 | 6314 | 6325 |
| 43 | .6335 | 6345 | 6355 | 6365 | 6375 | 6385 | 6395 | 6405 | 6415 | 6425 |
| 44 | .6435 | 6444 | 6454 | 6464 | 6474 | 6484 | 6493 | 6503 | 6513 | 6522 |
| 45 | .6532 | 6542 | 6551 | 6561 | 6571 | 6580 | 6590 | 6599 | 6609 | 6618 |
| 46 | .6628 | 6637 | 6646 | 6656 | 6665 | 6675 | 6684 | 6693 | 6702 | 6712 |
| 47 | .6721 | 6730 | 6739 | 6749 | 6758 | 6767 | 6776 | 6785 | 6794 | 6803 |
| 48 | .6812 | 6821 | 6830 | 6839 | 6848 | 6857 | 6866 | 6875 | 6884 | 6893 |
| 49 | .6902 | 6911 | 6920 | 6928 | 6937 | 6946 | 6955 | 6964 | 6972 | 6981 |
| 50 | .6990 | 6998 | 7007 | 7016 | 7024 | 7033 | 7042 | 7050 | 7059 | 7067 |
| 51 | .7076 | 7084 | 7093 | 7101 | 7110 | 7118 | 7126 | 7135 | 7143 | 7152 |
| 52 | .7160 | 7168 | 7177 | 7185 | 7193 | 7202 | 7210 | 7218 | 7226 | 7235 |
| 53 | .7243 | 7251 | 7259 | 7267 | 7275 | 7284 | 7292 | 7300 | 7308 | 7316 |
| 54 | .7324 | 7332 | 7340 | 7348 | 7356 | 7364 | 7372 | 7380 | 7388 | 7396 |
| 55 | .7404 | 7412 | 7419 | 7427 | 7435 | 7443 | 7451 | 7459 | 7466 | 7474 |
| 56 | .7482 | 7490 | 7497 | 7505 | 7513 | 7520 | 7528 | 7536 | 7543 | 7551 |
| 57 | .7559 | 7566 | 7574 | 7582 | 7589 | 7597 | 7604 | 7612 | 7619 | 7627 |
| 58 | .7634 | 7642 | 7649 | 7657 | 7664 | 7672 | 7679 | 7686 | 7694 | 7701 |
| 59 | .7709 | 7716 | 7723 | 7731 | 7738 | 7745 | 7752 | 7760 | 7767 | 7774 |
| 60 | .7782 | 7789 | 7796 | 7803 | 7810 | 7818 | 7825 | 7832 | 7839 | 7846 |
| N | 0 | 1 | 2 | 3 | 4 | 5 | 6 | 7 | 8 | 9 |

**Prop. Parts**

(43–31; see next page.)

| | 30 | 29 | 28 |
|---|---|---|---|
| 1 | 3.0 | 2.9 | 2.8 |
| 2 | 6.0 | 5.8 | 5.6 |
| 3 | 9.0 | 8.7 | 8.4 |
| 4 | 12.0 | 11.6 | 11.2 |
| 5 | 15.0 | 14.5 | 14.0 |
| 6 | 18.0 | 17.4 | 16.8 |
| 7 | 21.0 | 20.3 | 19.6 |
| 8 | 24.0 | 23.2 | 22.4 |
| 9 | 27.0 | 26.1 | 25.2 |

| | 27 | 26 | 25 |
|---|---|---|---|
| 1 | 2.7 | 2.6 | 2.5 |
| 2 | 5.4 | 5.2 | 5.0 |
| 3 | 8.1 | 7.8 | 7.5 |
| 4 | 10.8 | 10.4 | 10.0 |
| 5 | 13.5 | 13.0 | 12.5 |
| 6 | 16.2 | 15.6 | 15.0 |
| 7 | 18.9 | 18.2 | 17.5 |
| 8 | 21.6 | 20.8 | 20.0 |
| 9 | 24.3 | 23.4 | 22.5 |

| | 24 | 23 | 22 |
|---|---|---|---|
| 1 | 2.4 | 2.3 | 2.2 |
| 2 | 4.8 | 4.6 | 4.4 |
| 3 | 7.2 | 6.9 | 6.6 |
| 4 | 9.6 | 9.2 | 8.8 |
| 5 | 12.0 | 11.5 | 11.0 |
| 6 | 14.4 | 13.8 | 13.2 |
| 7 | 16.8 | 16.1 | 15.4 |
| 8 | 19.2 | 18.4 | 17.6 |
| 9 | 21.6 | 20.7 | 19.8 |

| | 21 | 20 | 19 |
|---|---|---|---|
| 1 | 2.1 | 2.0 | 1.9 |
| 2 | 4.2 | 4.0 | 3.8 |
| 3 | 6.3 | 6.0 | 5.7 |
| 4 | 8.4 | 8.0 | 7.6 |
| 5 | 10.5 | 10.0 | 9.5 |
| 6 | 12.6 | 12.0 | 11.4 |
| 7 | 14.7 | 14.0 | 13.3 |
| 8 | 16.8 | 16.0 | 15.2 |
| 9 | 18.9 | 18.0 | 17.1 |

| | 18 | 17 | 16 |
|---|---|---|---|
| 1 | 1.8 | 1.7 | 1.6 |
| 2 | 3.6 | 3.4 | 3.2 |
| 3 | 5.4 | 5.1 | 4.8 |
| 4 | 7.2 | 6.8 | 6.4 |
| 5 | 9.0 | 8.5 | 8.0 |
| 6 | 10.8 | 10.2 | 9.6 |
| 7 | 12.6 | 11.9 | 11.2 |
| 8 | 14.4 | 13.6 | 12.8 |
| 9 | 16.2 | 15.3 | 14.4 |

TABLE II—FOUR-PLACE LOGARITHMS OF NUMBERS    301

| N | 0 | 1 | 2 | 3 | 4 | 5 | 6 | 7 | 8 | 9 |
|---|---|---|---|---|---|---|---|---|---|---|
| 60 | .7782 | 7789 | 7796 | 7803 | 7810 | 7818 | 7825 | 7832 | 7839 | 7846 |
| 61 | .7853 | 7860 | 7868 | 7875 | 7882 | 7889 | 7896 | 7903 | 7910 | 7917 |
| 62 | .7924 | 7931 | 7938 | 7945 | 7952 | 7959 | 7966 | 7973 | 7980 | 7987 |
| 63 | .7993 | 8000 | 8007 | 8014 | 8021 | 8028 | 8035 | 8041 | 8048 | 8055 |
| 64 | .8062 | 8069 | 8075 | 8082 | 8089 | 8096 | 8102 | 8109 | 8116 | 8122 |
| 65 | .8129 | 8136 | 8142 | 8149 | 8156 | 8162 | 8169 | 8176 | 8182 | 8189 |
| 66 | .8195 | 8202 | 8209 | 8215 | 8222 | 8228 | 8235 | 8241 | 8248 | 8254 |
| 67 | .8261 | 8267 | 8274 | 8280 | 8287 | 8293 | 8299 | 8306 | 8312 | 8319 |
| 68 | .8325 | 8331 | 8338 | 8344 | 8351 | 8357 | 8363 | 8370 | 8376 | 8382 |
| 69 | .8388 | 8395 | 8401 | 8407 | 8414 | 8420 | 8426 | 8432 | 8439 | 8445 |
| 70 | .8451 | 8457 | 8463 | 8470 | 8476 | 8482 | 8488 | 8494 | 8500 | 8506 |
| 71 | .8513 | 8519 | 8525 | 8531 | 8537 | 8543 | 8549 | 8555 | 8561 | 8567 |
| 72 | .8573 | 8579 | 8585 | 8591 | 8597 | 8603 | 8609 | 8615 | 8621 | 8627 |
| 73 | .8633 | 8639 | 8645 | 8651 | 8657 | 8663 | 8669 | 8675 | 8681 | 8686 |
| 74 | .8692 | 8698 | 8704 | 8710 | 8716 | 8722 | 8727 | 8733 | 8739 | 8745 |
| 75 | .8751 | 8756 | 8762 | 8768 | 8774 | 8779 | 8785 | 8791 | 8797 | 8802 |
| 76 | .8808 | 8814 | 8820 | 8825 | 8831 | 8837 | 8842 | 8848 | 8854 | 8859 |
| 77 | .8865 | 8871 | 8876 | 8882 | 8887 | 8893 | 8899 | 8904 | 8910 | 8915 |
| 78 | .8921 | 8927 | 8932 | 8938 | 8943 | 8949 | 8954 | 8960 | 8965 | 8971 |
| 79 | .8976 | 8982 | 8987 | 8993 | 8998 | 9004 | 9009 | 9015 | 9020 | 9025 |
| 80 | .9031 | 9036 | 9042 | 9047 | 9053 | 9058 | 9063 | 9069 | 9074 | 9079 |
| 81 | .9085 | 9090 | 9096 | 9101 | 9106 | 9112 | 9117 | 9122 | 9128 | 9133 |
| 82 | .9138 | 9143 | 9149 | 9154 | 9159 | 9165 | 9170 | 9175 | 9180 | 9186 |
| 83 | .9191 | 9196 | 9201 | 9206 | 9212 | 9217 | 9222 | 9227 | 9232 | 9238 |
| 84 | .9243 | 9248 | 9253 | 9258 | 9263 | 9269 | 9274 | 9279 | 9284 | 9289 |
| 85 | .9294 | 9299 | 9304 | 9309 | 9315 | 9320 | 9325 | 9330 | 9335 | 9340 |
| 86 | .9345 | 9350 | 9355 | 9360 | 9365 | 9370 | 9375 | 9380 | 9385 | 9390 |
| 87 | .9395 | 9400 | 9405 | 9410 | 9415 | 9420 | 9425 | 9430 | 9435 | 9440 |
| 88 | .9445 | 9450 | 9455 | 9460 | 9465 | 9469 | 9474 | 9479 | 9484 | 9489 |
| 89 | .9494 | 9499 | 9504 | 9509 | 9513 | 9518 | 9523 | 9528 | 9533 | 9538 |
| 90 | .9542 | 9547 | 9552 | 9557 | 9562 | 9566 | 9571 | 9576 | 9581 | 9586 |
| 91 | .9590 | 9595 | 9600 | 9605 | 9609 | 9614 | 9619 | 9624 | 9628 | 9633 |
| 92 | .9638 | 9643 | 9647 | 9652 | 9657 | 9661 | 9666 | 9671 | 9675 | 9680 |
| 93 | .9685 | 9689 | 9694 | 9699 | 9703 | 9708 | 9713 | 9717 | 9722 | 9727 |
| 94 | .9731 | 9736 | 9741 | 9745 | 9750 | 9754 | 9759 | 9763 | 9768 | 9773 |
| 95 | .9777 | 9782 | 9786 | 9791 | 9795 | 9800 | 9805 | 9809 | 9814 | 9818 |
| 96 | .9823 | 9827 | 9832 | 9836 | 9841 | 9845 | 9850 | 9854 | 9859 | 9863 |
| 97 | .9868 | 9872 | 9877 | 9881 | 9886 | 9890 | 9894 | 9899 | 9903 | 9908 |
| 98 | .9912 | 9917 | 9921 | 9926 | 9930 | 9934 | 9939 | 9943 | 9948 | 9952 |
| 99 | .9956 | 9961 | 9965 | 9969 | 9974 | 9978 | 9983 | 9987 | 9991 | 9996 |
| N | 0 | 1 | 2 | 3 | 4 | 5 | 6 | 7 | 8 | 9 |

**Prop. Parts**

| | 15 | 14 | 13 |
|---|---|---|---|
| 1 | 1.5 | 1.4 | 1.3 |
| 2 | 3.0 | 2.8 | 2.6 |
| 3 | 4.5 | 4.2 | 3.9 |
| 4 | 6.0 | 5.6 | 5.2 |
| 5 | 7.5 | 7.0 | 6.5 |
| 6 | 9.0 | 8.4 | 7.8 |
| 7 | 10.5 | 9.8 | 9.1 |
| 8 | 12.0 | 11.2 | 10.4 |
| 9 | 13.5 | 12.6 | 11.7 |

| | 12 | 11 | 10 |
|---|---|---|---|
| 1 | 1.2 | 1.1 | 1.0 |
| 2 | 2.4 | 2.2 | 2.0 |
| 3 | 3.6 | 3.3 | 3.0 |
| 4 | 4.8 | 4.4 | 4.0 |
| 5 | 6.0 | 5.5 | 5.0 |
| 6 | 7.2 | 6.6 | 6.0 |
| 7 | 8.4 | 7.7 | 7.0 |
| 8 | 9.6 | 8.8 | 8.0 |
| 9 | 10.8 | 9.9 | 9.0 |

| | 9 | 8 | 7 |
|---|---|---|---|
| 1 | 0.9 | 0.8 | 0.7 |
| 2 | 1.8 | 1.6 | 1.4 |
| 3 | 2.7 | 2.4 | 2.1 |
| 4 | 3.6 | 3.2 | 2.8 |
| 5 | 4.5 | 4.0 | 3.5 |
| 6 | 5.4 | 4.8 | 4.2 |
| 7 | 6.3 | 5.6 | 4.9 |
| 8 | 7.2 | 6.4 | 5.6 |
| 9 | 8.1 | 7.2 | 6.3 |

| | 6 | 5 | 4 |
|---|---|---|---|
| 1 | 0.6 | 0.5 | 0.4 |
| 2 | 1.2 | 1.0 | 0.8 |
| 3 | 1.8 | 1.5 | 1.2 |
| 4 | 2.4 | 2.0 | 1.6 |
| 5 | 3.0 | 2.5 | 2.0 |
| 6 | 3.6 | 3.0 | 2.4 |
| 7 | 4.2 | 3.5 | 2.8 |
| 8 | 4.8 | 4.0 | 3.2 |
| 9 | 5.4 | 4.5 | 3.6 |

| | 43 | 42 | 41 | 40 | 39 | | 38 | 37 | 36 | 35 | | 34 | 33 | 32 | 31 | |
|---|---|---|---|---|---|---|---|---|---|---|---|---|---|---|---|---|
| 1 | 4.3 | 4.2 | 4.1 | 4.0 | 3.9 | 1 | 3.8 | 3.7 | 3.6 | 3.5 | 1 | 3.4 | 3.3 | 3.2 | 3.1 | 1 |
| 2 | 8.6 | 8.4 | 8.2 | 8.0 | 7.8 | 2 | 7.6 | 7.4 | 7.2 | 7.0 | 2 | 6.8 | 6.6 | 6.4 | 6.2 | 2 |
| 3 | 12.9 | 12.6 | 12.3 | 12.0 | 11.7 | 3 | 11.4 | 11.1 | 10.8 | 10.5 | 3 | 10.2 | 9.9 | 9.6 | 9.3 | 3 |
| 4 | 17.2 | 16.8 | 16.4 | 16.0 | 15.6 | 4 | 15.2 | 14.8 | 14.4 | 14.0 | 4 | 13.6 | 13.2 | 12.8 | 12.4 | 4 |
| 5 | 21.5 | 21.0 | 20.5 | 20.0 | 19.5 | 5 | 19.0 | 18.5 | 18.0 | 17.5 | 5 | 17.0 | 16.5 | 16.0 | 15.5 | 5 |
| 6 | 25.8 | 25.2 | 24.6 | 24.0 | 23.4 | 6 | 22.8 | 22.2 | 21.6 | 21.0 | 6 | 20.4 | 19.8 | 19.2 | 18.6 | 6 |
| 7 | 30.1 | 29.4 | 28.7 | 28.0 | 27.3 | 7 | 26.6 | 25.9 | 25.2 | 24.5 | 7 | 23.8 | 23.1 | 22.4 | 21.7 | 7 |
| 8 | 34.4 | 33.6 | 32.8 | 32.0 | 31.2 | 8 | 30.4 | 29.6 | 28.8 | 28.0 | 8 | 27.2 | 26.4 | 25.6 | 24.8 | 8 |
| 9 | 38.7 | 37.8 | 36.9 | 36.0 | 35.1 | 9 | 34.2 | 33.3 | 32.4 | 31.5 | 9 | 30.6 | 29.7 | 28.8 | 27.9 | 9 |

TABLE IV—COMMISSIONERS *1941* STANDARD ORDINARY MORTALITY
TABLE

| Age | Number Living $l_x$ | Number Dying $d_x$ | Rate of Mortality $q_x$ | Age | Number Living $l_x$ | Number Dying $d_x$ | Rate of Mortality $q_x$ |
|---|---|---|---|---|---|---|---|
| 0 | 1,023,102 | 23,102 | .02258 | 50 | 810,900 | 9,990 | .01232 |
| 1 | 1,000,000 | 5,770 | .00577 | 51 | 800,910 | 10,628 | .01327 |
| 2 | 994,230 | 4,116 | .00414 | 52 | 790,282 | 11,301 | .01430 |
| 3 | 990,114 | 3,347 | .00338 | 53 | 778,981 | 12,020 | .01543 |
| 4 | 986,767 | 2,950 | .00299 | 54 | 766,961 | 12,770 | .01665 |
| 5 | 983,817 | 2,715 | .00276 | 55 | 754,191 | 13,560 | .01798 |
| 6 | 981,102 | 2,561 | .00261 | 56 | 740,631 | 14,390 | .01943 |
| 7 | 978,541 | 2,417 | .00247 | 57 | 726,241 | 15,251 | .02100 |
| 8 | 976,124 | 2,255 | .00231 | 58 | 710,990 | 16,147 | .02271 |
| 9 | 973,869 | 2,065 | .00212 | 59 | 694,843 | 17,072 | .02457 |
| 10 | 971,804 | 1,914 | .00197 | 60 | 677,771 | 18,022 | .02659 |
| 11 | 969,890 | 1,852 | .00191 | 61 | 659,749 | 18,988 | .02878 |
| 12 | 968,038 | 1,859 | .00192 | 62 | 640,761 | 19,979 | .03118 |
| 13 | 966,179 | 1,913 | .00198 | 63 | 620,782 | 20,958 | .03376 |
| 14 | 964,266 | 1,996 | .00207 | 64 | 599,824 | 21,942 | .03658 |
| 15 | 962,270 | 2,069 | .00215 | 65 | 577,882 | 22,907 | .03964 |
| 16 | 960,201 | 2,103 | .00219 | 66 | 554,975 | 23,842 | .04296 |
| 17 | 958,098 | 2,156 | .00225 | 67 | 531,133 | 24,730 | .04656 |
| 18 | 955,942 | 2,199 | .00230 | 68 | 506,403 | 25,553 | .05046 |
| 19 | 953,743 | 2,260 | .00237 | 69 | 480,850 | 26,302 | .05470 |
| 20 | 951,483 | 2,312 | .00243 | 70 | 454,548 | 26,955 | .05930 |
| 21 | 949,171 | 2,382 | .00251 | 71 | 427,593 | 27,481 | .06427 |
| 22 | 946,789 | 2,452 | .00259 | 72 | 400,112 | 27,872 | .06966 |
| 23 | 944,337 | 2,531 | .00268 | 73 | 372,240 | 28,104 | .07550 |
| 24 | 941,806 | 2,609 | .00277 | 74 | 344,136 | 28,154 | .08181 |
| 25 | 939,197 | 2,705 | .00288 | 75 | 315,982 | 28,009 | .08864 |
| 26 | 936,492 | 2,800 | .00299 | 76 | 287,973 | 27,651 | .09602 |
| 27 | 933,692 | 2,904 | .00311 | 77 | 260,322 | 27,071 | .10399 |
| 28 | 930,788 | 3,025 | .00325 | 78 | 233,251 | 26,262 | .11259 |
| 29 | 927,763 | 3,154 | .00340 | 79 | 206,989 | 25,224 | .12186 |
| 30 | 924,609 | 3,292 | .00356 | 80 | 181,765 | 23,966 | .13185 |
| 31 | 921,317 | 3,437 | .00373 | 81 | 157,799 | 22,502 | .14260 |
| 32 | 917,880 | 3,598 | .00392 | 82 | 135,297 | 20,857 | .15416 |
| 33 | 914,282 | 3,767 | .00412 | 83 | 114,440 | 19,062 | .16657 |
| 34 | 910,515 | 3,961 | .00435 | 84 | 95,378 | 17,157 | .17988 |
| 35 | 906,554 | 4,161 | .00459 | 85 | 78,221 | 15,185 | .19413 |
| 36 | 902,393 | 4,386 | .00486 | 86 | 63,036 | 13,198 | .20937 |
| 37 | 898,007 | 4,625 | .00515 | 87 | 49,838 | 11,245 | .22563 |
| 38 | 893,382 | 4,878 | .00546 | 88 | 38,593 | 9,378 | .24300 |
| 39 | 888,504 | 5,162 | .00581 | 89 | 29,215 | 7,638 | .26144 |
| 40 | 883,342 | 5,459 | .00618 | 90 | 21,577 | 6,063 | .28099 |
| 41 | 877,883 | 5,785 | .00659 | 91 | 15,514 | 4,681 | .30173 |
| 42 | 872,098 | 6,131 | .00703 | 92 | 10,833 | 3,506 | .32364 |
| 43 | 865,967 | 6,503 | .00751 | 93 | 7,327 | 2,540 | .34666 |
| 44 | 859,464 | 6,910 | .00804 | 94 | 4,787 | 1,776 | .37100 |
| 45 | 852,554 | 7,340 | .00861 | 95 | 3,011 | 1,193 | .39621 |
| 46 | 845,214 | 7,801 | .00923 | 96 | 1,818 | 813 | .44719 |
| 47 | 837,413 | 8,299 | .00991 | 97 | 1,005 | 551 | .54826 |
| 48 | 829,114 | 8,822 | .01064 | 98 | 454 | 329 | .72467 |
| 49 | 820,292 | 9,392 | .01145 | 99 | 125 | 125 | 1.00000 |

# Answers to Exercises

*Note.* Answers to most of the odd-numbered problems are given here. Answers to even-numbered problems are available in a separate pamphlet when ordered by the instructor.

## Exercise 1, page 6

**1.** 0      **3.** $-8$      **5.** 9      **7.** 24      **9.** 81      **11.** 16

**13.** 5/6      **15.** 15/8      **17.** $-5/3$      **19.** 1/3      **21.** 35/12

**23.** 112/15      **25.** 4      **27.** 2/15      **29.** 6      **31.** 82/27

**33.** $-5xy$      **35.** $-6ax$      **37.** $x - 5y + 6$      **39.** $-12y + 12x$

**41.** 2/21      **43.** 4/3      **45.** 125/27      **47.** $-16$      **49.** 64

**51.** $x^2$      **53.** $x^9$      **55.** $v^6$      **57.** $x^4 y^8$      **59.** $16x^8$      **61.** $1/3x^3$

**63.** $x^4/y^4$      **65.** $x^6 y^{12}$      **67.** $-27w^6$      **81.** 1/10 or .1

**83.** $1/10^4$ or .0001      **85.** $1/x^3$      **87.** $y^3/x^2$      **89.** 1/72

## Exercise 2, page 12

**1.** {2, 4}, {2, 6}, {2, 8}, {4, 6}, {4, 8}, {6, 8}      **5.** 5      **7.** 7

**9.** $10 - 13x - 3x^2$      **11.** $ab - k(a + b) + k^2$      **13.** $x^2 + 2xy + y^2$

**15.** $x^4 + 4x^2 y^3 + 4y^6$      **17.** $x^3 - 7x + 6$      **19.** $x^4 - y^2$

**21.** $2x^2 + 7xy - 15y^2$      **23.** $a^2 - 6ab + 9b^2$      **25.** $x^2 - 4xy + 4y^2$

**27.** $a(b^2 + 3a + a^2)$      **29.** $(a - x)(a + x)$      **31.** $(y - 3x)(y + 3x)$

**33.** $(b + 3)^2$      **35.** $(2x - y)^2$      **37.** $(11 - 2xy)(11 + 2xy)$

**39.** $(x + 4)(x + 3)$      **41.** $(2x + 5)(x - 1)$      **43.** $(3y + 1)(y + 2)$

**45.** $(2y + 3a)^2$      **47.** $(3x - 2y)(x + 3y)$      **49.** $\pm 7$      **51.** $\pm 1/2$

**53.** 6/5      **55.** 7/8      **57.** $3x$      **59.** $7x^3$      **61.** $8x^2 y^3$

**63.** $7a^2 b^3$      **65.** $y^2/3$      **67.** $a^2 x/7y^3$      **69.** $3\sqrt{5}$      **71.** $3\sqrt{2}$

**73.** $\sqrt{2}/2$      **75.** $\sqrt{15}/5$

## Exercise 3, page 18

**1.** $3i$    **3.** $10i$    **5.** $i/3$    **7.** $5i/12$    **9.** $9i/2$    **11.** $\pm 7i$

**13.** $\pm 5i$    **15.** $\pm .3i$    **17.** $9y^2i$    **19.** $4x^2i/9$    **21.** $i$    **23.** $i$

**25.** $-3\sqrt{3}$    **27.** $-3\sqrt{10}$    **29.** $7 + 26i$    **31.** $41$

**33.** $21 - 22i$    **35.** $-5 + 12i$    **37.** $61$    **39.** $-35 + 12i$

**41.** $12; 2/9; 6/5$    **43.** $3; 5; 10; .1$    **45.** $-b$    **47.** $10$    **49.** $2$

**51.** $31$    **53.** $5$    **55.** $4$    **57.** $2$    **59.** $2$    **61.** $-2$

## Exercise 4, page 23

**1.** $3$    **3.** $5/7$    **5.** $3$    **7.** $9$    **9.** $C = (5F - 160)/9; -17\frac{7}{9}; 0; 100$

**11.** $\pm\sqrt{6}/2$    **13.** $\pm 2\sqrt{21}/7$    **15.** $3, -1/2$    **17.** $1, -5/3$

**19.** $0, -7/3$    **21.** $2/5, 2/5$    **23.** $(3 \pm i\sqrt{3})/2$    **25.** $2, -5/3$

**27.** $-2, -5/3$    **29.** $5, -2$    **31.** $-5/6, 3/4$    **33.** $(1 \pm 2\sqrt{7})/3$

**35.** $(2 \pm i)/2$    **37.** $0, 5/3$

## Exercise 5, page 26

**1.** $5; -7; -11; -9; 2; 7$    **3.** $\overline{AB} = -11; \overline{BC} = 2; \overline{AC} = -9$

**5.** $\overline{AB} = -3; \overline{BC} = -4; \overline{AC} = -7$

## Exercise 6, page 29

**1.** $x < 3$    **3.** $6 < x$    **5.** $x < \dfrac{10}{3}$    **7.** $\dfrac{11}{5} \leqq x$    **9.** $-\dfrac{6}{5} < x$

**11.** $x < \dfrac{10}{3}$    **13.** $\dfrac{82}{21} \leqq x$    **15.** $x \leqq \dfrac{75}{38}$

## Exercise 7, page 34

**1.** $B' = \{1, 2, 3, 4, 5\} \cup \{$all integers greater than $12\}$;
$A \cap B = \{6, 7, 8, 9\}$; $A \cup B = \{4, 5, \cdots, 12\}$;
$A \cup B \cup C = \{4, 5, \cdots, 14\}$; etc.

**3.** $\{$John$\}$, $\{$Mary$\}$, $\{$Ruth$\}$, $\{$John, Mary$\}$, $\{$John, Ruth$\}$, $\{$Mary, Ruth$\}$, and the empty set, $\varnothing$

**5.** $35$    **9.** $\{3; 2; 39; 61\}$

## Exercise 8, page 39

**1.** $-3 < x < 2$    **3.** $-6 < x < -2$    **5.** $x \leqq -3$

**7.** $H = \{-4 \leqq x\}$; $K = \{x < 0\}$    **9.** $H = \{-3 < x\}$; $K = \{x < 2\}$

**11.** $H = \{-2 < x\}$; $K = \{x < 2\}$    **13.** $S = \{x < -5\}$; $T = \{5 < x\}$

**15.** $V = \{x < 0\}$; $W = \{4 < x\}$    **17.** $V = \{x \leqq -3\}$; $W = \{-1 \leqq x\}$

**19.** $S \cap T = \{0 < x \leqq 2\}$; $S \cup T = \{-5 < x \leqq 4\}$

**21.** $S \cup T = \{x \leqq -3\} \cup \{3 < x\}$; $S \cap T = \varnothing$

**23.** $S \cap T = \{|x| \leqq 4\}$; $S \cup T = \{$all $x\}$

**25.** $S' = \{|x| \leqq 3\}$    **27.** $(A \cup B)' = \{-2 \leqq x \leqq 4\}$

## Exercise 9, page 42

**1.** $4 < x < 6$     **3.** $3 \leqq x < 6$     **5.** Solution set is $\varnothing$

**7.** $-20 < x < -\dfrac{13}{8}$     **9.** $-2 < x < -1$     **11.** $-4 < x < 4$

**13.** $\{-4 < x - 3 < 4\}$; solution is $\{-1 < x < 7\}$
**15.** $\{-1 < x + 2 < 1\}$; solution is $\{-3 < x < -1\}$

## Exercise 10, page 45

**13.** $(-1, 5)$     **19.** On $OX$, $(3, 0)$; on $OY$, $(0, -3)$

## Exercise 11, page 47

**1.** $4; 4$     **3.** $-8; 8$     **5.** $-4; 4$     **7.** $-12; 12$     **9.** $12; 12$
**11.** $13$     **13.** $4\sqrt{2}$.     **15.** $\sqrt{65}$     **17.** $6$     **25.** $12$

## Exercise 12, page 52

**1.** $(x = 5, y = -3)$     **3.** $(x = 2, y = 13/2)$     **23.** $k = -3/4$

## Exercise 13, page 55

**1.** $7/4$     **3.** $3$     **5.** $-1/4$     **19.** $y = -3/2$

## Exercise 14, page 58

**1.** $y = 4$     **5.** $y = 2 - 4x$     **7.** $y = -3 + 6x$     **9.** $y = 6x - 23$
**11.** $y = -2x - 14$     **13.** $y = -3x + 5$     **15.** $11x + 5y = 8$
**17.** $5x - 2y = -10$     **19.** $2x + 3y = 12$     **21.** $4x - 3y = 0$
**23.** $3y - 4x = 12$     **25.** $4x - 5y = 20$     **27.** $5x + 3y = 15$
**29.** $5x + y = -5$     **31.** Slope $- 2/5$; $y$-int. $- 4/5$
**33.** Slope $5/3$; $y$-int. $- 5$     **35.** Slope $2/7$; $y$-int. $4/7$
**37.** $3x - y = 9$     **39.** $x + 4y = -26$     **41.** $7x + 2y = 4$

## Exercise 15, page 62

**3.** $R = \{-12, -9, -6, -3, 0, 3, 6, 9\}$     **5.** $R = \{0, 2, 4, 6, 8, 10, 12\}$

## Exercise 16, page 65

**1.** $5$     **3.** $-7/4$     **5.** $169$     **7.** $32$     **9.** $9c^2 - 6c + 5$
**11.** $2/7$     **13.** $-5/4$     **15.** $(x + 4)/(x - 6)$     **17.** $78$
**19.** $14/9$     **21.** $28$     **23.** $11$
**25.** $-16; 9/13; 16/11; (9 + x); (20 - x - 12x^2)$

## Exercise 17, page 70

**15.** $y = \tfrac{1}{2}(3x - 18)$; $x = \tfrac{1}{3}(2y + 18)$
**17.** $y = \tfrac{1}{2}(7x + 15)$; $x = (2y - 15)/7$     **19.** $x = \tfrac{1}{2}(4y^2 + 8y - 7)$

### Exercise 18, page 73

**11.** $(x - 4)^2 + (y - 1)^2 = 4$      **13.** $x^2 - 4x + y^2 = 21$
**15.** $x^2 + 6x + y^2 - 4y + 12 = 0$      **17.** $C:(1, 2); r = 3$
**19.** $C:(-2, 0); r = \sqrt{3}$      **21.** $\varnothing$

### Exercise 20, page 85

**1.** $x = 4, y = -1$      **3.** $x = 5, y = -1$
**5.** Inconsistent; lines distinct and parallel      **7.** $x = -1, y = -3$
**9.** $x = 0, y = 0$      **11.** $x = 5/3, y = 2/15$
**13.** $x = -37/21, y = -19/7$      **15.** $x = .42, y = .19$
**17.** $x = 5, y = -2/5$      **19.** $x = 2/a, y = -b/2$
**21.** $x = a/2b, y = b/a$

### Exercise 21, page 89

**1.** (b) $x = 8$; (c) \$2; (d) \$3; $x = 4$      **3.** (b) $x = 9$; (c) \$1; (d) \$2; $x = 6$
**5.** (b) $x = 16$; (c) \$50; (d) \$1; $x = 8$
**7.** Producer, \$1.60; consumer, \$3.60; equi. quantity, $x = 3.6$
**9.** Producer, \$$\frac{7}{12}$; consumer, \$$\frac{7}{6}$; equi. quantity, $x = 20/3$
**11.** Producer, \$$\frac{8}{3}$; consumer, \$$\frac{2}{3}$; equi. quantity, $x = 28/3$

### Exercise 24, page 98

**9.** $x + y \geqq 4, 5y - 2x \leqq 20$, and $5x - 2y \leqq 13$
**11.** $y - 2x \leqq 4, x + y \leqq 4, x - y \leqq 2$, and $x + y \geqq -2$

### Exercise 25, page 104

**1.** Max. = 22; min. = 6      **3.** Max. = 15; min. = 9
**5.** Max. = 12; min. = $-18$      **7.** Max. = 26; min. = $-7$
**9.** Max. = 19; min. = 1, along a side of polygon
**11.** Max. = 14; min. = $-10$      **13.** Min. = 0; no max.

### Exercise 26, page 109

**1.** 150 of type $A$; 450 of type $B$
**3.** 60 of $A$, 25 of $B$, 85 of $C$
**5.** 43.75 lbs. of $R$, 6.25 lbs. of $S$, 50 lbs. of $T$
**7.** In liters, 600 of $A$, 150 of $B$, and 250 of $C$
**9.** 20%, $A$; 30%, $B$; 50%, $C$
**11.** 300 from (I) to $A$; 300 from (I) to $B$; 100 from (II) to $B$; 500 from (II) to $C$

### Exercise 27, page 119

**1.** 11      **3.** (a) 24; (b) 64; (c) 18      **5.** (a) 12
**7.** (a) 43,200; (b) 30      **9.** (a) 180; (b) 240
**11.** (a) 240; (b) 24; (c) 720      **13.** 125      **15.** 1956      **17.** 48

## Exercise 28, page 124

**1.** 20    **3.** 720    **5.** 504    **7.** 560    **9.** 288    **11.** 56
**13.** 216    **15.** 86,400    **17.** 2    **19.** 265

## Exercise 29, page 129

**3.** 35; 56    **5.** 30, 240; 252    **7.** 10; 6
**9.** (a) 1287; (b) 495; (c) 165    **11.** (a) 55; (b) 700; (c) 65; (d) 7000
**13.** (a) 36; (b) 84    **15.** 63    **17.** 900
**19.** (a) 4; (b) 4; (c) 108    **21.** 8

## Exercise 30, page 135

**1.** $a^4 + 4a^3b + 6a^2b^2 + 4ab^3 + b^4$
**3.** $x^7 + 7x^6y + 21x^5y^2 + 35x^4y^3 + 35x^3y^4 + 21x^2y^5 + 7xy^6 + y^7$
**5.** $32u^{10} + 80u^8v^3 + 80u^6v^6 + 40u^4v^9 + 10u^2v^{12} + v^{15}$
**7.** $729u^6 + 1458u^5v + 1215u^4v^2 + 540u^3v^3 + 135u^2v^4 + 18uv^5 + v^6$
**9.** $21u^2v^5$    **11.** $-160x^3y^3$    **13.** $1120u^4v^4$    **15.** 252
**17.** 128    **19.** 31

## Exercise 31, page 143

**1.** (a) 5/12; 3/4; (b) 1/22; 14/33; 5/22; 19/66; 19/33
**3.** For tosses of {2, 3, 4, 5, 6, 7, 8, 9, 10, 11, 12}, probabilities
   {1/36. 1/18, 1/12, 1/9, 5/36, 1/6, 5/36, 1/9, 1/12, 1/18, 1/36};
   $P(2 \text{ or } 7) = 7/36$
**5.** 1/16; 9/16    **7.** 1/10
**11.** With $E$ the desired event, and $E'$ the event "*no defectives shipped*:"
   $P(E') = 11,594/27,417$;
   $P(E) = 15,823/27,417$, the probability of rejected shipment
**13.** (a) 9/22; (b) 12/55; (c) 10/11    **15.** (a) 1/216; (b) 5/18; (c) 5/72
**17.** (a) 1/32; (b) 5/16    **19.** 203/225    **21.** 11/30

## Exercise 32, page 149

**1.** Value space is {2, 3, 4} with probabilities {$\frac{1}{2}$, $\frac{1}{3}$, $\frac{1}{6}$}
**3.** Value space is {4, 5, 6, 7, 8} with probabilities {$\frac{1}{5}$, $\frac{2}{5}$, $\frac{1}{15}$, $\frac{1}{5}$, $\frac{2}{15}$}

## Exercise 33, page 154

**1.** 6.75    **3.** 7/12    **5.** 2.75    **7.** $4.80
**9.** $p = 5/8$; $12.50    **11.** $22.50    **13.** 872,098/968,038
**15.** 26,955/454,548    **17.** $9394, in dollars due at end of 10 years.
**19.** Value space is {8, 10, 12, 14, 16, 20} with probabilities in 190ths,
   {45, 60, 15, 40, 24, 6}; $E(X) = $11.60$

## Exercise 34, page 159

**1.** 3/4    **3.** 15/32; 3/32; 7/16; 17/32    **5.** 1/216
**7.** 1/64; 1/16; 8/2197    **9.** 2/25; 23/25

**11.** 4/25; 12/25; 21/25     **13.** (a) .32 (b) .384; (c) .096; (d) .104
**15.** (a) .00018; (b) .00016; (c) .001; (d) .243

### Exercise 35, page 163

**1.** 9/64; 5/32; 63/64     **3.** 15/64; 21/32; 11/32
**5.** 17/1944; 919/5832     **7.** .001; .033     **9.** .015; .999
**11.** 25     **13,** 63 and 64

### Exercise 36, page 168

**1.** Probabilities in 256ths are {81, 108, 54, 12, 1} for $x = $ {0, 1, 2, 3, 4}
**5.** .246; .377; .172     **7.** (a) .914; (b) .086; (c) .375
**9.** (a) .989; (b) .011; (c) .677
**11.** (a) .999; (b) .001; (c) .878     **13.** (a) .215; (b) .042

### Exercise 37, page 175

**1.** $P(boy) = 3/8$; $P(girl) = 5/8$; $P(T) = 3/8$; $P(boy \cap T) = 1/8$;
    $P(girl \cap T) = 1/4$; $P_c(T, given\ girl) = 2/5$; $P_c(T, given\ boy) = 1/3$;
    $P_c(girl, given\ T) = 2/3$; $P_c(boy, given\ T) = 1/3$
**3.** $P(T_1) = 1/4$; $P(T_2) = 2/3$; $P(T_1 \cap T_2) = \frac{1}{6} = \frac{1}{4} \cdot \frac{2}{3}$  Yes     **5.** 5/9
**7.** (a) 8/125; (b) 1/30     **9.** (a) 1/5; (b) 1/3; (c) 8/15; (d) 5/8
**11.** 3/16     **13.** 376/5525     **15.** 35/12,168     **17.** 2/15
**19.** (a) .343; (b) .294; (c) .363

### Exercise 38, page 179

**1.** $P_c(E, given\ male)$ and $P_c(E, given\ female)$;
    $P_c(male, given\ E) = 27/49$; $P_c(female, given\ E) = 22/49$
**3.** With $D$ meaning "*in favor of decision,*"
    $P_c(Dem., given\ D) = 4/25$; $P_c(Rep., given\ D) = 21/25$
**5.** (a) 1/7; (b) 6/7     **7.** (a) 6/31; (b) 10/31; (c) 15/31

### Exercise 39, page 185

**1.** 21     **3.** 3     **5.** 3/5     **7.** 6/5     **9.** 2     **11.** 4/7
**13.** Limit is 0

### Exercise 40, page 192

**1.** (a) $\dfrac{\Delta y}{\Delta x} = 5 + \Delta x$; (c) 5; (d) $y = 5x - 4$     **3.** $2x$     **5.** $8x + 3$
**7.** $3 + 2t$     **9.** $h'(x) = 4$     **11.** $f'(t) = 3t^2$
**13.** $g'(y) = -2/y^3$     **15.** $x^{-1/2}/2$     **17.** $h'(t) = -1/2t\sqrt{t}$

### Exercise 41, page 197

**1.** $f'(x) = 21x^2$     **3.** $y' = x$     **5.** $f'(x) = 9x^2 + 8x - 5$
**7.** $y' = -8x^3 - 6x + 4$

**9.** (*a*) ($x = 1, y = 1$); (*b*) Tangents are $y + 2x = 2$ and $y = 2x - 2$; (*c*) $f'(x) > 0$ and $f(x)$ increasing when $x > 1$; $f'(x) < 0$ and $f(x)$ decreasing when $x < 1$

**11.** (*a*) ($x = -2, y = 9$); (*b*) tangents are $y = 2x + 14$ and $y + 4x = 5$; (*c*) $f'(x) > 0$ and $f(x)$ increasing when $x < -2$; $f'(x) < 0$ and $f(x)$ decreasing when $x > -2$

**13.** $y' = -18/x^4$; $y' = -40/x^6$     **15.** $4x - 6/x^3$

**17.** $18(3x + 5)^6$     **19.** $30s(3s^2 + 4)^4$

**21.** $(24t^2 - 12)(2t^3 - 3t + 1)^4$

### Exercise 42, page 201

**1.** $v = 480 - 32t$. At $t = 3$, $v = 384$; at $t = 5$, $v = 320$. Average velocity is 352. Highest at $t = 15$, when $s = 3600$.

**3.** $v = 4$; $v = 76$     **5.** $v = 29$; $v = 5$     **7.** 30; 29; 25

**9.** (*a*) 900; 300. (*b*) 150. (*c*) 840; 900. (*d*) Positive when $x < 150$; negative when $x > 150$; 0 when $x = 150$.

**11.** (*a*) $P = 840x - 2.9x^2 - 1600$. (*b*) 840; 782; 260. (*c*) Positive when $x < 145$; negative when $x > 145$; 0 when $x = 145$. (*d*) When $x = 145$

### Exercise 43, page 206

**1.** Local min. $f(3) = 0 =$ absolute min.

**3.** Local max. $f(-2) = 56$; local min. $f(3) = -69$

**5.** Local max. $f(4) = 87$; local min. $f(-2) = -21$

**7.** Local max. $f(1) = 5$; local min. $f(-3) = -27$

**9.** No local max. or min. Stationary point at ($x = -2, y = -13$)

### Exercise 44, page 209

**1.** 40 and 40     **3.** 75 by 50     **5.** 12     **7.** On 67th day

**9.** $x = 10$

**11.** (*a*) $p = 50.19$; (*b*) $R' = C' = 12.38$; (*c*) $.4975\alpha$

**13.** $w(x) = -x^3 + 12x^2 - 21x - 25$. (*a*) $x = 7$; (*b*) $R' = C' = 13$

**15.** $x = 3.3$

### Exercise 45, page 213

**1.** $\frac{dy}{dx} = 3$     **3.** $\frac{dy}{dx} = -5 - 4x^3$     **5.** $\frac{dz}{dx} = -15x^2$     **7.** $dy = 1.8$

**9.** (*a*) $.6\pi$; (*b*) $2.4\pi$     **11.** $60\pi$ cubic in.

**13.** $4\pi$ cubic in.     **15.** 6.25     **17.** 6.5

### Exercise 46, page 216

**1.** $\frac{dy}{dx} = 12x - 1$     **3.** $\frac{du}{dx} = 20x^3 - 6x^2 - 6x + 15$

**5.** $f'(s) = 5s^4 + 4s^3 - 15s^2 - 6s - 3$

**7.** $y' = -72x^2 - 80x + 46$

**9.** $y' = -\dfrac{26}{(2 + 5t)^2}$    **11.** $f'(z) = \dfrac{2z^4 - 6z^3 - 12z + 9}{(z^3 + 3)^2}$

**13.** $y' = -\dfrac{18}{(3x + 2)^2}$    **15.** $-9x^{-4}$    **17.** $-\dfrac{35x^{-6}}{2}$

**19.** $y' = \dfrac{5x^{3/2}}{2}$    **21.** $y' = 5x^{2/3}$    **23.** $y' = \dfrac{9t^2}{2\sqrt{3t^3 + 1}}$

**25.** $f'(x) = -3(2x - 5)^{-3/2}$    **27.** $y' = -2x(x^2 - 4)^{-3/2}$

**29.** $\dfrac{dy}{dt} = \dfrac{5}{2(3t - 2)^{1/2}(t + 1)^{3/2}}$

## Exercise 47, page 221

**1.** $2xy + x^2 \dfrac{dy}{dx}$    **3.** $\left(y - x\dfrac{dy}{dx}\right)/y^2$    **5.** $4(3x - y)^3\left(3 - \dfrac{dy}{dx}\right)$

**7.** $\dfrac{dy}{dx} = -\dfrac{3}{4y}; \dfrac{dx}{dy} = -\dfrac{4y}{3}$    **9.** $\dfrac{dy}{dx} = -\dfrac{y}{x}; \dfrac{dx}{dy} = -\dfrac{x}{y}$

**11.** $\dfrac{dy}{dx} = \dfrac{x}{y}; \dfrac{dx}{dy} = \dfrac{y}{x}$    **13.** $\dfrac{dy}{dx} = \dfrac{3y - 2x}{2y - 3x}; \dfrac{dx}{dy} = \dfrac{2y - 3x}{3y - 2x}$

**15.** $\dfrac{dy}{dx} = -\dfrac{2xy}{x^2 + 3y^2}; \dfrac{dx}{dy} = -\dfrac{x^2 + 3y^2}{2xy}$

**17.** $\dfrac{dy}{dx} = -\dfrac{2\sqrt{y}}{3\sqrt{x}}; \dfrac{dx}{dy} = -\dfrac{3\sqrt{x}}{2\sqrt{y}}$    **19.** $\dfrac{dy}{dx} = -\dfrac{4x}{9y}; \dfrac{dx}{dy} = -\dfrac{9y}{4x}$. Horizontal at

$(x = 0, y = \pm 2)$; vertical at $(x = \pm 3, y = 0)$

**21.** $\dfrac{dy}{dx} = 3x^2; \dfrac{dx}{dy} = \dfrac{1}{3x^2}$. Horizontal at $(x = 0, y = 0)$; no vertical tangent

**23.** $\dfrac{dy}{dx} = \dfrac{x}{4y}; \dfrac{dx}{dy} = \dfrac{4y}{x}$. No horizontal tangent; vertical at $(x = \pm 4, y = 0)$

**25.** $f'(x) = 15x^4 - 12x^2 + 3; f''(x) = 60x^3 - 24x; f'''(x) = 180x^2 - 24$

**27.** $C' = 2; C'' = -.04$

**29.** $C' = .006x^2 - .08x + 25; C'' = .012x - .08; .04$

**31.** At $x = 10, C'' = .04$

## Exercise 48, page 227

**1.** $s = -2t^2 + 3t + 5$    **3.** $s = \frac{1}{3}t^3 - \frac{3}{2}t^2 + 4t - \frac{20}{3}$

**5.** $s = -\frac{1}{3}t^3 - \frac{3}{2}t^2$    **7.** $y = \frac{3}{2}x^2 - 2x - 5$    **9.** $y = \frac{1}{3}x^3 - x^2$

**11.** $y = -\frac{2}{3}x^3 + \frac{3}{2}x^2 - 4x + \frac{13}{3}$    **13.** $R = 100x - \frac{3}{2}x^2 - \frac{2}{3}x^3$

**15.** $P = 500x - .95x^2 - 5000$

## Exercise 49, page 232

**1.** $S_3 = 17.5; S_6 = 17.875$    **3.** 10.75    **5.** (a) 11.9375; (b) 9.875; (c) 14.375

## Exercise 50, page 237

**1.** 22    **3.** $-142\frac{1}{2}$    **5.** 4/3    **7.** $26\frac{1}{3}$    **9.** $10\frac{2}{3}$    **11.** 4/3

**13.** 71/6    **15.** 4/3

## Exercise 51, page 241

**1.** 70     **3.** $17\frac{13}{15}$     **5.** $\bar{x} = 5\frac{2}{21}$     **7.** 55/67

## Exercise 52, page 246

**1.** (a) $k = 1/3$; (b) $1/6$; (c) $F(x) = (x - 2)/3$

**3.** (a) $k = 3/56$; (b) $91/448$; (c) $F(x) = \dfrac{x^3}{56} - \dfrac{125}{448}$

**5.** (a) $k = 2$; (b) $.11$; (c) $F(x) = 2x - x^2$

**7.** (a) $k = 2/27$; (b) $11/27$; (c) if $0 \leqq x \leqq 3$, then $F(x) = 2x/9$;

   if $3 \leqq x \leqq 6$, then $F(x) = \dfrac{12x - x^2 - 9}{27}$

## Exercise 53, page 248

**1.** $\mu = 7/2$; $\sigma^2 = 3/4$     **3.** $\mu = 45/14$; $\sigma^2 = 291/980$

**5.** $\mu = 1$; $\sigma^2 = 1/6$

## Exercise 54, page 251

**1.** $\begin{bmatrix} -4 & 12 \\ -16 & -8 \end{bmatrix}$     **3.** $\begin{bmatrix} 9 & 11 & -1 \\ -3 & 7 & 26 \end{bmatrix}$     **5.** $\begin{bmatrix} 13 \\ -18 \end{bmatrix}$

**7.** $[-6 \quad 0 \quad 3 \quad 12]$     **9.** $\begin{bmatrix} (9 - x) \\ (29 - y) \\ -(17 + z) \end{bmatrix}$

**11.** $(x = 3, y = 5)$     **13.** $(x = -3/4, y = -3, z = -3/2)$

## Exercise 55, page 254

**1.** $(x = 5, y = -1)$     **3.** $(x = 2, y = -1, z = 2)$

**5.** $(x = -2, y = 3, z = -3)$     **7.** $(x = -3/2, y = 2, z = -1)$

**9.** $(x = -1/3, y = -3/2, z = 2)$     **11.** Inconsistent

## Exercise 56, page 257

**1.** $(x = 4, y = -1)$     **3.** $(x = 5, y = 1)$

**5.** Cannot be solved by use of determinants because the determinant of the coefficient matrix is zero

**7.** $(x = -1, y = -3)$     **9.** $(x = 0, y = 0)$

**11.** $(x = 5/3, y = 2/15)$     **13.** $(x = -37/21, y = -19/7)$

## Exercise 57, page 260

**1.** $-43$     **3.** 36     **5.** 5

## Exercise 58, page 262

**1–6.** See Exercise 57     **7.** 67     **9.** $-548$

## Exercise 60, page 266

**1.** $\begin{bmatrix} 6 & 10 \\ 5 & -8 \end{bmatrix}$    **3.** $\begin{bmatrix} -6 & 8 \\ -14 & 16 \end{bmatrix}$    **5.** $\begin{bmatrix} 2 \\ -17 \end{bmatrix}$

**7.** $\begin{bmatrix} 3 & 8 & 0 \\ 0 & -6 & 3 \\ 1 & 16 & 20 \end{bmatrix}$    **9.** For both: $\begin{bmatrix} 3 & 8 & 5 \\ 7 & 4 & 9 \\ 9 & 6 & 4 \end{bmatrix}$    **11.** $\begin{bmatrix} 3 \\ -8 \\ 21 \end{bmatrix}$

**13.** $2x - 3y = 3$ and $x + 2y = 5$; $(x = 3, y = 1)$

**15.** $\left. \begin{array}{l} -2x + 4y = -2, \\ 3x - y + 3z = 3, \\ x + 2y + 2z = 5 \end{array} \right\}$; $(x = 13, y = 6, z = -10)$

**17.** $\begin{bmatrix} 1 & 2 \\ 3 & 5 \end{bmatrix} \cdot \begin{bmatrix} x \\ y \end{bmatrix} = \begin{bmatrix} 3 \\ 10 \end{bmatrix}$    **19.** $\begin{bmatrix} 1 & -3 & 1 \\ 2 & 1 & -2 \\ 2 & -3 & 1 \end{bmatrix} \cdot \begin{bmatrix} x \\ y \\ z \end{bmatrix} = \begin{bmatrix} 7 \\ -1 \\ 9 \end{bmatrix}$

**21.** The elements are the pounds of carbohydrates, fats, and proteins, respectively, in the mixture: [130  220  120]

## Exercise 61, page 271

**1.** $\dfrac{1}{23} \begin{bmatrix} 5 & 2 \\ -4 & 3 \end{bmatrix}$    **3.** $\begin{bmatrix} 1 & 1 \\ 4 & 3 \end{bmatrix}$    **5.** $\begin{bmatrix} -5 & 2 \\ 3 & -1 \end{bmatrix}$

**7.** $\dfrac{1}{5} \begin{bmatrix} -5 & 0 & 5 \\ -6 & -1 & 4 \\ -8 & -3 & 7 \end{bmatrix}$    **9.** $-\dfrac{1}{26} \begin{bmatrix} 1 & -3 & 13 \\ -2 & 6 & 0 \\ -5 & -11 & 13 \end{bmatrix}$

**11.** $-\dfrac{1}{16} \begin{bmatrix} 3 & 2 & 7 \\ 2 & -4 & 10 \\ 8 & 0 & 8 \end{bmatrix}$    **13.** $-\dfrac{1}{96} \begin{bmatrix} 18 & -6 & 10 \\ -15 & 21 & -3 \\ 48 & -48 & 48 \end{bmatrix}$

**15.** No inverse exists because the determinant of the matrix is zero

## Exercise 63, page 281

**1.** $-56/5$    **3.** $-30$    **5.** 30    **7.** 25    **9.** $x_1^2 + x_2^2 + \cdots + x_7^2$

**11.** $x_1 + x_2 + x_3 + x_4 + y_1 + y_2 + y_3 + y_4$

**13.** $v_1 + v_2 + v_3 + v_4 + 12$    **15.** 13; 79; 55

**17.** $\bar{x} = 29$; $s_x^2 = 13\frac{1}{3}$    **19.** $\bar{x} = -6$; $s_x^2 = 44\frac{1}{3}$

**21.** $\bar{x} = 5$; $s_x^2 = 8\frac{8}{13}$    **23.** 5.1

**25.** 4.3; integral weights {18, 3, 4, 8, 18}

**27.** 137.1 lb    **29.** 73.7

## Exercise 64, page 286

**1.** $x = 44/31$; $y = 87/31$    **3.** $x = 28/15$; $z = -53/45$

**5.** $x = 2.51$, $y = -1.04$, $z = -2.17$

### Exercise 65, page 292

**1.** $a = 27/34; b = 13/34$    **3.** $a = 67/117; b = -3/13$
**5.** $y = 6.05t + 41.4$    **7.** $y = 3.52t + 82.85$
**9.** $y = 21.87t + 274.90$    **11.** $y = 2.606t + 48.27$

### Exercise 66, page 297

**1.** $y$ on $x$:   $y = .7941x + .3823;$
  $x$ on $y$:   $x = .7200y + 2.0800; r = .756$
**3.** $y$ on $x$:   $y = .5726x - .2308;$
  $x$ on $y$:   $x = 1.1754y + .8597; r = .820$
**5.** $r = .926$    **7.** $r = .044$

# INDEX